Environmental Sociology

The Ecology of Late Modernity

Second Edition

Thomas J. Burns
University of Oklahoma
and
Beth Schaefer Caniglia
Regis University

Published by:

Mercury Academic ™
Norman, OK

Mercury Academic ™ issues a number of textbooks in print, ebook and audio format.

Visit us at our website: mercuryacademic.com.

Editorial Staff:
Terry Best
Michelle Wicker

Book Design and Graphic Design:
David Fetter

Cover:
iStock Photos

ISBN: **978-1-62667-039-6**

For Chris Contreras (1948 - 2013)

About the Authors

Thomas J. Burns (PhD, 1990, University of Maryland) is Professor of Sociology at the University of Oklahoma, where he is active in the Environmental Studies and Religious Studies programs and the Center for Social Justice. His research focuses on social institutions from a comparative and historical perspective, particularly as they pertain to issues of well-being and sustainability. He has published widely on topics that include deforestation, pollution, health and well-being outcomes, environmental ethics, social movements, theory, and religion and the environment.

Professor Burns was formerly at the University of Utah, where he was a member of the Sociology Faculty, and Chaired the interdisciplinary Master of Statistics (MStat) Program. He has served on the Executive Board of the Society for Human Ecology, is currently the Book Review Editor of *Human Ecology Review*, and is a member of the Editorial Board of *The Journal of World-Systems Research*. He has won teaching awards at the Universities of Utah and Oklahoma, and is recipient of the Society for Human Ecology's Distinguished Leadership Award.

Beth Schaefer Caniglia (PhD University of Notre Dame) is Professor and founding Director of the Sustainable Economic & Enterprise Development (SEED) Center at Regis University in Denver, Colorado, and conducts research focused at the intersection of social movements, organization, and policymaking, especially related to environmental movements. For over a decade, she has collected extensive data on the Multi-stakeholder dialogues at the United Nations Commission on Sustainable Development, where she also served as a consultant to the NGO Steering Committee. Her more recent work has turned toward the interaction of science, social movements and public opinion in the creation of climate change and fresh water policy. Dr. Caniglia was chosen as a Global Climate Leader by the State of the World Forum in recognition of her commitment to link academic scholarship to global carbon cycle transformation. She is Past Chair of the Section on Environment and Technology of the American Sociological Association.

For "Exemplifying the highest standards of scholarly work in the field of Human Ecology," Professors Burns and Caniglia won the Gerald L. Young Book Award at the 2016 International Conference of the Society for Human Ecology.

Contents

About the Authors *iv*
Table of Contents *v*
List of Supplemental Features *xiii*

Preface 14
Acknowledgements 16

1 INTRODUCTION: LATE MODERNITY AND THE NATURAL ENVIRONMENT 19

2 THE SOCIOLOGICAL VIEW AND THE UNIQUE VISION OF ENVIRONMENTAL SOCIOLOGY 31

3 THE NATURAL ENVIRONMENT AND THE CULTURE OF LATE MODERNITY 45

4 SCIENCE AND TECHNOLOGY 65

5 ECONOMICS—THE CAPITALIZATION OF EVERYTHING OR NATURAL CAPITAL? 88

6 GOVERNANCE, POLICIES, AND INSTITUTIONS 105

7 HEALTH, WELL-BEING, AND THE ENVIRONMENT 126

8 COLLECTIVE BEHAVIOR AND SOCIAL MOVEMENTS 144

9 LATE MODERNITY AND THE ENVIRONMENT IN EMERGING ECONOMIES 160

10 CATALYSTS FOR CHANGE AND GROWING CONCIOUSNESS 170

11 BRINGING IT TOGETHER AND MOVING AHEAD 189

REFERENCES AND SUGGESTED READINGS 207

ILLUSTRATIONS 249

INDEX 253

Annotated Table of Contents

1 INTRODUCTION: LATE MODERNITY AND THE NATURAL ENVIRONMENT

People have always had to survive in the environments of which they are part. In so doing, they have sometimes lived in harmony with the natural environment and at other times have not. With the advance of industrial society across the planet, there were profound changes in the ways people relate to the environment. In this chapter, we explore these issues and particularly focus on ways in which the processes of late modernity have significantly affected the environment in industrialized nations and emerging economies. We close the chapter with a vision of what environmental sociology can offer, and give a brief plan for the rest of the book.

- *Environmental Problems Are Not New*
- *Our Problems Now Are as Pressing as Ever and We Can Address Them*
- *Natural Ecosystems and Human Society*
- *The Trajectory of Large-Scale Social Change and Why It Matters*
- *Environmental Problems Particular to Late Modernity*
- *Economics as the Default Lens of Late Modernity*
- *The Unique Place of Environmental Sociology*
- *Our Plan for the Book*
- *Chapter 1 Summary*

2 THE SOCIOLOGICAL VIEW AND THE UNIQUE VISION OF ENVIRONMENTAL SOCIOLOGY

The discipline of sociology developed in the nineteenth century as people struggled to understand society and the many problems posed by modernity. The classical sociologists had many insights, but did not sufficiently take the environment into account. In the late twentieth century, environmental sociology developed out of the struggle to understand ecological problems coming about as a result of human-environmental interactions. It applies insights from the rich tradition of the social sciences, even as it comes to grips with what about the environment is unique. Environmental sociology is in some ways comparable to other subfields, but in many ways is distinct. It necessarily requires its own sets of theories, measures and analytical tools. The stakes are high and rising. Environmental sociology is a vibrant field; this is necessary, because it is studying a rapidly moving and globalized target.

- *Major Influences in the Rise of Sociology*
- *The Critical Need to Think Ecologically and the Limits of the Pioneers of Sociology*

- *Thought, Discourse, and the Natural World*
- *Contemporary Theories about the Environment*
  - o *Work in the Critical Tradition*
  - o *Work in the Functional Tradition*
  - o *Work Crossing Traditional Boundaries*
  - o *Human Ecology*
  - o *Some Other Notable Environmental Voices*
- *Using Sociology to Understand Environmental Problems*
- *Chapter 2 Summary*

3 THE NATURAL ENVIRONMENT AND THE CULTURE OF LATE MODERNITY

Culture is the milieu in which people live, find meaning, make decisions, think, and communicate. Culture can change in response to external circumstances, but typically does so slowly. In a world where there are rapid changes in the material world in areas such as technology, communication, and transportation, the cultural adaptation may lag significantly behind. This mismatch between rapid environmental change on the one hand, and the culture adequate to make sense of it and to act in a manner appropriate for long term survival and sustainability on the other, has become perhaps the defining social problem of our day. We review contemporary cultural characteristics of the United States and the emergence of a global culture that attempts to address the urgent need for environmental reform. We examine these processes and consider ways in which we may go about addressing them in ways that will make the problems less acute rather than worse.

- *What Is Culture?*
- *Understanding Environmental Problems through the Lenses of Culture*
- *Culture and the Trajectory of Modernity*
- *The Individual and Society in Late Modernity*
- *The Problem Writ Large: Mismatches between Culture and Sustainability*
  - o *Mismatches between Evolution and Technology*
  - o *Mismatches between Large-Scale Economies and the Natural Ecology*
- *Why Institutional Fixes by Themselves Often Are Ineffective*
- *Conclusions: Take-Away Lessons about Culture and the Environment*
- *Chapter 3 Summary*

4 SCIENCE AND TECHNOLOGY

Science and technology are at once blamed for many environmental problems as well as touted as its only solution. Problems like climate change and water and air pollution have been explicitly linked to the rise of the Industrial Revolution. Yet, proponents of "ecological modernization" argue that it is only through more technological development that we will solve current environmental problems. Others argue, just the opposite, that we need to voluntarily simplify our lifestyles to conserve natural resources and regain our connection to nature. A middle-ground approach called the precautionary principle was adopted at the 1992 Rio Earth Summit. This chapter will review these perspectives on the ways technology and science relate to environmental problems. We also consider the potential for technology transfer from more to less industrialized nations and the related process of leapfrogging by developing nations.

- *Technology and Social and Environmental Change*
- *Technological Development and Cultural Lag*
- *Science and Technology as Tools of Progress, but Sometimes as Hubris*
- *Paradoxes of Technological Innovation*
- *Technology and the Economy in Advanced Capitalism*
- *The Effect of Technology Is Best Understood as It Interacts with Other Macro-Level Variables*
- *Standards of Knowledge and Proof*
    - o *The Impacts of Technology and Environmental Assessment*
    - o *Developing New Ecological Measures: Coming Full Circle*
- *Conclusions: Take-Away Lessons on Science, Technology, and the Environment*
- *Chapter 4 Summary*

5 ECONOMICS—THE CAPITALIZATION OF EVERYTHING OR NATURAL CAPITAL?

The economy is an institution that brings incredible prosperity. At the same time, unchecked economics is often blamed for ecological destruction. According to public opinion surveys, people believe corporations should be held responsible through taxes and other means for the costs of deforestation, climate change, and air and water pollution. We are much less likely to agree to higher taxes or higher prices when the goods we purchase contribute to those environmental costs. In this chapter, we will look at the connections between the economy, corporations, and the consumptive behavior of individuals across the globe. We further examine the complex balance that must be struck among collective, corporate, and individual responsibility, which naturally leads to questions of environmental ethics and justice and the roles that might be played by national and international finance institutions.

- *The Discipline of Economics and How It Came About*
- *What Is the Value of Nature?*
- *Economic Truisms and Their Limits*

- o *Economies of Scale*
- o *Externalities*
- o *Comparative Advantage*
- o *Perpetual Expansion*
- o *The Invisible Hand of the Free Market*
- *Individual and Collective Interests: The Drama and Tragedy of the Commons*
- *Distributions of Wealth and the Environment*
- *The Treadmill of Production and Consumption*
- *Contributions and Limitations of Environmental Economics*
- *Economic Incentives: When and How Do They Work?*
- *What Can Societies Do Now? Adapting Old Ideas to Contemporary Problems*
- *Conclusions: Take-Away Lessons on Economics and the Environment*
- *Chapter 5 Summary*

6 GOVERNANCE, POLICIES, AND INSTITUTIONS

In democratic societies, political institutions are the sites where potential solutions to social problems are adjudicated and public policy is created. This chapter will review the relevant political institutions involved in environmental policy making. Specific challenges arise when faced with environmental problems that cross national boundaries and/or defy the ability of a single nation to protect its people from unwanted environmental degradation. Recent trends in national, regional, and global environmental governance will be evaluated from a distinctly sociological point of view. We examine cross-cutting axes of power, which complicate environmental governance. We also examine the mismatch that often occurs between the scale of environmental problems and legalized solutions. Finally, we will consider the question of legitimacy in governance.

- *Background: Ways in Which Political Systems Work and Don't Work*
  - o *What is Governance?*
  - o *Classical Sociological Theories of Governance*
  - o *Contemporary Sociological Theories of Governance*
  - o *Ecological Modernization Theory*
  - o *World System Theory*
  - o *World Polity Theory*
- *Private Property and Market Mechanisms of Environmental Governance*
  - o *Who Should Govern the Commons?*
  - o *Private vs. Public Land Ethic*
  - o *Optimists in the Commons*
- *Institutional Mismatch and Adaptive Approaches to Environmental Governance*

- *Institutional Mismatch*
- *Macro-Level Environmental Problems and Nation-States*
- *Civil Society and Hybrid Governance*

- *Conclusions: Take-Away Lessons about Environmental Governance*
- *Chapter 6 Summary*

7 HEALTH, WELL-BEING, AND THE ENVIRONMENT

Imbalances in the natural environment caused by human activity adversely affect the health and well-being of those dependent upon that environment. Darwinian medicine theorizes that our bodies are governed by the principle of adaptation by natural selection. In this chapter, we explore the role of environmental imbalance in this process of adaptation as humankind strives to achieve the optimal balance point to ensure survival in each population's specific environment. Many diseases arise from out-of-balance environments, and these diseases can spread globally. Exposure to toxins in the air and water, the use of modern agricultural practices such as herbicides and pesticides, chemical additives in our foods, and the transfer of diseases from animal populations, all symptomatic of environmental imbalance, have negative effects on our health and well-being. Often, the poor and undeveloped countries face the greatest risk of disease, as well as societal problems such as violence and political instability related to the unequal distribution and scarcity of environmental resources. We look here, at the toll modernity has taken on human and societal health.

- *Public Health and the Environment*
  - *Why We Get Sick: A Darwinian Approach to Health*
  - *Sickness as a Function of an Environment Out of Balance*
- *Inequality, Scarcity, Marginalization, and Social Breakdown*
  - *Environmental Justice and Health*
  - *Close to Home, Far from Safe*
  - *Poisoning and Premature Deaths from Pollution*
- *Conclusions: Takeaway Lessons about Health, Well-Being and the Environment*
- *Chapter 7 Summary*

8 COLLECTIVE BEHAVIOR AND SOCIAL MOVEMENTS

Social movements have been a powerful force on behalf of the environment. In this chapter, we describe the range of actors who make up the environmental movement and review some of their successes and failures. We consider the role of national and international institutions as targets of, obstructions and partners to, the environmental movement. We review possible effects of social movements on the hearts and minds of citizens around the world, and consider whether, and to what degree, the environmental movement influences actual environmental outcomes.

- *Background: Who or What Is the Environmental Movement?*
  - o *Environmental Movement Strengths*
  - o *Institutional Change*
  - o *The International Environmental Movement*
- *Changing Hearts and Minds*
- *Environmental Movement Limitations*
  - o *Conflicting Priorities and the Two-Party System in the United States*
  - o *Challenges to the Environmental Movement in the International Arena*
- *Conclusions: Take-Away Lessons about Social Movements and the Environment*
- *Chapter 8 Summary*

9 LATE MODERNITY AND THE ENVIRONMENT IN EMERGING ECONOMIES

While environmental degradation is a huge problem worldwide, environmental challenges often present themselves differently in different places. Of particular concern for the environment are emerging economies of the "BRIC" countries (Brazil, Russia, India and China), which have huge numbers of people and large amounts of natural resources that are rapidly diminishing. Reviewing the special needs of these countries provides insights into the environmental challenges confronting developing nations and emerging economies around the world.

- *The Environment and the Modern World-System*
- *The Recursive Structure of the World-System: Replicating Itself at Different Levels of Analysis*
- *The Environmental Kuznets Curve*
- *The Netherlands Fallacy and the Ecological Footprint*
- *The Environment and Health in Developing Countries*
- *Chapter 9 Summary*

10 CATALYSTS FOR CHANGE AND GROWING CONSCIOUSNESS

A central theme of this chapter is that of the catalyst—a small addition to a mix that helps to bring about a large change. We review a variety of approaches set forth by experts for comprehensive changes to our society that can transform our personal behaviors, as well as our institutions, in ways that reorient our behaviors to be more in line with nature and environmental limits. The Global Marshall Plan illustrates the outcomes of a world-wide cooperative effort, while other approaches, focusing on the need to reconnect to nature and build our lifestyles in ways that deeply integrate respect and reverence of our non-human plant and animal relatives, explore the indigenous perspective and the idea of reenchantment with nature. We conclude with an analysis of the structural and cultural dimensions of these perspectives and the ways social scientists understand the roles of structure and personal change, while recognizing the value of both perspectives working together to achieve solutions to our environmental problems.

- *Introduction*
- *Global Marshall Plan for the Environment*
- *Today's Date: 1 E.C.E.*
- *Ecological Revolution*
- *Indigenous Realism*
- *Reenchanting Nature*
- *Structure vs. Agency or Infrastructure vs. Personal Change*
- *Conclusions: Take-Away Lessons about Catalysts for Change and Growing Consciousness*
- *Chapter 10 Summary*

11 BRINGING IT TOGETHER AND MOVING AHEAD

In the previous sections, we have looked at different approaches to addressing environmental issues. While each of these approaches, such as technological, political, and economic changes are vitally important; they still are likely to be ineffective if implemented in a vacuum. Rather, there needs to be a synergy among approaches. What will be the glue to hold the approaches together such that there can be coherent change for the better? Here we look to an emergent ethos that has a set of common norms and frameworks for thinking about the environment and people's place in it. Is a global culture or ethic powerful enough to effect change, or are place-based ethics focused closer to home necessary? In articulating ways in which we see an environmental ethos emerging, we bring together ideas from previous chapters.

- *The Transformations of Modernity*
- *Thinking About Institutions*
- *Thinking About Time*
- *Transforming the Tragedy of the Commons into the Drama of the Commons*
- *Rebuilding Connection With the Natural Environment*
- *Toward a Comprehensive Model of Humankind's Interaction with the Natural Environment*
- *Chapter 11 Summary*

List of Supplemental Features

Figure 1.1 What Is An Ecosystem? 21
Figure 1.2 What Is Modernity? 24
Figure 1.3 Environmental Problems of Late Modernity 26
Figure 1.4 Some Hidden Problems With Economistic Thinking 27
Figure 2.1 Key Ideas of Classical Sociologists on the Perversities of Modernity 33
Figure 3.1 Enantiodromia: Nature Senses Imbalances and Pushes Back 52
Figure 3.2 Cultural Lag and Cultural Diffusion 56
Figure 4.1 Genetically Modified Crops and the Precautionary Principle 68
Figure 4.2 Jevons Paradox: Where Technology Meets the Unintended Consequences of the Free Market 74
Figure 4.3 The Scale of the Fishing Industry: Technology and Ecosystems 78
Figure 5.1 Perversities of Scale: Desertification of the American Breadbasket 90
Figure 5.2 The Harsh Reality of Externalities: Living Downstream of Moneyed Interests 94
Figure 6.1 The Tragedy of the Commons 112
Figure 7.1 Supernormal Stimulus 128
Figure 8.1 Brulle's Analysis of U.S. Environmental Movement Diversity 146
Figure 8.2 Representative Environmental Activist Bios 151
Figure 8.3 Dimensions of the Political Opportunity Structure 153
Figure 9.1 Industrial Accidents in Developing Countries 166
Figure 10.1 Action Items from the Earth Charter Secretariat 176
Figure 11.1 The United Nations Climate Change Conference in Paris (COP21) 196

Preface

People have always had to survive in the environments of which they are part. In so doing, they have sometimes lived in harmony with the natural environment, and at other times have not. With the advance of industrial society across the planet, there were profound changes in the ways people relate to the environment. In this book, we explore these issues and particularly focus on ways in which the processes of late modernity (or what some have come to refer to as the "Anthropocene Age"), have significantly affected the environment in industrialized nations and emerging economies.

The discipline of sociology developed in the nineteenth century as people struggled to understand society and the many problems posed by industrialization and the related processes of modernization, such as urbanization, rising crime, and alienation. The classical sociologists had some tremendous insights into a wide array of social problems, but, with some exceptions we note in the text, did not sufficiently take the natural environment into account.

In the late twentieth century, environmental sociology developed out of the struggle to understand ecological problems coming about as a result of human-environmental interactions. It applies insights from the rich tradition of the social sciences, even as it comes to grips with what about the environment is unique. Environmental sociology is, in some ways, comparable to other subfields, but in many ways is distinct. It necessarily requires its own sets of theories, measures and analytical tools. The stakes are high and rising. Environmental sociology is a vibrant field; this is necessary, because it is studying a rapidly moving target.

As environmental sociologists, we apply the vision of sociology to what, historically, has been its most neglected problem—the connection between humankind and the natural environment. That neglect is itself a function of how profoundly the culture of modernity has influenced everything in its wake, including how disciplines coming into their own in the nineteenth century, particularly sociology and economics, largely ignored this most basic of all relationships. As brilliant as the early sociologists were, and clever as the economists were, this neglect threatens to limit the relevance of the disciplines even as the very intellectuals so desperately needed to focus on these crucial problems fail to grasp their significance.

The approach we take in this book is to focus on environmental problems associated with modernity. With increases in the size and concentration of populations, economies of scale, advanced technological capabilities, elaborate divisions of labor, and widely skewed access to resources and wealth, there also have arisen large ecological imbalances which, in turn, have manifested in myriad ways. These include air and water pollution, deforestation, global climate change, and rises in environment-based diseases in plant, animal, and human life.

This leads us to one of the wicked problems of modernity itself: we have the ability now, and perhaps even the propensity, to create problems beyond our ability to address them in sustainable ways. Here, it is crucial to think as human ecologists—to be open to multi-disciplinary approaches to what are complex problems that do not fall neatly into the predefined disciplinary categories of the academy.

In spite of this frustrating predicament, the book takes a decidedly optimistic approach, examining in detail solutions stemming from major institutions and local communities, as well as individual lifestyle changes that can bring us closer in harmony with the natural environment. As such, the book goes beyond merely describing environmental problems, to discuss catalysts for change across an array of perspectives and on multiple levels. Because we examine such a diverse set of institutions, the interdisciplinary nature of environmental problems and solutions takes center stage.

The central theme of this book is that humankind has gradually lost connection with the natural environment. This is reflected in its institutions and culture; because of that, continuing to harm the environment is part of the norm and, in so doing, we harm our own health and well-being. It is thus vital to recover that connection. We focus attention on the various aspects of that disconnection—whether it be in terms of the political process, the economy, technology, or the culture, and, in each case, then consider some possible ways to unwind those processes on various levels, from the individual to the global, to help heal the connection.

Acknowledgements

Somewhere between Norman and Stillwater, on a country road in the Oklahoma version of the middle of nowhere, a small retreat complex sits quietly. When we first decided to collaborate on the book you now hold in your hands, we wanted a place for our weekly meetings, and the library of the St. Francis of the Woods retreat complex turned out to be pretty much perfect for a couple of refugees from the madding crowd, writing their book on humankind's relationship with the environment in late modernity, surrounded by chirping birds in a variety of pine, oak, and elm trees. Either of us could come early or stay late and meditate, or take a walk and think through things while enjoying the backdrop of the Cross Timbers. St. Francis of the Woods is a special place. We are grateful for being able to come together there to do our work.

Most of the weeks we met at the library of St. Francis of the Woods, there was only one other person there. Chris Contreras was the librarian. Chris was uniformly gracious. He was a monk at the time in one of the Eastern Orthodox sects, and seemed to know a good deal about other paths, in a quiet sort of way. When we mentioned one time that he seemed to embody the Confucian virtue of Chun Tzu about as well as anyone, he immediately knew what that was, without explanation. Being both magnanimous and humble, he took the compliment graciously, but without embellishment. Chris was there, week in and week out. We would chat pleasantly, sometimes about small things, sometimes about big issues. Once we turned to our work, Chris would leave us alone, but he had a peaceful presence that pervaded the place. He was the kind of person you could be comfortable with, even in silence. Chris did not live to see the completed book, but his spirit very much lives on, and we dedicate this book to him. R.I.P. Chris.

We are grateful to our mentors, family and friends, who have provided intellectual, spiritual and moral support over the years. Tom's dissertation advisor in particular, Jerry Hage, was a masterful teacher who had a habit of developing increasingly elaborate class handouts until, at some point, they reached something close to the critical mass of a book. This book started humbly enough, with both of us finding ourselves having ever-larger packets of class notes to hand out. What started as a series of class handouts have, over the years, developed into what you now hold in your hands, and years of student feedback have helped us tremendously as we have honed and modified throughout this process. There is no audience in the world to parallel students for being candid and honest about what works and what does not pedagogically, and we owe a debt of gratitude to the students we have had over the years, at all levels from high school seniors taking freshman college courses, through PhDs and postdocs, for offering their feedback. What you hold in your hand now, is pretty close to what students who have gone before you seem to think works for them. Tom also extends his heartfelt appreciation to Tom Boyd, whose wisdom and spirit serve as an inspiration to all who know him. Thank you, my friend.

Beth is grateful to Penelope Canan and Patricia Bell for their mentorship throughout her career. Beth's entire family, including her husband Jason, her mother and father, her brother, sister-in-law, nieces and nephews, and extended family members have been a source of strength and happiness. Finally, Beth wants to thank her friends Rebecca and Kelli for hours of commiseration and celebration.

We very much appreciate the thorough reading and helpful insights offered by peer reviewers of earlier parts of our manuscript. Richard Borden of College of the Atlantic, Lori Hunter of the University of Colorado, Andrew Jorgenson of Boston College, and Richard York of the University of Oregon each took the time and energy to give our work a careful reading, and offered supportive and helpful feedback. We appreciate their input, and have taken their suggestions to heart. We have no doubt the book is better for it. Any remaining problems are our own doing.

Working with the folks at Mercury Academic Publishing has been delightful. John Cox's vision to establish a College Textbook Division that is of the highest caliber, and to reach out to connect with us to be an integral part of that, is an inspiration. Our Developmental Editor, David Fetter, was a steady presence throughout the project. Michelle Wicker's keen eye for sociological detail and Terry Best's proofreading have been helpful and professional throughout the process of completing this book. Thank you all for your hard work and good cheer. The arduous process of developing a book has been, with you folks, a great experience. Thank you all.

Chapter One - Introduction: Late Modernity and the Natural Environment

Our world abounds in environmental problems. Deforestation, overgrazing and overfishing, the degradation of croplands and once plentiful natural resources, and the alarming increase in polluted air, water, and toxic contaminated land threaten human life and planetary survival. Just in our lifetimes, numerous plants and animals have gone extinct. Global warming has led to a number of problems, including the melting of polar ice caps, climate and tidal extremes in some areas, and desertification in others. Deeper understanding of the human and ecological aspects of the problems is crucial; taking decisive, positive, informed action is vital.

Environmental Problems Are Not New

The problems are daunting, and yet humankind has faced environmental challenges before. Many such difficulties, including those others, or we, may attribute to "natural causes," have had a human hand in their making. In Mesopotamia, the "Cradle of Civilization," over-foraging in the early horticultural period, and over-planting in agrarian times led to environmental degradation serious enough to threaten human sustainability. Many people attributed desertification, dramatic crop declines, and famine to natural occurrences or acts of God. Yet, human practices and a lack of knowledge were primarily to blame.

In hindsight, we now know that at least some "natural" disasters, such as the Irish Potato Famine of the 1840s, and the Dust Bowl tragedies of the 1920s and 1930s, resulted from human practices and policies. In nineteenth-century Ireland, absentee landlords, eager to maximize profits from cash crops, implemented mono-cropping and other techniques which eventually resulted in massive famine and human suffering. In the early twentieth century, landowners in Oklahoma and elsewhere in the American South and Southwest removed natural land breaks to facilitate extensive plowing, thereby exacerbating dust storms and other natural or weather-induced disasters. We can look back to past ideology and practices and rationalize such mistakes because people at the time did not know better. But ignorance of the environmental impact of human actions can no longer be an excuse for many so-called "natural" disasters.

Our Problems Now Are as Pressing as Ever and We Can Address Them

Still, we continue to make serious mistakes. Consider a few of the previous decade's natural disasters. Hurricane Katrina hit the Gulf Coast of the United States in 2005. Its damaging winds and rains may have been unavoidable, yet we cannot help but wonder whether some climate extremes caused by global environmental change made a bad situation worse. On the other hand, we do *know* that post-storm health hazards involved widespread exposure to water-borne toxins that had collected at the mouth of the Mississippi River for decades. Well before Katrina crashed the Gulf Coast, the patterns and prevalence of certain diseases had medical sociologists and epidemiologists referring to the Mississippi Delta region as "Cancer Alley" (Freudenburg et al. 2009; Laska and Morrow 2006).

More recently, not only did Hurricane Sandy barrage the East Coast, but the summer of 2012 was one of the hottest and driest on record in many parts of the country. The "American Heartland" took a particularly hard hit—in some states, harvests of corn and wheat were about one-fifth of the average yield. In 2015, as we write this, the same area is experiencing devastating flooding. As environmental sociologists, we look beyond the facile "natural disaster" label, inquiring into the human, social, and institutional contributors. How much of these extremes—the drought of 2012 and the flooding of 2015—may be the result of human action, including economic policy, social and cultural practices (Peek et al. 2002; Tierney 2007; Gill et al. 2011)?

Environmental problems manifest on a number of levels, ranging from the local to the national, and the international to the planetary. They involve complex interactions stemming from multiple causes involving ecosystems and social systems. As Garrett Hardin (1968) pointed out in his essay *The Tragedy of the Commons*, technology now has the ability to create problems it cannot solve. In his landmark work, Hardin writes of a class of environmental problems going beyond "requiring change only in the techniques of the natural science, demanding little or nothing in the way of changes in human values or ideas or morality."

Put another way, environmental problems can seem overwhelmingly complex, stemming from multiple causes that *at our current level of knowledge*, are difficult to disaggregate. They inevitably point to hard ethical questions. By their nature, environmental problems invite an approach that attends to several causal streams at once, from the natural to the social. Environmental sociologists look for answers in this nexus between the social and the ecological.

Figure 1.1 What Is An Ecosystem?

Redwood Creek Overlook, Redwood National Park, California.

An ecosystem is a community of interdependent life forms, and of the non-living things that are important for those life forms to continue. While there are countless instances of an ecosystem, let us consider the example of a pond, replete with algae, worms, frogs, and smaller and larger fish. The non-living things are just as important, for without them, there would be no ecosystem. These non-living components include such essential elements as the water of the pond, the ground in which the water is contained, and the sunlight that provides warmth and energy for the flora and fauna of the pond.

An ecosystem can be healthy or sick. Biodiversity, or a multitude of life forms, living in some semblance of equilibrium, is a characteristic of a healthy ecosystem. With high levels of biodiversity, systems become more complex, sustaining greater numbers of interdependent parts. While there are exceptions, a complex ecosystem often is more robust in the face of disruptions than are more simple ecosystems.

If an ecosystem loses some of its elements (e.g., the algae is killed or major parts of it are contaminated through the introduction of toxins such as poly-chlorinated bi-phenyls or PCBs), it can cause a disruption to the entire system. Put another way, losing part of an ecosystem is analogous to knocking out a moving piece from a well-working machine. The machine may still function for a time, laboring on with difficulty; in catastrophic cases, it may shut down altogether.

We can think of small ecosystems being nested in larger and more encompassing ecosystems. A pond, for example, has a multitude of living entities, all working together in one way or another. The algae on the pond capture energy from the sun through photosynthesis; this helps nourish small organisms, which in turn provide sustenance for worms. Small fish may eat the worms and minute organisms. The smaller fish then may be eaten by larger predatory fish and so on.

For much of history, humankind has lived with the ecosystems available to it. By staying within the natural cycle of an ecosystem and keeping the disruptions in its balance to a minimum, people often can subsist on its fruits indefinitely. Ecologists warn of overshoot, when the natural biodiversity is pushed beyond its limit. This can occur when small imbalances increase in magnitude until reaching a tipping point. When an ecosystem no longer can sustain life to the extent it had, ecologists characterize this as ecosystem collapse. Ecosystems in various regions around the world are near a state of collapse, due to the heavy load of environmental degradation, pollution, and the overall demand on the resources of the system.

Sources: Kareiva et al. (2011); Meadows et al. (2004); Walker et al. (2006).

Natural Ecosystems and Human Society

This book focuses on environmental problems associated with social changes over the past few decades. Massive population growth and density with attendant economies of scale, advanced technological capabilities, elaborate divisions of labor, and widely skewed access to resources and wealth, have caused large ecological imbalances. Such imbalances manifest themselves in myriad ways, including air and water pollution, deforestation, global climate change, biodiversity loss, and rises in environment-based diseases in plant, animal and human life (Houghton 1997; McNeill 2001; Hughes 2009; Ponting 2008).

While ecosystems can handle the natural metabolic cycles of production and consumption, growth and death within certain natural ranges of tolerance (e.g., a moderate number of livestock on a small family farm, integrated into the natural balance of the land), when we exceed those limits (e.g., concentrated agricultural feeding operations or "CAFOs," where thousands of animals, such as hogs, chickens or cattle, are forced to live in cramped quarters to make growth and slaughtering more efficient), the ability of the land and local ecosystem to handle the feeding and waste is overwhelmed (Edwards and Ladd 2000; Ladd and Edwards 2002). In such instances, otherwise healthy and life-sustaining operations become toxic and dangerous.

Changes in magnitude can be sustained up to a tipping point, after which additional increases become part of the problem. Modern theorists of any discipline, particularly those placing a faith in the *bigger is better* principle, would do well to heed the age-old story of the straw that broke the camel's back, and to pay closer attention to the natural limits of ecosystems. Economic decision-making often suggests that bigger is necessarily better. For ecological systems, such thinking needs to be tempered with prudence, caution, and keen attention to how human actions impact the ecosystems upon which we all ultimately depend. Large-scale systems tend to overwhelm the natural ecologies on which they ultimately depend. Put succinctly, *in ecological systems, "small is beautiful" thinking is vital* (Schumacher 1973).

The Trajectory of Large-Scale Social Change and Why It Matters

Taking a long view of human history, we can see a number of interrelated processes, all of which contribute to the complexity of life on the planet; not just for society, but also for the way society interacts with the natural environment (for reviews and discussion, see Giddens 1990 and 1991; Beck 1992; Berman 1982; Wagner 2012). Human population has increased tremendously. Early in the third millennium, we are past the seven billion mark and rising, but consider that planet Earth only passed its first billion in the mid-nineteenth century, several decades into the Industrial Revolution. During that time, we have gone from over 95 percent of the people in the world making their living directly connected to the land (in most cases, farming, fishing or herding), to over 95 percent of people in developed countries working in ways unconnected directly with land or sea. Meanwhile, over half of the world's population, for the first time in history, now lives in cities.

These factors alone have contributed in no small measure to how we use resources and relate to the natural environment, yet they are but a part of the picture of modernity. Technology has increased dramatically and, with it, the size and scale of human manufacturing and enterprise have ballooned. The first assembly line for automobile production was developed for the Model T Ford in the early twentieth century, using the "scientific management" principles articulated by Frederick Winslow Taylor. Since then, scale of production and consumption has increased dramatically (for in-depth discussion of the tradeoffs involved, see Braverman 1974/1998). While this has led to efficiencies in certain kinds of manufacturing, it has also led to greater concentrations of waste to such degrees that the natural ecological systems become overwhelmed.

These changes have inspired highly positive things too. Technological development allowing for global communication has forever changed the scope and depth of knowledge production and human communication, for example.

Since industrialization, however, technology has allowed us to circumvent many natural environmental constraints, but to do so in increasingly risky ways. Our technological innovation, driven in no small measure by a culture of consumption, has brought us to the point where we have created problems that technology has not, or the culture will not, address.

One of the perverse aspects of technology is that it increases the use of resources and produces certain kinds of waste dramatically, but rarely addresses the resulting environmental degradation or waste production in a balanced, ecological way (Gille 2010). Consider that virtually every piece of plastic that has ever been manufactured still exists—it has not degraded to its natural state, or the state of the original components. Much of that, including every plastic cup used by fast food restaurants, winds up somewhere—landfills, discarded by the side of the road or into a waterway. As of this writing, a collection of garbage has amassed in the Pacific Ocean (sometimes simply called the "Pacific Trash Vortex") that by some accounts is larger in area than the state of Texas. This has come about, not just in the past 200 years, but mostly in the last 20 years.

Thus, while modernization itself is not a bad thing—and we certainly do not advocate going back to a time before industrialization—some of the ways in which our world has modernized, have caused dangerous imbalances in the natural ecology and in our human systems. Ironically, one of the Enlightenment ideals that, at least in part, informed the spirit of modernity was that of balance. But other ideas of modernity, including a tremendous emphasis on expanding markets and scales of production, came to trump moderation and harmony. In the world as it is currently—far into the trajectory of modernity—we find many of these problems having reached a tipping point.

Figure 1.2 What Is Modernity?

Carnegie Steel, Ohio.

As societies modernize, they become more complex in a number of ways. They have a more elaborate division of labor in which there are more specialties and more levels of hierarchy; they have extreme concentrations of wealth and poverty. There now are more people alive on the earth than at any previous time in history, and only recently, did the majority of those people become city dwellers. In a related vein, modes of production have become more concentrated over time. Factories and other industrial entities are large and have commodity chains that include many countries, often from different continents.

Modernity involves an increasing complexity on a number of levels: a rise in industrialization and a gradual transformation to a more complex division of labor characterized by a wide array of disciplines and an elaborate hierarchy of social stratification; a decline in traditional authorities such as religion and feudal systems, and a concomitant rise in the faith that people put in science. These processes were accompanied by a number of related social changes, not the least of which were rises in literacy and formal education, urbanization, and a profound shift from agrarian, farm-based to industrial and postindustrial societies. Over the last two and one half centuries, for example, countries that industrialized went from over 95 percent of their populations involved in farming and related agrarian activities to having fewer than 5 percent so employed.

On the heels of the Enlightenment, we can place the beginning of widespread industrialization, or the Industrial Revolution in the latter half of the eighteenth century. Adam Smith's publication of *The Wealth of Nations* in 1776 is as good a date as any to mark the beginning of a system of modern economic thought to go along with the rise of industrialization.

Technology of one sort or another has always been part of the human condition, as have population changes and divisions of labor. Yet, with modernity, the culture struggles to integrate technological innovation coming in rapid-fire fashion that is able to make broader and deeper incursions than ever before; there are greater numbers of people than in previous eras, many of whom are concentrated in huge urban agglomerations; scales of production and consumption are broader than ever in the past, even as concentrations of wealth and poverty are perhaps as profound as at any time.

These processes of modernity brought the mechanization of production, not only in factories, but they also have profoundly affected farming. In terms of machinery, the cotton gin, the tractor, the mechanized plow and the combine would change farming forever; but the effects even of these were perhaps not as great as the chemical revolution in farming. The widespread adoption of pesticides, herbicides, chemical fertilizers, growth hormones and other related synthetics would make large-scale farming feasible. In a related vein, at the time of this writing, the ubiquity of antibiotic use is such in high-density factory farms (e.g., where every chicken for generations now has been on a steady diet of antibiotics for its entire life) that a large majority of all antibiotics is going directly to animals, with one unintended consequence being the rise of resistant strains of germs that can have a profound effect on human as well as animal populations).

An integral part of the process of modernity is that a large majority of people become less obviously dependent upon the natural environment. This perception in turn becomes increasingly embedded in culture so that now, late into the trajectory of modernity, much of human culture struggles not to lose sight of the natural ecology of which it is necessarily a part.

Sources: Wagner (2012); Burns (2009); Beck (1992); Giddens (1990).

Environmental Problems Particular to Late Modernity

The contemporary world comes as a product of millennia of social and environmental interactions. Those of the last few centuries, and particularly since World War II, have been especially important in shaping the current situation. Because of technological developments, and the scale of human population and its institutions, we are now at a time unprecedented in history. We can characterize this as *late modernity*.

Late modernity has several distinctive features that make it particularly problematic for the interface between humanity and the natural environment. These factors include: unprecedented technological development, often coupled with the inability of cultural norms to keep apace of it; the scale of human population is larger than ever before, increasingly concentrated in urban agglomerations; increasingly unequal ecological exchange, in which resources from one part of the planet can be moved in large scales out of their natural ecological niches; and the consumption of resources and the production of waste at paces that far exceed the natural ecology's ability to accommodate them. Combine with that a culture of consumption and wildly unequal distributions of wealth and power on a global scale, and the potential for environmental catastrophe is daunting.

Through time, human institutions such as economic, educational, and political systems have grown more complex. In the face of this complexity, there arises a tendency, understandable but ultimately perverse, to see solutions in narrow, artificially simplified ways. Examples abound of people, often smart and well-meaning, who see solutions through the limited scope of their own disciplines, disembodied from a larger ecological consciousness.

Economists, for example, tend to see environmental problems as most appropriately addressed with economic measures such as "cap and trade," or other monetary incentives. In such a scheme, companies or even countries are seen as having a "right" to pollute to a degree determined by some arbiter, such as past polluting activity. They may then sell or trade those rights. People with a more political bent tend to see solutions in political terms. "Let us pass more laws!" People with a "hard science" perspective tend to perceive environmental problems as something that can and should be addressed through hard science. Such a view tends to discount a broader holistic perspective, taking account of each of these views, but in the context of what is healthy and sustainable for the natural environment and the life depending upon it.

Economics as the Default Lens of Late Modernity

The rise of large factories in the Industrial Revolution came to out-compete many smaller-scale operations, particularly in things like textiles and, later, in automobiles and large machinery. Large-scale farming did not take off so quickly, but has caught up with a vengeance in the post-World War II period. One of the cultural truisms arising from the work of Adam Smith (1776/1937) and those following in his wake in the economic and global business tradi-

Figure 1.3 Environmental Problems of Late Modernity

Many cities' roadways and interstate highways are plagued by "traffic jams" and gridlock during rush hours.

Environmental problems have been with us at least since the dawn of civilization, and probably even before that. Over-foraging, even back in our hunting and gathering past, impacted human conditions. And history tells us that even in the Mesopotamian cradle of civilization, there was environmental depletion. Yet in the last two centuries, ecological degradation has come to previously unseen levels. Particularly in the last half-century, many of the problems have, if anything, become more severe than ever in human history. The scale of environmental devastation, and the rapidity with which it is accelerating has increased exponentially since the middle of the twentieth century. Humanity is at a crossroads, where many ecosystems stand in danger of collapse.

While the world has always been changing, the processes of the last few centuries have taken these changes to such new levels, that we can now think of them not only quantitatively, but as qualitatively different from times past. Some of the problems becoming particularly acute in the late twentieth century include unsustainable rates of deforestation, global climate change, erosion of topsoil, declining fish stocks and catastrophic losses of biodiversity, air and water pollution. Recent work indicates, for example, that a rise of 4 degrees Celsius could result in about an 85 percent loss in the Amazon rainforest within this century.

As society modernizes and becomes more complex, we develop technologies that outrun our abilities to manage them. This leads to situations such as strip mining entire mountains with disregard to the local ecosystems or of the people relying on them, and accessing and using fossil fuels more rapidly than we can figure out ways to use resources sustainably. If the technology has been developed to strip mine—and it has—under current conditions of normative development, much of the thinking goes that of course strip mining is the thing to do, and to oppose it is wrong. It can always be justified with emphasizing some pieces of modernity such as job growth (think of all the people it will employ, etc.) over others (why not employ people in ways that are more ecologically feasible, for example?).

We now have more people than ever before—seven billion and counting—living on a planet with finite resources. The vast preponderance of people are disconnected from the basic workings of nature, such as the germination of seeds, and the birth and death of animals. In the division of labor on the eve of the Industrial Revolution, over 95 percent of the world's population was involved in food production. In contemporary society, that ratio is precisely the opposite—well over 95 percent of people are no longer engaged in farming or related activity. For those who are involved in primary food production, there is an increasing tendency to be part of large-scale technology and chemical intensive operations.

This, in turn, leads to a situation in which a large and growing majority of people are, at least potentially, alienated from significant aspects of the natural world. This change has been paralleled by a move from small farms to ever larger and extensive agribusiness farms, and a concomitant rise in pesticides, herbicides and other practices that interfere with nature. The enormity of these processes has resulted in some wild imbalances in the natural environment. We live in a time when our actions can worsen problems significantly and perhaps catastrophically, if we do not engage them in significant ways and take action to address them.

Sources: World Resources Institute (www.wri.org); Worldwatch Institute (www.worldwatch.org); The World Health Organization (www.who.int/globalchange/environment/en/); The United Nations Environmental Program (http://www.unep.org/geo/GEO4/report/GEO-4_Report_Full_en.pdf).

Figure 1.4 Some Hidden Problems with Economistic Thinking

Adam Smith, who wrote the influential, *An Inquiry into the Nature and Causes of the Wealth of Nations*.

Perhaps, in part, because the discipline of economics came into being well before people developed a fuller awareness of the social and institutional contributors to environmental problems, many economists and business people have tended to ignore non-monetary costs such as the loss of a healthy environment. There are countless examples of what economists and others came to refer to euphemistically as externalities. This externalization, or (sometimes willful) ignorance of the true costs of production, commerce and consumption, has become a central feature of standard business practices. In some ominous ways, the widespread adoption of this narrowly economistic way of thinking has paralleled the mechanization of production and the concomitant alienation of humankind in modern society from the natural environment .

Conceptually, an externality is a substantive variable we fail to account for and leave out of an analysis. Many economists, as well as those relying on them as they frame their own thinking (such as politicians and business investors), tend to externalize variables that do not have a monetary cost associated with them. An externality is, in this case, what we don't take into account. For example, if someone has a business that relies on fresh, clean water, and does not pay anything for that water, or take steps to replenish it in kind, clean water is an externality.

Many times, there is a tendency to take such resources for granted. As population pressures grow and more people begin to compete for, or to have claims on, that resource, externalizing it can become a political issue. Even so, a company may continue to use the resource as long as it can get away with it.

An enterprising business person may, for example, start a leather tanning business (perhaps with kudos and support from local politicians for "creating jobs"). This brings us to another major aspect of externalities—taking something from an ecosystem or putting wastes into it, that do not naturally recycle in a time frame that will not overwhelm the system.

A small imbalance in the ecosystem may still not cause a major disruption, but as a general rule, imbalances are made worse with larger scales. Put another way, as a small problem gets bigger, it also tends to get worse, perhaps heading eventually to a tipping point, beyond which the system moves into catastrophic collapse. Take for example the case of animal feed lots and the manure they produce. Small scales may be good for the local ecosystem, but in large quantities, tend to overrun the system. This has contributed to, for example, a large "dead zone" in the Gulf of Mexico, in which the collective toxins from runoff from mega-farms and other ecologically marginal enterprises into the Mississippi River, sometimes from hundreds of miles away, have accumulated to the point where that part of the Gulf can no longer sustain the marine life that once thrived there.

This propensity to externalize and hence to off-lay social or ecological problems to the natural environment has significantly contributed to many of the staggering environmental problems we experience in modern society. In addition, the growing tendency to make significant aspects of the production and consumption chains of increasingly larger scale has proven to be a potent combination indeed.

Sources: Daly and Cobb (1994); Lux (1990).

tions, was that large-scale production was the wave of the future, and that large-scale production would, with its efficiency, generally trump smaller-scale production.

While the efficiencies of large-scale production may make sense from an economic standpoint, they rarely do from an *ecological* perspective. The reasons for this are complex, and we will touch on aspects of why this is throughout the book. At the risk of oversimplification, however, let us mention two important ideas for now: externalization and scale effects.

Economistic thinking is particularly problematic when taking the effects of human activity on the environment into fuller consideration. Environmental sociology developed in no small part as a corrective to the excesses and imbalances of economistic thinking.

The Unique Place of Environmental Sociology

A comprehensive social scientific perspective examines the human interface with the natural environment, considers important processes of modernity, and articulates their impact on social institutions. Such an approach tunes into not just the individual parts of a system, but attunes to the system as a whole. Put another way, the respective institutions such as the economy and the polity are vital, but to reduce thinking and action about environmental problems to a strictly economic, or solely political issue, ignores the larger perspective. This sort of caricature almost invariably leads to serious imbalances, as it privileges part of the overall picture by minimizing others. Environmental sociology acknowledges the importance of each of the parts of systems. At its best, the sociological perspective goes beyond that and takes seriously the elusive, but crucial, balance among the various parts of the complex interweaving of human and ecological systems.

In environmental sociology, we seek to adopt such a perspective. Thus, while we often measure quantitative things like numbers of people, their age and sex distributions and living patterns, such as urbanization and rural migration, national rates of CO2 emissions and other greenhouse gases, and deforestation and pollution, it is not the measurements per se, but *the questions we ask to make sense of them*, that distinguishes sociology as a uniquely effective lens through which to analyze the local and global environmental problems. In the words of C. Wright Mills (1959), at its best, the sociology "[connects local or personal] troubles into public issues, and public issues into their human meaning."

In environmental sociology, we apply what Mills characterized as the *sociological imagination*, or the continual search for connections between what is happening in a given time and place (e.g., the landfill in our neighborhood is overflowing and its runoff is seeping into the local stream), and larger unfolding historical processes (e.g., growing population pressures and earlier cultural adaptations to environmental constraints encountered in the transition to modernity).

Our Plan for the Book

Our work offers an extended examination of the uneasy tension between the logic of late modernity on one hand, and the constraints on earth's abundance on the other. The long processes of change have brought well-developed and highly differentiated institutions, each with their own logic and norms. Most notably, science and technology, the economy, the polity, and education systems have all intertwined, while social movements have arisen largely as a reflective conscience of these institutions and related processes. And so we take a long look at these dynamics, considering each institution on its own terms, but also as part of the larger picture as society now finds itself far into the trajectory of modernity. These factors interact, as their impact on the environment is considerable.

People who do not learn from the past, as goes the old saw, are doomed to relive it. Thus, we look to the past for lessons. The history of human-environmental interaction offers important lessons, hard-won from past experience. Put bluntly, humanity can ill afford to repeat the mistakes of our environmental past.

Still, we look with hope for an alternative vision of how we may live on the planet from now on. We spend the last chapters examining what an environmentally conscious culture would look like, what its institutions might be, and how they might interact. We also look at catalysts for change. What sorts of things could, can and should happen, from the individual to the institutional, from the local to the global, to move humankind toward a sustainable future?

We present this book in the spirit of stimulating serious discussion and environmental praxis. This is a young field, but a crucial one. We are glad to have fellow travelers on this journey.

Chapter 1 Summary

- Modernity refers to the profound social changes that came about in the eighteenth, nineteenth, and twentieth centuries. These changes included dramatic rises in population and urbanization, higher levels of literacy and formal education, labor force differentiation, rises in individualism, technological innovation, unprecedented levels of industrial production and also of the consumption of resources, greater faith in science, and a decline in religious authority.

- Environmental problems are not new to modern society. These problems can be seen stretching throughout history and affecting many generations.

- Particularly in the last half-century, many environmental problems have become more severe than ever in human history. The scale of environmental devastation, and the rapidity with which it is accelerating has increased exponentially since the middle of the twentieth century.

- World population is larger than it has ever been before and continues to grow. Also, for the first time in human history, there are now more people living in urban areas than out of them. The vast preponderance of people now make their living on something other than the land, and rely on technology, either directly or indirectly, for much of their livelihood. All social changes have tradeoffs, and while these changes do have a number of arguable advantages, humankind has become increasingly alienated from the land.

- Economic decision-making often suggests that bigger is typically better. Such thinking needs to be tempered with prudence, caution, and keen attention to how human actions impact the ecosystems upon which we all ultimately depend. The small is beautiful principle is important to keep in mind as we consider ecologically viable systems.

- Technological innovation, driven in no small measure by a culture of consumption, has brought us to the point where we have created problems that technology has not, or the culture will not, address.

- A comprehensive social scientific perspective examines the human interface with the natural environment, considers important processes of modernity, and articulates their impact on social institutions. Such an approach tunes into not just the individual parts of a system, but to the system as a whole.

Chapter Two - The Sociological View and the Unique Vision of Environmental Sociology

Sociology as a discipline came into being in the nineteenth century as social thinkers were attempting to make sense of the problems and complexities of modernity, and, if possible, at least to point the way toward addressing them. The most influential figures in the developing discipline of sociology were Karl Marx, Max Weber, and Émile Durkheim. Other figures, such as Georg Simmel and William Ogburn, added important insights. As perceptive as they were at identifying problems with aspects of modernity, with few notable exceptions, they took the natural environment as something outside of human interaction or concern. They did not spend considerable time or attention on humankind's complex interactions with the natural environment.

Major Influences in the Rise of Sociology

Karl Marx (1867/1967) articulated a number of ideas relevant to environmental sociology. His view of modernity included a thoroughgoing critique of the problems of large-scale production and the concentration of wealth in the hands of the few, juxtaposed with the immiseration of the many.

Marx also theorized about *metabolic rift,* in which the primary production of one place was taken to another. In Marx's time, as in our own, this typically was from rural to urban areas. Increasingly, in the contemporary era of global economies, this includes taking goods or natural resources from one place—typically a poorer, less developed area, and consuming them in another area, typically more affluent and perhaps on the other side of the world. Additionally, we see with increasing regularity, the phenomenon of *commodity chains,* in which natural resources are taken from one place, assembled somewhere else, and consumed yet elsewhere. This, in turn, is connected with an alienation of consumers from the productive process. In our time, for example, the ready availability of chicken at a cheap price seems like a "natural" aspect of the world, becoming more real than the myriad ecological abuses that went into making that chicken available at the local superstore or fast-food establishment.

Marx attributed these problems primarily, but not solely, to capitalism, in which inequalities of distributions of resources hardened themselves into class differences. These problems on the macro level profoundly influenced individuals as well—Marx saw that in class-based societies, and coming to a boiling point under modern capitalism, there were rampant problems of *alienation.* This included a separation from the *product* as well as from the *process* of one's labor, from other people in the society—and ultimately from our own human potential. In contemporary society we can see problems with alienation from the natural environment as much as, or perhaps more than, any time in history.

Max Weber (1921/1968; 1896/1976), sometimes known irreverently as "the Bourgeois Marx," developed a number of relevant ideas; many of which complement and extended Marx's thinking. Weber clearly saw that with modernity came rises in levels of bureaucracies, red tape, rules, and regulations. These may have made sense on some level when they were first instituted, yet over time, they tend to take on a life of their own and spin out of control.

Much as Marx saw the potential for perversities to multiply and metastasize in large-scale systems, so too did Weber. It also bears noting that Weber influenced a number of different lines of theorizing, from critical to functional, and organizational to cultural.

Weber also had a number of helpful ideas in terms of *methods* of study. He introduced the notion of *ideal types* to the social sciences. These would become a yardstick against which to measure actual instances. Weber also used the term *Verstehen*, or deep cultural empathy. It was important to understand the intent of social actors, the context in which they acted, and to attempt to put understanding before judgment.

Weber stressed the importance of culture, and particularly focused on how ideas, and the ethics associated with them, came to influence outcomes in the material world. He saw that some ideas become "legitimate," as they are accepted and internalized by a critical mass of people. While a person may or may not like it, *organizing behavior around something* is what lends it legitimacy (for example, a person may be angry and disgusted by receiving a traffic ticket, even while lending legitimacy to it and to the system of which it is part, by going to court and participating in the proceedings). That legitimacy could then come to pervade an entire culture.

Émile Durkheim (1893/1964; 1912/1965) also had a number of powerful ideas, germane to our discussion. He examined social structure, and the idea of the sacred, including a sense of place, and had a fascination with totemism. Durkheim also focused on culture and the importance of norms to hold a society together. To make sense of social structure, Durkheim introduced the concept of *social facts*, such as the overall division of labor and the norms that held a culture in place, as "external to, and coercive of, the social actor." In a pivotal essay with Marcel Mauss (Durkheim and Mauss 1902/1961), he further articulated how modes of thought are profoundly shaped by the social structure in which they arise.

Georg Simmel (1908/1955) saw the importance of social networks. Social action, including environmental action, often takes place in the context of social systems. Communities, polities, and social movements springing from them, involve social networks, replete with their own meanings and norms.

William Ogburn (1932/1961) coined the term *cultural lag*. In looking at connections between culture and natural environment, this concept is absolutely

Figure 2.1 Key Ideas of Classical Sociologists on the Perversities of Modernity

Karl Marx

Karl Marx wrote extensively about the large-scale ("macro" level) and, albeit to a lesser extent, of the interpersonal ("micro" level) problems particular to capitalistic economic systems arising as an integral aspect of modernity.

Key ideas of Marxist theory include a focus on the perversities of capital accumulation in the hands of a few, juxtaposed with the immiseration of the masses of people. This macro-level condition was, for Marx, intimately tied with the problem of alienation, in which people felt isolated from the product and process of their labor, from one another, and from the natural environment. Alienation from the land, particularly as people moved away from rural agriculture and into cities, contributed to a metabolic rift between town and country. With metabolic rift, the natural wealth, such as crops or natural resources, are taken from one place to another for consumption. This ties in with increasing inequalities between the rich and the poor on the human level, but also contributes to imbalances in ecosystems. With the rapidly globalizing economy, the metabolic rift has become more widespread geographically. The demand for food and resources has led to dramatic increases in resource transfers from poor agrarian regions, to richer, often urbanized ones, sometimes in a different part of the globe.

Max Weber

Max Weber saw modernity as a set of processes leading to a rise in formal rationality, characterized by increases in quantification, calculability and the rise of uniformity and bureaucratization. While these in and of themselves were not necessarily problematic, they did lend themselves to increasing uniformity and tremendous economies of scale.

Weber also made a contribution through his study of ethics, or a set of norms, values and beliefs held and practiced by a community. In his landmark work *The Protestant Ethic and the Spirit of Capitalism*, for example, Weber articulated how a set of norms, values and beliefs could shape how members of a religious community related to the secular world.

In the closing pages of that work, Weber focuses on some of the perverse outcomes of the processes he discusses, and introduces the idea of the iron cage of rationality, in which the rules and institutions people create come to hold such sway over their lives, that the human impulses that created the system in the first place come to be crushed and twisted.

Émile Durkheim

Émile Durkheim examined how traditional societies become modern through such social facts as population size and density, and the norms and values of society. Durkheim saw these social facts as "external to, and coercive of" the people whose behavior they constrained and influenced.

Durkheim's first major work was *The Division of Labor in Society*, in which he examined how social organization in modern society came about, with a particular emphasis on the rise of specialties and systems of inequality.

He also saw modernization of society as responsible for the rise in individualism. In Durkheim's words, "...[T]he individual is born of society–not the society of individuals." For Durkheim, this could have perverse consequences, such that an individual felt cast asunder from the society. He characterized this as egoism. In a related vein, when people do not feel constrained by the norms of society, there is a state of anomie.

These two problems–egoism and anomie–were, for Durkheim, at the root of an array of social pathologies such as suicide, delinquency and crime. A number of social problems that were not articulated for the social sciences until later, but which have huge implications for how human social arrangements impact the natural environment (e.g., what Garrett Hardin and others came to call the tragedy of the commons), can be traced to an uneasy relationship between the individual and the larger social collective.

With the exception of Marx's ideas about metabolic rift (which Marx himself did not particularly emphasize), the classical social theorists almost completely ignored ecological problems. While they were tuned into many of the problems of modernity such as inequality, alienation, egoism, anomie, and the iron cage of rationality, almost without exception, they stopped short of using these ideas to shed light on how human institutions and social arrangements profoundly impacted the environment. This was perhaps a function of the sheer enormity of natural resources which, at the time they were writing, may have seemed limitless. Whatever the reason(s) for this oversight, environmental sociology comes into the academy as somewhat of an orphan discipline. While the study of social inequality, for instance, is well worn by now, having been a preoccupation of much of the thinking of the classical theorists, environmental sociology is a newer addition to the sociological family. That, notwithstanding, we now struggle to understand the causes as well as the consequences of environmental degradation as perverse legacies of modernity.

Sources: Ritzer (2011); Turner (2002); Burns and Kick (2015).

crucial. Cultural systems do tend to adapt to external circumstances such as a change in technology or a geographic discovery. However, the theory of cultural lag points to the social dislocation that takes place as the culture struggles to catch up. In contemporary society, perhaps more than at any time in history, the phenomenon of cultural lag cannot be ignored. The environment is being strained by ever larger numbers of people with increasingly sophisticated technology, and yet the normative systems that would help make sense of those changes and informed ways of dealing with them are not keeping pace. As a result, people treat resources as if they were still plentiful, even as their behavior contributes to an increasing scarcity.

The Critical Need to Think Ecologically, and the Limits of the Pioneers of Sociology

While the pioneers of sociology, particularly Marx, Weber, Durkheim and Simmel, offer tremendous insight into earlier periods in the trajectory of modernity, they did not emphasize the centrality of environmental issues, even in their own time. Yet, given the tremendous environmental degradation that the world has witnessed since the Industrial Revolution, and particularly since the middle of the twentieth century, it is becoming increasingly apparent that we continue to ignore the environment at our peril.

The early sociologists did offer powerful ways of looking at, and thinking through, some of the serious problems modernity had wrought, such as runaway bureaucracies, growing disparities of wealth and poverty, alienation, and a sense of social dislocation. With some exceptions noted, the early theorists did not engage questions of how human society and culture have impacted the natural environment to the extent they did these other issues.

Yet human-induced environmental problems have wildly outstripped what the early theorists encountered and engaged. Environmental sociologists now struggle with how to move beyond the original formulations. As the discipline of sociology has unfolded in these traditions, it has struggled with how to incorporate insights about how societies operate, with more recent empirical findings about how some of those very social factors have impacted the environment in myriad ways, such as global warming, deforestation, declines in biodiversity, and runaway pollution (Tindall 1995).

A partial antidote, and necessary first step, is for humankind to develop the ability and propensity to think ecologically. This involves thinking not only in terms of solving an immediate problem (e.g., keeping American oil flowing and keeping the prices down), but also in terms of the bigger picture over the long run.

Thought, Discourse, and the Natural World

In addition to the macro level, or the "big picture" structural view of society, sociology also looks at society from the standpoint of idea systems. Symbolic interaction and phenomenology look at how people come to see the world as they do, and the social constructions they make in the process.

In their landmark work, *The Social Construction of Reality: A Treatise in the Sociology of Knowledge*, Peter Berger and Thomas Luckmann (1967) develop a theory based in phenomenology about how cultures come to be as they are, and how they socialize new members and even entire generations in older ways of thinking about, and living in, the natural world.

An important idea here is that of *reification*. People come to see the world in a certain way, and that worldview tends to be tempered profoundly by the cultures of which we are part. Those cultures are very slow to change. A central problem of the contemporary era is that while the environment is changing rapidly, and many times for the worse in terms of deforestation, greenhouse gas emissions, pollution, resource depletion, and desertification, our cultures often are not adapted to deal with these issues or even to see them clearly.

We also do well to heed past failures of vocabulary in ways we talk and even think about the environment and our relationship with it. Put another way, it is important to consider questions that at first blush may seem so obvious as to be not worth posing—how do we think about a problem in the first place? In a related vein, particularly in social movements that address environmental concerns, a crucial issue is how to "frame" a problem; and prior to framing something for public consumption, it is first necessary to conceptualize it, to think about it in useful ways (Benford and Snow 2000); (Goffman 1974).

These conceptual considerations come to pervade the culture, manifesting themselves particularly through the many ways its institutions interact with one another. Consider, for example, the political arena in modern societies. It is often here in which economic incentives are implemented. As we will see, for example, a truly free market exists almost solely in the realm of ideas. In practice, political action, particularly around narrow special interests, constrain the free market. The ethics of what "should" be done typically are embedded in the broader culture, and one of the tasks of environmental sociology is to examine and articulate them.

Debates about whether and how to raise taxes on one group relative to another (e.g., the rich, the poor, the middle class, smokers, polluters, tourists, etc.) often unfold against a cultural backdrop. Claims of fairness or unfairness take place in this milieu as well.

That said, sociology as a discipline has been lacking, as have other disciplines, in articulating a clear vision of the many complex ways in which humankind is interconnected with the natural environment. To be sure, the pioneers of sociology such as Marx, Weber, Durkheim, Simmel, and others had ideas and theories that are applicable in many ways. However, it is also the case that these theories were developed at a time in the trajectory of modernity where the focus was on something other than the environment.

These problems, of course, are not unique to sociology. Many economists, as we have seen, tend to treat the environment and natural resources as "externalities"—things that can be taken for granted; and it often fails to fully realize problems caused by "economies of scale." Yet, even as we take a sociological view, we must be aware of the limits of the discipline of sociology. That said, it is important to apply a sociological vision, or the sociological imagination, to environmental problems.

Some of the recent work in the social construction of nature may be fruitful in this regard. The work of William James Gibson extends the ideas of classical thinkers, such as Max Weber, as it seeks to understand how a "disenchantment of nature" has come to be so firmly embedded in major swaths of modern culture. In a related vein, the work of Andy Weigert (Weigert 1997) and others grapples with how people in late-modern cultures come to be alienated from the natural environment, and suggests ways in which cultures might effectively address this.

In the grand tradition of Marx, Weber, Durkheim, and other sociologists, it is important to acknowledge problems with certain aspects of modernity and its many manifestations—including late modernity and post-modernity. Marx focused on the alienation attendant to a class system, Weber on a system of formal rationality that took on a life of its own, coming to dominate and disenchant people's lives, and Durkheim focused on an egoism run amok and a breakdown in society's abilities to promulgate a system of norms to hold itself in place in some sort of a functional way.

We hasten to point out that none of these theorists advocated going back to pre-modern times. Rather, ways of addressing the problems would necessarily take into account the trajectory of modernity itself. In the tradition of the pioneers of sociology, we also see environmental problems through the lenses of modernity. But also in that tradition, we see ways of addressing them embedded in modern society.

Contemporary Theories about the Environment

Much of the contemporary ways of thinking about the environment build on aspects of classical theories. However, because classical theories did not have a thoroughgoing view of the natural environment, contemporary theories that stem from them tend to be somewhat piecemeal.

Work in the Critical Tradition

In the critical tradition of Karl Marx and, to a slightly lesser extent, Max Weber, we now have separate but related lines of research focused around a number of given aspects of the overall system. Here, we consider research and theorizing about: metabolic rift, the treadmill of production and consumption, recursive resource exploitation, the ecological footprint, and environmental justice theories.

Each of these lines of research in the critical tradition have a common focus around inequality, particularly as it pertains to access to resources and exposure to risk. Work in metabolic rift emphasizes how resources are taken from one place and consumed in another. In an increasingly globalized economy, this process that separated town and country in prior times often involves moving resources around the world. Recent research on the ecological footprint phenomenon emphasizes not so much environmental degradation in a given place, as it does on how consumption patterns in one place (typically a richer one) *cause* ecological degradation in another place (often a poorer one).

In a related vein, work in environmental justice gives close consideration to how, even as abundant resources accrue to the socially and economically privileged, environmental risk tends to be disproportionately borne by the marginalized—people of color, poor, and indigenous peoples. Toxic waste dumps, for example, tend to be sited in places with large proportions of marginalized people who are not politically connected enough to be effective at keeping such projects at bay. Those who are more politically influential can off-lay environmental risk to someone else in what has been characterized as the "not in my back yard" (or NIMBY) phenomenon.

Recursive exploitation theory recognizes the multi-level, or fractal, nature of environmental problems. On the most macro level, well-connected and politically powerful nations enjoy a high ecological footprint at the expense of the poorer, less-connected and dependent nations. Yet, these processes replicate themselves at virtually all levels of social organization—within a nation-state, richer and poorer regions engage in metabolic rift processes, constituting environmental *injustice*. And within each of *those* regions differentiation occurs, and the processes of rift and injustice replicate themselves yet again (Clausen and Clark 2005).

Work emphasizing the treadmill of production focuses on the ever expanding nature of capitalism. As markets for goods and services get bigger, the demand for those increase as well. Businesses must expand or die, and expansion is typically at the expense of the natural environment which provides the raw materials, but also the sinks for pollution and waste. This leads to depletion of natural resources, and also to phenomena such as global environmental change, as the treadmill pumps ever increasing amounts of greenhouse gases into the environment. The environment cannot sustain this in the long run. Rather, such patterns lead humankind to overshoot the carrying capacity of various regions and, ultimately, of the planet in general (Gould, Pellow and Schnaiberg 2008).

Work in the Functional Tradition

Theories of ecological modernization and world polity follow in the functionalist tradition. World polity theory focuses on a growing uniformity of institutions across cultures and nations. With this uniformity comes a rise in bureaucratic structures that should, in the ideal, protect the environment (e.g. Frank et al 2000 a & b).

Ecological modernization theory does see the inevitability of the processes of modernity and advanced industrialization. It seeks to make the best of that situation by stressing environmentally responsible action (from overall environmental reform to more focused initiatives, such as recycling in an age of mass consumption, for example). Through the lenses of ecological modernization, the solution lies in a hypermodernity and rational use of technology, in which societies move beyond the heavily polluting stages inherent in earlier industrialization, coming to a post-material stage in which people will tread more lightly on the earth (Sonnenfeld 2002).

We hasten to note that these theories are not without criticism. Any thoughtful consideration of them would necessarily take account of their drawbacks—and rest assured that we do just that in the chapters that follow. Yet we do so not to denigrate, but in the spirit of coming to an understanding of the complexities of the problems at hand.

While ecological modernization theory does, as its name implies, look at certain aspects of modernity, its thrust is quite different from a more encompassing socio-ecological examination of the complexities and perversities of modernity and late modernity. Ecological modernization theory should not be confused with the broader project of environmental sociology, as it strives to make sense of a number of large, otherwise seemingly unrelated, phenomena. More generally, as environmental sociology matures as a discipline, it will be important to continue to focus on the large social and ecological processes that comprise late modernity.

Work Crossing Traditional Boundaries

It also should be noted up front that environmental theories do not necessarily fall neatly into one or the other of critical, constructivist/phenomenological, or functionalist camps. Phenomenological theories, and those related to them, emphasize the effects of ideas and culture on the environment. These include cultural lag theory, for example, work in culture and cognition, and research organized around communication and framing.

We hasten to point out that even these categories do not constitute a perfect fit. For example, William Ogburn, the father of cultural lag theory, was highly influenced by theories of historical materialism, particularly the work of Karl Marx.

Human Ecology

Early in the Industrial Revolution, a British clergyman, Thomas Malthus (1798/ 1993) observed that human population had begun to grow in what he was afraid would be an unsustainable way. He saw a world that was on the brink of having its first billion people, and he warned of "overpopulation" (a term Malthus coined, and which has been in usage ever since). Malthus thought that overpopulation would put a strain on the ability to provide the basic necessities, and would ultimately lead to a world on the brink of an apocalypse, accompanied by the "Four Horsemen" of: war, famine, plague and pestilence. Various thinkers have adopted a Malthusian approach. Most notably, in the late twentieth century, Paul Ehrlich and Anne Ehrlich (1990; also see P. Ehrlich 1968), continue to warn of the dangers of a "population explosion."

Building on insights of Malthusian thinking, as well as that from the traditional social sciences, human ecologists developed the *"POET"* model, which emphasized the interplay among *Population*, human *Organization*, the natural *Environment*, and *Technology* (Commoner 1971, 1992; Hawley 1981).

The next generation of theorizing in this line emphasized trying to specify a series of mathematical equations to predict environmental *Impact* as an outcome. With the input variables of *Population*, *Affluence* and *Technology*, this so-called *IPAT* model focused on what researchers saw as the major influences on environmental outcomes (Dietz and Rosa 1994; Burns et al. 1994, 1997; Kick et al. 1996). A variant of the IPAT framework, the so-called *STIRPAT* model, followed in this tradition, with a focus on the probabilistic (or *Stochastic*) nature of the problem (York, Rosa, and Dietz 2003a, 2003b). Another crucial concern of Human Ecology, is linking the local with the global, in terms of the natural environment, as well as of human interactions (e.g., Givens and Jorgenson 2012; Marquart-Pyatt 2013).

Work in the POET/IPAT/STIRPAT Tradition continues to evolve. One promising model, which we discuss more in the final chapter, is characterized by the word POETICAA, where (P)opulation, Human (O)rganization, the (E) nvironment, (T)echnology, Environmental (I)llness & Health, (C)ulture, (A) ffluence, and ways of (A)ddressing problems are all taken into account (Burns & Kick 2015).

Some Other Notable Environmental Voices

Rachel Carson, author of *Silent Spring*. Written in 1962, it illuminated the devastating effects of pesticides (particularly DDT) on the environment.

More recently, researchers have begun taking the environment more seriously, not only as an outcome of social processes, but also as a predictor of human outcomes including health and well-being, risk, and violence. In this book we give brief discussion and due consideration to each of these theories, and evidence that might tend to support or refute them. Following in the tradition of the prophetic work of Rachel Carson for example, Sandra Steingraber and others (e.g., Colborn et al. 1997) have pieced together a compelling narrative based on collective and individual historical accounts as well as on a rapidly growing body of hard scientific evidence, of some of the profound effects of environmental irresponsibility on planetary and human health (Zavestoski et al. 2004; Frickel 2004).

Some of these themes show up in popular non-fiction as well. For example, Thomas Homer-Dixon's (1999) *Environment, Scarcity and Violence* brings together a wide array of work linking environmental depletion with social outcomes such as collective violence. Thomas Friedman's (2008) *Hot, Flat and Crowded* looks at relationships among climate change, population pressures, rising standards of living (particularly in large, rapid-growth societies such as India and China), and broader globalization processes.

One of the goals of this book is to consider a broad array of ideas about, and research into, the complex and nuanced variety of interfaces between humankind and the natural environment. We seek to make sense of environmental problems through the lenses of modernity—the huge macro-level processes that have been operating for hundreds of years and which influence us all so profoundly, even now and moving into the third millennium.

So we offer this book in the spirit of furthering discussion. Environmental sociology is a living and vibrant field, albeit relatively young. It builds on older, more established traditions, even as it strives to make sense of a truly pressing set of issues and problems. We believe it is becoming increasingly clear that the most pressing problem of the twenty-first century and beyond will be the question of how and whether people can live in the natural environment and can do so sustainably.

The larger project of planetary survival unfolding over the course of this century will necessarily involve *un*doing much of the damage that was caused in earlier phases of modernity. We believe that only through an integrated way of thinking about the environment, not as something to be tacked on as an afterthought, but as an integral part of the human condition, can humanity hope to come abreast of the problems at hand.

Using Sociology to Understand Environmental Problems

As early theorists of modernity pointed out, population growth and changes in living patterns, such as dramatic rises in urbanization, are themselves intimately connected with other aspects of modernity such as technological change, economies of scale leading to a greater degree of interconnectedness and predatory globalization, increasing levels of bureaucratization, a rise in the faith that people have in science, increasing institutional differentiation, and dramatic growth in consumption. These, in turn, has led to unsustainable increases in resource depletion, social dislocation, concentrations of wealth on the one hand and poverty and risk on the other, uneven development, and many of the environmental problems that go with it (Brechin et al. 2003).

Modern society witnessed the rise, as well, of individualism. A number of theorists saw this as a mixed blessing. To be sure, modernity did see a decline in feudalism and slavery along with an increased awareness of, and respect for, human and civil rights. The abolition of slavery in the United States of the nineteenth century and the civil rights movement and legislation of the twentieth century were, in no small measure, some of the fruits of modernity. The importance of these can hardly be overstated.

Yet, as Durkheim and others pointed out, with the rise of modernity also came the rise, not only of individualism that celebrated human potential and dignity, but of a darker kind of individualism—disconnected, alienated, estranged from, the larger collective. This type of individualism brought with it a host of problems around selfish behavior; these include what Durkheim (1893/1964) singled out as egoism and Freud (1923/1990; 1930/2010) saw as narcissism, even as Marx (1867/1967) decried alienation.

It is a rise in selfishness that fuels the phenomenon that has come to be known as *the tragedy of the commons* (Hardin 1968, 1993), where numerous individuals acting selfishly can have the aggregate effect of causing catastrophic damage to the earth's resources. The problem stems not so much with individualism *per se*, but with a disembodied, alienated individualism which itself arises as a perverse twist in modernity. This, in turn, leads to people externalizing environmental problems by not taking full responsibility for the environmental outcomes they have a hand in causing. This sometimes leads to a cascade of problems manifesting on a number of different levels of analysis, from the individual to the collective, or from one nation-state relative to another.

While managing one's conscious awareness is part of any number of grand spiritual traditions, it is perhaps more important now than ever. With perverse modernity and alienation come a number of problems that slip under our radar. For instance, we probably do not fully recognize the corrosive nature of the isolating technologies and frenetic noise that have become such integral components of contemporary culture.

We witness some of the perversities of modernity in the precipitous decline in availability of ecological resources such as forests, fresh air, and a stabilizing environment. What becomes of people who grow up in *ecologically* impoverished circumstances? Society has come, albeit grudgingly, to recognize how devastating it can be to grow up in socio-economic poverty; such circumstances can negatively affect, for example, a person's educational opportunities and the freedom to build their stock of human capital; but little, if any, thinking tends to go into what it will mean to current and future generations who are deprived of exposure to nature.

Will those people themselves develop into adults less likely to see its importance? To be sure, society offers plenty of alternatives to experiencing nature, many or most of which are embedded in advertising and the treadmill of production and consumption. The rise of shopping malls, video games, and such may be poor adaptations to being ecologically impoverished. Narcissistic, alienated consumption leads to the rise of noisy, polluting outdoor activities, emphasizes using, taking and consuming natural resources, rather than living in harmony with them.

The solution to environmental problems most certainly involves education. That is not to negate the gains in formal education of the last 200 years. It does, however, bear acknowledging that education must move in the direction of a rising ecological consciousness. In a similar vein to people taking a world religion class becoming, over time, less religiously intolerant and more understanding and ultimately less likely to engage in religious violence, an education in basic ecological principles may help to awaken an environmental consciousness. Far from being "propaganda" of some sort, the important point is to engage the sense of how ecosystems on the planet have helped shape, even as they are impacted by, human interaction.

As societies continue to get bigger and more complex, their institutions tend to become more differentiated and specialized. While this has some positive features, it also tends to lead to a situation that Weber predicted over 100 years ago—institutions developing a life of their own, following their own logic. In addition, *institutional disarticulation* arises, in which the logic of one institution (such as the economy, for example) does not dovetail with the logic of other institutions (the polity and civil society, for instance). From the individual, through the meso-level of institutions, to the planetary, problems arise in late modernity that present tremendous challenges to ecological sustainability.

Taking all these factors into consideration, the environmental problems of late modernity are wicked and daunting indeed. While the discipline of sociology offers a powerful set of insights and analytical tools, it is coming late to the game. Environmental sociology and human ecology, while fairly young sub-disciplines, have much to offer, but the problems are pressing. There is much at stake.

Chapter 2 Summary

- Important figures in sociology such as Karl Marx, Max Weber, and Émile Durkheim developed key concepts that social thinkers use to make sense of the problems and complexities of modernity, and point the way toward addressing them.

- Karl Marx theorized and addressed topics such as metabolic rift and contradictions of capitalism. He discussed his theory about the bourgeois class who made demands on the proletariat class through labor and the taking of resources for capitalistic gain.

- Max Weber introduced ideas such as ideal types and Verstehen. He influenced many different theories, and he stressed the importance of culture with a particular focus on how ideas and ethics associated with them can influence outcomes in the material world.

- Émile Durkheim's theories were based around social structure and the sacred, including the idea of totemism. He believed that cultures and, more particularly, norms hold societies together. He introduced the concept of social facts. He also saw modernization of society as responsible for the rise in individualism.

- People come to see the world in a certain way, and that worldview tends to be tempered profoundly by the cultures of which we are part. Those cultures are very slow to change.

- A number of theoretical ideas have come out of the critical tradition in sociology. These include: the treadmill of production, the ecological footprint, recursive exploitation, metabolic rift, and environmental justice.

- Environmental justice gives close consideration to how, even as abundant resources accrue to the socially and economically privileged, environmental risk tends to be disproportionately borne by the marginalized—people of color, poor, and indigenous peoples.

- Ecological modernization and world polity theories grew out of the functional tradition.

- Thomas Malthus coined the term overpopulation. Building on that premise, POET, IPAT and POETICAA models were constructed. These models lay out how population has a profound effect on the environment on a macro level.

- Other notable environmental thinkers, including Rachel Carson and Thomas Friedman, examined things such as water pollution and pesticides through collective and personal accounts, which show how the human footprint has forever changed the earth and its inhabitants. We believe it is becoming increasingly clear that the most pressing problem of the twenty-first century and beyond will be the question of how and whether people can live in the natural environment sustainably.

- As societies continue to get bigger and more complex, their institutions tend to become more differentiated and specialized. While this has some positive features, it also tends to lead to a situation that Weber predicted over 100 years ago—institutions developing a life of their own, following their own logic.

- Environmental sociology and human ecology are relatively late arrivals, coming into their own only in the second half of the 20th century. They offer powerful correctives to many of the gaps in traditional sociology, but there is much work still to be done on the most pressing of problems in coming to grips with the interface between humankind and the natural environment.

Chapter Three - The Natural Environment and the Culture of Late Modernity

What is Culture?

There is an old saw about two fish swimming past one another. In an attempt to strike up a conversation, the first fish inquires: "How's the water?" The other fish, looking puzzled, stops mid-stroke and asks: "What is water?"

Culture for humankind is something like water for the fish. It is so ubiquitous, so ever-present a part of our experience, that we may sometimes forget to notice that it is even there. This is particularly true in situations where people stay in the same place, hang around with the same people, listen to the same radio stations, and do not ever find themselves outside of their own familiar circumstances.

Culture is a system for organizing and prioritizing communication, belief, thought, value, and action in the context of an ethical framework (Weber 1978 [1921], 1948, 1985 [1904]). It enables us to prioritize the information that we perceive in our day-to-day existence, and ultimately, over the course of a lifetime. Each of us make sense of the world with the help of culture. Culture provides ethical meaning to our perceptions.

On a more down-to-earth level, culture is what we use to make meaning of things. It provides us with the "toolkit" (Swidler 2001) from which we choose possible ways to act toward, and in many cases to think about, the world we inhabit.

Although we humans may experience events using the same five senses, our resulting perceptions are not universal. Experience can be chaotic and overwhelming. A framework of meaning is necessary to impose order out of chaos — to make sense of the masses of data that each of us perceives. Therefore, perception is filtered through the prism of culture. Frameworks of meaning dictate much of how we see the world.

This system that we call culture informs our judgments. Opinions are formed and conclusions drawn based on shared culture. Culture can be thought of as an interpretive framework or framework of meaning. This *network of meaning* directs us in assigning correctness and value to actions. Culture, for each of us, determines what is right or wrong; good or bad; just or unjust; true or false. At first glance we may assume that these are universal values, but that is often not the case. While common norms, values, and beliefs are held within a culture they can vary from one culture to the next. Institutions and actions are judged relative to culture. There are unique cultural ways of seeing and acting.

Culture, for humankind, is something like water for the fish. It is so ubiquitous, so ever-present a part of our experience, that we may sometimes forget to notice that it is even there.

Networks of meaning determine which ideas and perceptions are valuable. Behaviors, mores, folkways, traditions, and different types of information are judged against the backdrop of culture. Centrality is a key feature of the prioritizing power of networks. As a rule, more central elements or "nodes" of the culture have a more powerful influence than those peripheral elements. The prioritizing nature of culture ensures that some ideas are more important and valuable than others. This prioritization is universal to *all* cultures (H. Simon 1990; Bourdieu 1984). When a lack of harmony occurs between an object of perception and a network of meaning, it is always the object of perception and not the culture, which is deemed *other* and rejected as strange and foreign. While we may think of ourselves as unbiased and open-minded, our judgments, perceptions, and ideas are influenced by our own culture.

Culture, by its very nature, is taken for granted by the participants. Culture works as a mechanism of socialization from birth. We are blind to our own culture because we cannot see it as uncommon. Culture is woven into our everyday existence. It is difficult indeed to view one's culture from a distance, given that culture is so personal. When something becomes so self-evident that it is taken for granted and rarely even noticed, it becomes a privileged and forceful part of culture. This inability to take stock of one's own culture is most commonly referred to by social scientists as *reification*.

A cogent example in American culture is the reverence given to individual choice. In contrast, many other cultures stress cooperation and societal harmony. As we shall see later, the spread of hyper-individualism among cultures of the modern world is one of the major contributing factors that make sustainability such a hard goal to achieve. Ways in which we have constructed ideas about individualism can sometimes be taken to extremes. For example, when individuals obsessed with their own rights, and not feeling constrained by a sense of social or ecological responsibility to counter-balance those rights, can drift into selfishness. As we will see later in the book, this sort of selfishness can aggregate to truly astounding proportions in causing significant and widespread environmental problems. We will discuss this in depth later, when we consider the phenomenon of *The Tragedy of the Commons,* but suffice it to say here, that selfishness and greed, while age-old problems to be sure (reliably showing up as problems in the canonical texts of virtually every one of the wisdom traditions, from the Bible, to the Bhagavad Gita, to the Analects of

Confucius, and pretty much everything in between!), have, if anything, seem to have gotten even more acute and problematic in the modern age.

Culture, then, is the water in which we humans swim. It remains, however, largely invisible to us, precisely because our own culture appears to us as self-evident "truth." In other words, we are so used to the culture of which we are part, that we take it for granted. In so doing, we cannot effectively separate ourselves from it. This cannot be separate from how we relate to the natural environment.

Understanding Environmental Problems through the Lenses of Culture

We have learned that culture organizes and prioritizes all of the data that we must make sense of to make our way in the world on a daily basis. The act of prioritization means that some ideas are more important than others. Therefore, culture assigns value. It is the act of assessing worth and importance that is so crucial to culture's impact on environmental problems. Man has always had an impact on the environment. Humanity's penchant for tool making and our unique uses of the natural world, coupled with the ability to harvest and gather natural resources at an unprecedented scale, set us apart and ensures that we will change the natural environment.

The need to survive and adapt to the environment at hand will inevitably give rise to cultures very much dictated by place. Institutions, classes, customs, arts, social mores, marriage and family structure, and all of the many hallmarks of culture are both limited and encouraged by place. The culture of the desert nomad is dictated by the need to survive in a hot, arid land, while the culture of Arctic peoples is similarly dictated by the harsh conditions of freezing sea, ice, and snow. Likewise, natives of tropical forests will develop a uniquely different culture than inhabitants of temperate climates. All of the variations that encompass the natural environment — climate, physical geography, vegetation, available game animals, suitable draft and pack animals, and many more factors — influence culture (Diamond, 1998).

Even the earliest civilizations were responsible for environmental degradation. Yet, some cultures have had a greater impact on the natural environment than others. Likewise, some cultures have had values of sustainability, while others have not. Still other cultures — the Native American tribes of North America come to mind — have placed a high priority on conservation and bequeathing a communal natural legacy to future generations. These cultures are often very dependent upon nature for survival and have a much closer bond to the natural world. Out of necessity, these cultures have made the environment a central organizing principle. It is no coincidence that modern Western cultures misunderstand these nature-friendly cultures.

Culture and the Trajectory of Modernity

Culture has changed as human societies have progressed from more primitive to more advanced forms over the last ten thousand years. The relationship between humans and the natural ecology has also changed profoundly. Two instances stand out as examples of this type of sweeping change. The first of these is referred to as the *Neolithic Revolution*, or, more aptly, the *Agricultural Revolution*. This first period is characterized by a gradual evolution from nomadic hunting and gathering to farming in one place. The second great change began in the eighteenth century and is known as the *Industrial Revolution*.

The Agricultural Revolution led to a gradual change in how humans organized themselves and to an increasingly complex society. The rooted (pun intended) nature of farming gave rise to new ways of organizing society and to new technologies. It is during the Agricultural Revolution that we see the development of village life, writing and record keeping, divisions of labor and specialization, and social classes. Our cultural references in older institutions such as religion have also been influenced by our agrarian past (think for example, of aphorisms like "as ye sow, so shall ye reap").

Our relationship with nature also changed due to the advent of agricultural technology as people began to engage in activities that facilitated larger harvests and greater yields of livestock. Some examples include the domestication of large animals for plowing the soil, slash and burn agriculture, selection and breeding of crops and livestock, irrigation and damming of waterways, and new methods for storing and preserving agricultural bounty.

As profound as the impact of the Agricultural Revolution was on culture and humankind's relationship with nature, even greater change was experienced as a result of the Industrial Revolution. Despite the sweeping changes experienced during the transformation from nomadic hunter-gatherers to farmers, people and nature still shared a powerful bond. In many ways, the Industrial Revolution severed this bond. Machines were invented to complete old tasks that had previously been done by animals or humans; and other machines were built to accomplish work that had never even been dreamed of on the farm. The nature of work changed, and people began to move from the countryside to the city in search of employment. Rural life was replaced by urban life, and the division of labor changed even more (Berry 2015). Gradually, as mechanization reached the farmer, a diminishing number of people supplied the food necessary to feed the growing industrial centers. Fewer people even thought about the natural world, much less retained a connection to it.

Additionally, the pace of change itself was greatly accelerated during this time period. We are, each of us, a product of our ancestral heritage. Both physically and culturally, we are who we are because of the slow and gradual progression from hunter-gatherer to farmer. We retain the traits that we acquired to survive and prosper from our earliest times to the present. Although we humans are unique in our ability to weather change, we are limited by our need to absorb change slowly over many generations. An accelerating change of pace made it difficult for culture to keep up.

The net effect of industrial and post-industrial era economistic thinking is a culture that emphasizes a hyper-individualism, capitalistic economies, and large-scale production and consumption.

In modern times, we retain composite characteristics of our hunter-gatherer, agrarian, and industrial selves. Yet, we in the developed world are immersed in a new post-industrial era. Tenets of this new cultural shift include: advanced technology and a corresponding high degree of faith and dependence upon it; a complex social differentiation of society and a hyper-individualism; and globalizing processes of *metabolic rift* that shuttle ever larger amounts of resources from one place to another far removed place; and ever increasing scales of production and consumption. These beliefs are so common and widely accepted that they are virtually unnoticed in our daily lives and have become the cultural yardstick by which we measure the world. Ominously, the culture of modernity has quickly become the norm that less developed countries strive to emulate. As the Western lifestyle, and the culture of acquisitiveness and consumption in particular, diffuses more generally, the toll on the planet increases with it.

The Individual and Society in Late Modernity

As the Western world transitioned from rural, agrarian village life to urban, industrial city life and culture was transformed, so, too, did the individual within society experience profound changes. The old support systems of extended family and clan began to break down. Social hierarchies that had existed for millennia lost their relevance as tenant farmers migrated from manor and farm to factory and office. Wages were the currency of the day. *Noblesse oblige*, that ancient code of responsibility and loyalty that bound master and subject, began to wane. The industrialist, merchant and businessman displaced the nobleman at the apex of power.

Just as in the past, an ideological and cultural belief system emerged to justify the new social order. *Enlightenment* thinkers had actually set the groundwork for these changes. Political philosophers such as Hobbes, Locke, Montesquieu, and Rousseau questioned the natural order and dared envision a world where the individual had rights and value beyond that of loyal subject. So too, the world watched as a bold new experiment in the former colonies of Great Britain put Enlightenment political theory into practice.

In the realm of economic theory, Adam Smith's seminal work *An Inquiry into the Nature and Causes of the Wealth of Nations* attempted to explain why some cultures prospered, while others did not. Published in 1776 at the beginning of the Industrial Revolution, *The Wealth of Nations* became holy writ for the new economic order. Core tenets of capitalism, such as the division of labor, supply and demand, wages, profit, investment, stocks, and the accumulation of capital were set forth in its pages. Practices that had once been suspect or immoral, like the charging of interest, now made good economic sense and became smart business. Economistic thinking was taken to new heights and business was catapulted to the most important of places in society. *Laissez-faire* economics and "free-market" culture defined modern nation economies.

In 1905, the German sociologist Max Weber published *The Protestant Ethic and the Spirit of Capitalism*. A central theme of his work is that individual hard work led to the rise of capitalism, and the accumulation of wealth in those countries where religious thinking (Protestantism generally, and its Calvinist branches most particularly) encouraged hard work and thrift. Likewise, Social Darwinism — the belief that natural selection and survival of the fittest applied to human society as well as the natural world — was a rationale used to justify what can only be described as economic domination and exploitation during the last decades of the nineteenth century and the beginning decades of the twentieth century. It follows that individuals in society who are hard-working, virtuous, and frugal will prosper, while those who are lazy, seek the easy way, and spend their wages unwisely are destined for the poor house.

In the latter third of the twentieth century and continuing into today, a growing belief in prosperity theology — the belief that God will financially bless believers — has also added to a general sense of entitlement on the part of the individual. Thus, material wealth is an outward manifestation of a life well lived and proof that one has worked harder than others. Taken even further, this line of reasoning posits that God has pre-ordained an entitlement of abundance to some individuals. What would have once been considered a moral shortcoming and the height of hubris — to center one's relationship with God upon individual wants and desires — is now seen by many to be proper religious doctrine (Bowler 2013).

The net effect of industrial and post-industrial era economistic thinking is a culture that emphasizes a hyper-individualism, capitalist economies, and large-scale production and consumption. This results in a common cultural rationale that the virtuous individual who plays by the rules and works hard is entitled to his or her success. Entitlement, taken to an extreme, leads to a sense that one's own rights are more important than anyone else's rights and removes any sense of responsibility relative to society. Furthermore, cultures with high levels of individualism are more likely to vote conservatively (Burns 1992) and to the detriment of the environment. In capitalistic, individualistic cultures, people seek to maximize their own short-sighted individual self-interests and to get as much as they can get away with (even if it means leaving nothing for everyone else), and simultaneously shifting the costs to the collective and/or the environment on which everyone depends. As we alluded earlier, this situation, in which individual rights trump communal rights, is referred to as *the tragedy of the commons*. Such a culture, by its very nature, allows the individual to hold environmentally unsustainable practices as legitimate.

The Problem Writ Large: Mismatches between Culture and Sustainability

Earlier, we touched upon the profound changes that occurred when humankind progressed from the Paleolithic to an agrarian lifestyle and again from agrarian to industrial society. These dramatic shifts in lifestyle caused correspondingly dramatic cultural shifts. Those traits that were useful to us during our previous incarnations are not easily dismissed. Like all animals, humans are capable of adapting to changing conditions — given enough time. In earlier times, the pace of change was much slower, and both evolution and culture had time to change too. We are, however, products of both our earlier selves and our modern world and have retained traits that were once valuable but are now less so. Evolution is slow — change in the modern world is fast. Our bodies, emotions, and minds struggle to keep up.

This "mismatch" between our inherited makeup and the modern conditions that we find ourselves in today can be most easily illustrated by the preponderance of *diseases of civilization*. Hypertension, cancer, type 2 diabetes, and asthma are examples of physical ailments that have a direct link to modern lifestyle. So too, it can be argued, an increase in disorders of the psyche such as anxiety, depression, and addiction are a manifestation of the stresses of a mismatch between our evolutionary selves and our modern everyday selves (Lieberman, 2013).

Mismatches between Evolution and Technology

Humankind's own technology has created mismatches between what our bodies are able to adapt to and the changes to the natural environment that occurs through the widespread use of technology (Epstein 2008). For example, the widespread use of pesticides and herbicides have provided an easy solution to an age-old problem — how to maximize food production by eliminating loss of crops to insects, pests, and plant diseases. Incredible leaps in production were realized with the advent of modern chemistry. At first, few questioned the wisdom of spraying chemicals that were known to cause health

Figure 3.1 Enantiodromia: Nature Senses Imbalances and Pushes Back

The tendency for an action to cause a reaction to itself is called *enantiodromia*. Often, the reaction has a greater impact than the original action. Reactions are typically unpredictable, and the larger the initial action, the greater the reaction.

Anyone who has taken ninth-grade science can say, almost reflexively, Isaac Newton's maxim that for every action there is an equal and opposite reaction. The reaction experienced in enantiodromia may in fact be *more* forceful or violent, particularly if it has gone past some tipping point (which may not have been apparent before the action took place).

The idea of enantiodromic processes has been present in the ideas of thinkers from ancient times to the modern. The psychiatrist Carl Jung relied heavily on enantiodromic processes to formulate his philosophy.

The idea of enantiodromia pre-dates Newton and, in the West, goes back to the pre-Socratic thinker, Heraclitus. Enantiodromia is a principle that can be found in many, if not most, wisdom traditions. The law of Karma in Hinduism and Buddhism, and the principle of Wu Chi, or the balancing of Yin and Yang energies in Taoism, and the idea of "As you sow, so shall you reap" in the Judeo-Christian tradition, all reflect this idea (Burns 2016).

The philosopher Aristotle built on these ideas in developing his framework of dialectics, which influenced the course of Western philosophy, becoming a pillar in the work of the German Enlightenment philosopher G.W.F. Hegel. Hegel, in turn, was highly influential on the work of sociologists Georg Simmel and, particularly, Karl Marx, whose theory of "dialectical materialism" held, *inter alia*, that the main driving force of history was the conflict between classes. Yet, as a keen observer of enantiodromic processes can readily discern, the dialectical relationships led to there being a fatal flaw, or *contradiction of capitalism*, such that "Capitalism produces its own grave diggers..." (Marx and Engels 1848/1948). The process would concentrate so much capital in so few hands, causing the system to become precariously imbalanced over time, that it would collapse of its own weight, most likely at the hands of a revolution of disenfranchised workers with "nothing to lose but [their] chains."

Building on the work of Marx and Engels, the environmental sociologist James O'Connor (1998) has pointed out a *second contradiction of capitalism*, in which, in virtually every exchange, resources are taken from the natural environment without their being replaced. What is given back to the earth is in the form of pollution or some other form of degradation. Intertwined with this is the process of *metabolic rift*, in which the resources from one locale are taken to another. While this may be from the local countryside into the town, it is, particularly in late modernity, increasingly more likely to be from one country or geographic region to another. The world economy operates with a logic that, in many ways, is out of sync with the natural ecological processes of the planet (Burns and Rudel 2015).

Enantiodromia has been used by other twentieth century thinkers in disciplines from history (Thompson 1971, 1981) to psychology (Jung 1959, 1960, 1970). Although the idea has, with some exceptions, largely been ignored by sociologists and human ecologists, it is nonetheless a useful tool in helping us analyze a wide array of phenomena.

Enantiodromia is a form of pushback — often a negative or unfavorable response to an action. In ecology, for example, small and seemingly ignorable problems, such as the overuse of pesticides and fertilizers, have resulted in enantiodromic processes that cause things such as cancers and birth defects. The release of greenhouse gases into the atmosphere have resulted in pushback by environmental forces that cause global warming, desertification, and climate change that, in turn, cause other problems, such as widening the vectors of exotic species and melting polar ice caps that, in turn, threaten the livelihood of various species, cause rising tides and sea levels which threaten a number of vulnerable areas, particularly along low-lying sea coasts, just to name a few.

The idea of enantiodromia is found in many of the world's wisdom traditions. The balancing of Yin and Yang energies in Taoism is one such example.

Enantiodromic processes occur in the culture, in terms of how ideas are met with opposition, and can, tragically, feed into self-fulfilling prophesies. Suppression of would-be "terrorists" by a powerful regime, for example, may so alienate and enrage an entire generation of people who feel so put down and degraded, that they may, as they come of age, ripen into a hatred of that regime and, perhaps, develop an animus to that regime and people and ideas they associate with it.

This principle takes place in social interactions at virtually all levels of analysis, from the overbearing act of a partner in a couple relationship being met with less than a harmonious response, to civic meetings and congressional actions. As one side of a debate or a controversy pushes their agenda over the edge, there is pushback. When the pushback does not occur in the social realm, it occurs in nature. For example, polluters and economic forces have placed the burden of proof upon those who oppose unsustainable and damaging practices, rather than the onus being placed upon those who would pollute to prove that their actions will not result in damaging pushback by the ecosystem. In our hyper-paced world, new products and technologies are introduced faster than they can be vetted (Steingraber 1998). Our culture may reflect what is expedient for business in the short-run, but not necessarily what is best in the long-run for environmental and societal well-being. The natural environment pushes back, and that is reflected in increased rates of diseases such as cancers.

The idea of enantiodromia, in the West, goes back to the pre-Socratic thinker Heraclitus.

The lesson from our observations of enantiodromic processes, as is the lesson from virtually any of the major wisdom traditions that have withstood the test of time, is that the laws of nature are in delicate balance. We disturb that balance at our peril. The farther out nature's balance gets pushed (for example, by strip mining, heavy and indiscriminate use of pesticides, fracking or dumping of toxic wastes), the harder nature pushes back. Ultimately, the law of nature is to seek balance, and that is true from the smallest to the largest scales. We do well to remember that. Learning to live with the natural balances of ecosystems, without pushing those limits we do not fully understand, may be the most important cultural lesson of all.

Sources: Jung (1959, 1960; 1970); Thompson (1971; 1981); Burns (2009; 2016) Burns and Rudel (2015); Steingraber (1998); Marx and Engels (1848/1948); James O'Connor (1998).

problems and even death, in high enough doses, on the foods that people eat. Yet, it soon became evident to scientists that these chemicals were entering the ecosystem and having unintended consequences on both nature and humans.

Likewise, the widespread use of additives, preservatives, and sweeteners, such as high-fructose corn syrup in the foods we consume have resulted in obesity, cancers, diabetes, and hypertension. The benefits of long shelf life and cheaper food comes at a high price for health. It seems too much of a good thing is a very human problem. The same can be said of many of the labor saving devices that we use every day. Lack of physical activity is a serious problem in the developed world. Unfortunately, the rest of the world (as evidenced by rising obesity rates in the developing world) seems to be rushing headlong to catch up.

The modern industrial/post-industrial era is but a brief interval in the timeline of human evolution. Much of basic human biology and culture developed during the earlier phases of our history (e.g., religion and its symbols, writing, early stratification systems), while things like modern economic systems, and advanced technology developed during the relatively shorter industrial/post-industrial eras, and have therefore, had less time to integrate into human culture. The resulting mismatches put the natural environment and the people who depend on it in a precarious position.

Mismatches between Large-Scale Economies and the Natural Ecology

Another important dilemma to consider is the immense mismatch between the large-scale production of modern economies and sustainable ecology. Once again, the catch-22 of technology — and also, of course, human nature — figure into this modern quandary.

The modern global economy is predicated on steady growth and greater productivity. Our financial institutions, stock markets and businesses, large and small, rely on greater and greater consumption to fuel economic expansion. So too, individuals are dependent on growth as the engine of employment and an increase in living standards. Steady growth encourages large-scale production. Large-scale production is enabled by the technologies of, first, the Industrial Revolution and, now in our own time, the post-industrial information age. This *"treadmill of production"* has profound environmental consequences. Human history has been a tale of growth and expansion. Stasis only happens in textbooks — it is rarely, if ever, the case in real life.

There is a basic mismatch between the time trajectories and feedback mechanisms of economic systems and ecological systems. The first is short, and the latter is long. To conflate the two is folly and invites catastrophe. Yet, that is precisely what the modern, global economy is predicated upon. This is especially true of the last century.

Additionally, in economies with large-scales of production and consumption, there tends to be a large disparity of wealth. The rich get richer and the poor get poorer. This condition can only go on for so long before consumption drops along with growth.

And, because ecological feedback loops may not be immediately evident, environmental damage from unchecked growth may not become known until lots of precious time has gone by, and the problem has become significantly worse than it otherwise would have been. The enthusiasm for economic growth can lead a country to ignore the natural limits of the ecosystem. This is all too often the case. Witness the possibly irreparable damage done to the rainforests and the oceans in the frenzied rush to harvest their natural resources by the most expedient means available.

Compare the steady growth model of our modern global economy to the "small is beautiful" model of an ecologically sustainable economy, in which living systems thrive and inhabit many smaller niches in a bio-diverse ecosystem (Schumacher 1973/1999).

Weak political leadership further compounds the problems inherent in a steady growth economy. All too often, rather than take into account the natural limits of ecosystems, political leaders court catastrophic ecological disaster when they seek to maximize short term economic gains at the expense of the ecology and, indeed, the long term well-being of humanity. Unfortunately, the needed political will is absent or weak. The future looks bleak unless those who wield power choose to look out for humankind's long-term best interests.

Why Institutional Fixes by Themselves Often Are Ineffective

Culture permeates the institutions of a society; and therefore cultures can be said to be meta-institutional. Institutions are a reflection of the culture in which they were created and all institutions are equally influenced by culture. Culture is the glue that connects and binds institutions to one another. Institutions such as commerce, banking, and the labor system are connected by culture in the same way that culture creates connections between family, school, and class. The affinity between culture and institutions is likely to make isolated changes in one institution ineffective.

This is why institutional "fixes" rarely are successful in solving a problem. An isolated fix in one institution is likely to trigger an *enantiodromic* process of cascading consequences. Culture seeks to restore the prior equilibrium across the entirety of society's institutions. A well-known recent example is the attempt to impose a Western-style democracy in a nation that retains widespread tribalism and has no system of formal education or free markets

Ever-increasing advances in technology allow us to impact the environment to a degree never imagined. Tools, such as the internal combustion engine,

Figure 3.2 Cultural Lag and Cultural Diffusion

New technology that relied on the burning of fossil fuels for power made raw materials like oil a valuable commodity and changed modern culture.

Culture changes in response to changing demographic, technological, and material conditions, such as the discovery of new resources. Yet, some institutions change more quickly than others. Culture may change quickly, but is more likely to unfold over long periods of time that may involve centuries or even millennia.

Early in the twentieth century, William Ogburn observed that there were two types of culture. The first he called material culture. *Material culture* is simply a material change, for instance, the development of a new technology or the discovery of new sources of natural resources. The second change he dubbed adaptive culture. *Adaptive culture* is the cultural response to the new material culture. For instance, culture adapted to the widespread use of the automobile by building housing a great distance from places of employment. The concept of distance changed in response to a new technology. Culture adapted to the new ability to travel greater distances at greater speed than was previously possible.

Ogburn also noticed that there is usually a time difference between a material cultural change and an adaptive cultural response. Sometimes, the gap between a material change and the adaptive change can be quite long. This gap, Ogburn referred to as *cultural lag*. Culture changes in response to material changes, but adaptation may take place gradually over a long period of time and often involves some disruption and social confusion.

In pre-industrial society, culture was better able to adapt to technological changes, but because the pace of change today is so rapid, the situation can easily become more complicated as culture struggles to keep up with an ever-increasingly rapid succession of material changes. This process is referred to as *cultural warp*. Over time, the process of cultural warp has intensified. The pace of change in the pre-industrial world was slower. Culture had a chance to catch up. People and institutions were able to adapt.

Additionally, because of globalization, change in one part of the world often causes change in *other* parts of the world. This phenomenon is called *cultural diffusion*. Change takes place first in more technologically advanced cultures. It then spreads to less technologically advanced cultures whether they want it or not. This cultural domination of one culture over another has been termed *hegemony* by the Italian social thinker Antonio Gramsci. The result is often resentment and conflict from the receiving culture.

In terms of environmental change, the material changes brought about by advances in technology have enabled humans to damage the ecology and to harvest natural resources on an unprecedented scale. Uniquely, Western values (especially in the United States) of hyper-individualism, a belief in limitless resources and of personal entitlement, set up a scenario in which people are unable or unwilling to adjust their attitudes toward the environment in ways that are more sustainable. This is especially true of people who may have been born into conditions that were more plentiful, either because they are older and have gotten "used to" having access to greater amounts of resources than are now realistic to expect, or perhaps they are from a sparsely populated area, where they learned to feel entitled to wide open spaces and easy access to resources. There is also the easy fallback position of thinking that one person doesn't make a difference and that we will let the other guy do something. In a related vein, there is the tendency to give oneself the benefit of the doubt, or to take a "pass" when using resources (social psychologists have a fancy name for this — fundamental attribution bias —

but the bottom line is that there is a tendency, particularly in cultures where "individualism" is privileged, for that individualism to edge dangerously into self-serving profligacy where the natural environment is concerned).

Thus far, we have been discussing cultural lag as if it responded to only one material change — but that is a simplification for explanatory purposes. In real life, a change in some material condition, such as a technological discovery or change (typically an increase, but in the case of, for example, the bubonic plague in Middle Age Europe, or the massacre of the Khmer Rouge in Cambodia in the twentieth century, a decrease) in population, there follows, over time, a change in culture. That change tends to unfold over long periods of time such as decades, or even centuries.

During that time, of course, other technological and demographic changes occur that trigger their own adaptations, and so the process goes on in perpetuity. As a general rule of thumb, the more technological and demographic changes there are, the more cultural changes come in their wake. At the dawn of the third millennium technological innovation happens as quickly, and perhaps more so, than ever in history. At a time when we have more people on the planet than at any time, concentrated in urban areas more than ever before, putting strains on resources at unprecedented rates, the sociological implications of these material conditions cannot be overstated.

As the process of adaptation to a major change unfolds, other shocks to the system happen that have their *own* processes of cultural lag. Here, as always, a concrete example can help tremendously. As there was crowding in Europe, and keen competition for resources, a new set of natural resources opened up in the form of the "discovery" (by Europeans, at least) of the "New World."

A number of artifacts of the way the United States developed are still part of the culture that make little or no sense in light of the current material conditions. Using the Electoral College to decide the presidency instead of popular vote is a hold-over from a time way before voting tallies were readily available on the national news, and sending a few representatives to the national capital to represent the various states made sense. The fact that it is still around (and still making a difference, as the supporters of Al Gore found out the hard way in the 2000 election, when he garnered more votes than George W. Bush, yet, still lost the election because of this holdover from a prior time). The school year is, with a few exceptions here and there, still organized around the nine-month calendar with three months off during the summer. This is a holdover from a time when the country was largely agrarian, and children were expected to help on the family farm during the prime growing season of the summer. Only after the first harvest in the fall, did school start.

While these processes may seem relatively benign, consider how cultural lag affects how people see themselves relative to the natural environment. Here, it is crucial to give a long and serious look at how these processes occur and how values become embedded in the culture and, once there, become the solid foundation from which people make their decisions about what they see as "right" and ethical.

People will tend to use resources in a way commensurate with their cultural expectations. If those expectations are born of a time of plenitude, *even though that time may be long gone*, people can still be expected to over consume, if the culture has not yet adapted to the newer conditions (such as the shortage). At the time of our writing this book, as we examine differences in environmental attitudes around the United States, for example, we can observe expectations in many of the Western mountain states to push for loosening of environmental restrictions and oversight by the government. This has come to a head from time to time in, for example, the "Sagebrush Rebellion" of the 1970s and 1980s, or the "Bundy Standoff," of 2016 coming to a head when a group of ranchers occupied U.S. federal lands in Oregon with demands for less or no government oversight of public land and resources.

Sources: Ogburn (1932/1961); Burns (2009); Bowler (2013); Burns (1999); Burns and LeMoyne (2003); Wuthnow (1987); Burke (1969); Fischer (1978); Grubler (1991); Inglehart and Baker (2000); Inglehart (1990); Swidler (2001)

computers, chain saws, chemicals, and huge fishing fleets, make finding and harvesting natural resources easier and more productive. As Martin Heidegger (1966 [1932], 1999, 2006) perceived the ideas, vocabularies, and feelings about technology become embedded, or "enframed, " in culture and integrated into each of us.

But aren't the nations of the world moving towards environmental stewardship? Won't we solve our environmental problems once the cultural lag process has played out, and we are able to "catch up" with environmental problems? This attitude — termed world polity theory — is problematic, at best, on a number of levels. Buttel (2000) has pointed out that despite the fact that developing countries have established environmental agencies and entered into environmental treaties, there is no guarantee of environmentally friendly action. Additionally, the problem of environmental degradation may be so widespread and rapid that it becomes impossible to make up the difference between the creation of environmental problems and the implementation of solutions. The gap between rapid technological change, together with the concentration of wealth in a few hands, and much slower cultural change is growing ever wider.

Our dependence and trust in the power of technology can also lead us to believe that technological fixes will "solve" environmental problems (J. Simon 1983). However, "Jevons paradox" shows that the more sweeping a technological change is, the more likely it is to upset the ecological balance unless there are also off-setting cultural adaptations.

Simply put, any increases in efficiencies due to technological change are likely to result in greater use of natural resources rather than conservation. History is replete with examples. For instance, greater fuel efficiency in automobiles resulted in a number of unintended consequences. As the *intended* effect of gas mileage increased, this, in turn, led to more cars being purchased and more miles driven. Families went from owning one car to two or three. Then there were increased costs and environmental degradation from road construction, infrastructure needs, and the expansion of suburbs and exurbs. Additionally, advances in technology used for oil extraction caused the price of gasoline to plummet, further increasing miles driven and quashing research and adoption of alternative energy products.

This is most certainly not to argue against the adoption of fuel efficiency. Rather, it is simply to point out the folly of thinking that a technological development will, in the absence of any positive cultural adaptation to accommodate it, "fix" a problem where human activity and social interaction are involved.

The modern world is fueled by mass production and consumption. Global markets exist to facilitate trade of far-flung natural resources and finished goods that are only possible because of economies of scale and concentrations of vast capital that were once unimaginable (Foster 1999). The steady march of technological prowess abets this process and increases its destructive powers. Without a global normative system to provide a check, meaningful ethical judgments are impossible and damage to the environment will only increase.

Sustainability will surely involve institutional solutions and political will. However, for true change to occur, a culture of sustainability must emerge. Given the fact that institutional and technological fixes often have unintended consequences and that cultural lag is inevitable, the creation of a sustainable culture is dependent upon a critical mass of committed individuals who internalize and practice sustainability as a core principle.

Pro-environmental values are increasing in some societies, especially at the extreme ends of international development — the very rich and the very poor. Among some, there is a noticeable regard for sustainability. For instance, the "*locovore*" movement is made up of people who choose to eat food that is locally grown to decrease the environmental impact of transporting food great distances.

Yet, there is also concerted pushback from global commerce and trade groups and conservative cultural and political forces. The rise of international corporations and global markets makes regulation, even by nation-states, difficult (Broadbent 1989; O'Neill 2002; Clarke 1988; Yeager 1987; Gareau and DuPuis 2009). The ease with which these players can move to take advantage of cheap labor and lax environmental regulations often forces developing countries to ignore environmental concerns in an effort to attract much needed jobs and capital. For poorer countries, environmentalism is seen as a luxury. The fact that this flies in the face of actual empirical research remains a moot point, as long as there is a complicity between officials in those countries (or localities within them) and foreign capital, which seeks to locate in places with the cheapest labor and laxest environmental regulations (Foster et al. 2011). Calls for stricter regulation on pollution and the depletion of natural resources by developed countries is often viewed as a paternalistic attempt to deny the growth and prosperity that has already taken place in these first world countries.

Although the formidable forces allied against sustainability have great power and influence, in the long run, they are dependent upon the good will and acceptance of individual members of society (Marshall and Picou 2008). Ultimately, market forces must react to consumers. That is why it is so important to grow awareness of environmental problems and to build a critical mass of individuals who make sustainability a central and organizing aspect of their ethos.

Conclusions: Take-Away Lessons about Culture and the Environment

Are we even capable of reversing the damage that has already been done to the environment, particularly since the time of industrialization? Given the all-encompassing nature of culture on each and every one of us, it is a daunting task to make natural ecology and sustainability a central concern of society, and yet this is precisely the challenge as society moves into the third millennium. In order to have a chance of success, it is vital to stem the tide of runaway consumption and unchecked use of limited resources. No longer can we afford to harbor dangerous rationalizations that unsustainable beliefs and activities are not a problem and a threat.

A culture cannot afford to celebrate wasteful and destructive ways of life as simply the well-deserved fruits of a virtuous people, and do so indefinitely (Szasz 2007). In a culture that celebrates hyper-individualism, individual choices have a collective impact on the environment (Givens and Jorgenson 2011). Some public critics have stated that it is the height of hubris to assume that humankind can have a lasting impact on the world that God has created. Yet, in the Anthropocene Age (Crutzen 2002), it is the epitome of irresponsibility to assume otherwise.

Because we have, from time immemorial, had such a bountiful planet, the bounty of nature has been taken for granted, and has been enframed into the culture. Modern culture has only multiplied belief in a world with limitless abundance. It was once thought that North America's aquifers could supply limitless amounts of water and that the fish in the oceans were a never ending and constantly renewable source of protein. Yet, the legacy of technology run amok and of unchecked growth and consumption can be seen in so many ways, including in today's meager seafood harvests due to overfishing and the drawing down to dangerous levels of our major reserves of ancient fresh water.

We are, each of us, immersed in culture and are barely able to notice its effect on us or to question its impact upon our beliefs and actions. We are like the fish swimming in polluted water until it dies — unable to reflect on the situation, let alone take action that might save its life. To solve a problem, one must first acknowledge the problem.

We must also prioritize the problem of a damaged and unsustainable ecology. We find ourselves in a time of mounting crises and concerns that require both time and money. Perhaps it would be a good idea to allocate some of the resources that have been assigned to a multitude of small fires, and instead concentrate a portion to the spreading conflagration of a deteriorating environment.

There is hope that people of good intent can make a difference and through smart leadership and example can educate and inspire others to take action. The more cynical among us may point out that despite many warnings, we have so far not risen to the challenge. They may also despair in light of the many powerful opponents of environmental action. Yet, the more optimistic among us can cite contrary instances in which, despite the opposition of many formidable institutions and individuals, change did, indeed, prevail.

About a century and a half ago, the United States was undergoing the most intense of societal transformations in history. Following a devastating civil war in which a staggering number of young men were killed, maimed and psychologically wounded in the first "modern" conflict, the victorious northern half of the country turned its attention from war and whole-heartedly set about creating a new industrial, urban, laissez-faire, capitalist society. The pace of change was dizzying, and the old rural, agrarian values were quickly being replaced with the modern values of the Industrial Revolution. As might be expected, the natural world took a back seat to progress.

Despite this, however, President Ulysses S. Grant, the former commander of the U.S. Northern forces, created Yellowstone National Park — the first national park in the world. As industrialization continued unabated into the early twentieth century and environmental damage mounted, however, President Theodore Roosevelt — having been inspired by John Muir — expanded the number of national parks, the first national forests and national monuments were established, and vast areas of natural beauty were set aside for the future enjoyment and recreation of the American people. It bears pointing out that Roosevelt and Congress acted during a time when the railroads and mining and timber interests wielded great power and influence, and the infant oil industry was starting to flex its muscles. Roosevelt known as the "Trust Buster," for breaking up the large monopolies of "trusts" of the day, such as Standard Oil, was not afraid to take on the powerful "robber baron" industrialists of the time.

In the 1960s and 1970s, the United States faced a growing problem of pollution caused by neglect and abuse. Air pollution and water pollution had become impossible to ignore. Rachel Carson, in her book *Silent Spring*, sounded the alarm concerning unregulated chemicals in our environment, and Richard Nixon, a Republican president, signed the law creating the Environmental Protection Agency. The 1970s (known popularly by many as the environmental decade) in particular, witnessed an unprecedented sustained and concerted battle against environmental degradation. Since that time, many Republicans have retreated on environmental issues, some becoming downright hostile, with some Democrats carrying the environmental torch, while others have come to take the support of environmentally conscious people for granted as they prioritize other causes at the expense of the environment (Burns and LeMoyne 2001). Could it be, that it is time for a new environmental consciousness that moves beyond party parochialism, and that puts the environment as the core organizing principle (Gore 1993)?

Past experience shows that leaders can be influenced to take concrete action if a few prescient and persuasive activists in the mold of a John Muir or a Rachel Carson can move the culture and its leaders toward a sustainable mindset. In the words of the great French writer, Victor Hugo, "There is nothing so powerful as an idea whose time has come." It is time, during these early years of the third millennium, that environmentally aware people of good will articulate the perils of our present situation and provide possible solutions that can be set into motion by a rising cultural consciousness.

Globalization and the awesome power of extractive technologies increases the scope and scale, and therefore the consequences, of whatever action is taken. Since the oil crises of the 1970s, we have had ample time and opportunity to change our direction and take a new path towards a sustainable future. Problems have only worsened, and the longer we ignore them the worse they will become and the harder to reverse. Viable alternatives to the old unsustainable technologies and lifestyles exist today, but receive scant attention, encouragement or resources from governments and other institutions.

Humankind long ago passed the point of benign human impact on the natural world. There are simply too many of us, and our technology is too powerful. Our cultural attitudes towards the environment still reflect earlier times when we were more intimately connected with, and perhaps nurtured by, the natural world. The earth's bounties were seen as the rightful harvest of humankind. Yet, the culture of modernity, even as it has devised ever more clever technologies, has alienated humankind from that close bond. As environmental sociologists, we now know that the earth's resources are not unlimited, nor were they ever. If we are to survive and thrive as a species, then we have no choice but to become better stewards of the world upon which we all depend.

Culture can change, but it necessarily does so slowly, almost glacially. This requires that the current way of doing and thinking be examined and understood by the people in the culture, as some of our most deeply held beliefs come to be challenged. New ideas that lead to a sustainable ecology can be introduced gradually, until they become routinized into daily life and thought. This is how culture changes — it is not some facile quick fix.

As we move into the third millennium, we face some of the most difficult and intractable problems in world history. As the term "Anthropocene Age" conveys, many of those problems are of human creation. The seriousness of the predicament calls for people of good faith to step forward and come to terms with it, confronting our own impact on the world, assessing the situation for what it really is in a sober manner, and awakening from complacency. Delay will only make matters worse, and further constrain future action.

As environmental sociologists, we seek to make sense of the many ways in which humankind interacts with the natural environment. It is incumbent upon us to try to understand these processes, even as there are endless levels of complexity. That understanding will, in turn, inform how we think about these crucial issues moving forward, and interact in the public sphere.

Culture is the way in which we make sense of the world both collectively and individually. Culture is the most profound of human creations. Cultural attitudes about the natural world have been problematic; yet, they can also be a source of salvation from our current crisis. Culture can play a critical role in restoring harmony between hummankind and nature.

Chapter 3 Summary

- Culture can be seen as an interrelated network of meanings, ideas, values, traditions, and perceptions. Within these networks are what we hold most central, or important. New information is judged against the backdrop of these networks of meaning.

- Culture for humankind is analogous to water for fish or air for birds. It is so ubiquitous, so ever-present a part of our experience that it becomes part of the taken-for-granted backdrop of our lives. As this taken-for-granted backdrop, much of culture has a profound influence on how we experience the world.

- Sometimes we can become so culturally embedded, that we become blind to it. Because of this phenomenon of being "swallowed by the culture" it is important to step out of it, and to examine it from a distance.

- Although people encounter events using the same five senses, the resulting perceptions are not universal. The culture we are a part of forms our judgments and opinions—our way of viewing the world.

- Humankind has always had an impact on the environment. It is the act of assessing worth and importance that is so crucial to culture's impact on environmental problems.

- The Agricultural Revolution led to a gradual change in how humans organized themselves, causing them to become an increasingly more complex society. During this time, with the development of village life, writing and record keeping, divisions of labor and specialization, and social classes, there were profound cultural changes as well.

- The Industrial Revolution brought about more profound cultural changes, including ways in which humankind relates to the natural environment. There is now a distance between humankind and nature, largely mediated by technology, and characterized by a "treadmill of production" and mass consumption.

- Consider the phenomenon of "cultural lag," which refers to the time between the change in a material condition, and the cultural adaptation to it. In a time of rapid technological change, such as the present day, even when culture changes rapidly in response, it still may be falling behind the leading technological change.

- Problems of environmental degradation are so widespread and rapid, that it becomes close to impossible to make up the difference between the creating of environmental problems and the implementing of solutions without moving to a culture based less on consumption and more on values of sustainability.

- The legacy of technology run amok and of unchecked growth and consumption can be seen in many ways, including in today's meager seafood harvests due to overfishing and the drawing down to dangerous levels of major reserves of ancient fresh water. In order to have a chance of success in being able to reverse the damage done, it is vital to stem the tide of runaway consumption and unchecked use of limited resources.

- Past experience shows that leaders can be influenced to take concrete action if a few prescient and persuasive activists in the mold of a John Muir or a Rachel Carson can help move the culture and its leaders toward a sustainable mindset. In the words of the great French writer, Victor Hugo, "There is nothing so powerful as an idea whose time has come."

Chapter Four - Science and Technology

Science and technology are at once blamed for environmental problems, as well as touted as their most likely (in some extreme cases, their only) solution. Troubles such as climate change and water and air pollution have been explicitly linked to the rise of industrialization. This chapter will review perspectives on ways technology and science relate to environmental problems. We also consider the potential for technology transfer from more to less industrialized nations and related processes of leapfrogging by developing nations. The 2015 United Nations Conference on Climate Change in Paris considered how industrialization may well bring the planet to the point of catastrophe if humankind does not come to grips with effects of advanced technologies on the environment. We consider the long view of science and technology, and effects on the environment, not only in isolation but in a combination with other human creations, such as the economy and culture.

Technology and Social and Environmental Change

Looking back over the span of the last two and a half centuries, we can see unprecedented social and environmental change. Much of the changes that society has witnessed in this time have been intimately intertwined with the technological developments beginning with the Industrial Revolution and coming forth since then (Burns and Jorgenson 2007; Moore 2015). Their magnitude has become even greater in the post-World War II period (McNeill 2000).

In fact, the effect of humankind on the earth and its atmosphere has been so profound, to a degree unprecedented in history, that observers have puzzled over whether from this industrialization period on be given its own name. The Pleistocene era lasted until the end of the last Ice Age, about 11,700 years ago. The Neolithic era, when hunters and gatherers slowly began to become horticulturalists and agrarians, started shortly after that.

The term "*Anthropocene*" was coined by a Dutch chemist and Nobel Prize winner, Paul Crutzen, who sought to give a meaningful term to an age in which, for the first time ever, human beings have made significant and lasting changes on the planet earth. While the precise dates are a matter of debate and discussion, the advent of the Industrial Revolution in the late eighteenth century is a commonly held tipping point in the process (Ponting 1991; Purdy 2015; McNeill 2000; Burns 2009).

The terminology is telling, but the broader point is well taken. Technology has, over time, afforded ever greater mastery over the planet. At some point (the precise placement of which may be up for debate, but the existence of which is beyond any reasonable doubt) the "mastery" over the planet becomes so profound, that those effects go beyond what can be simply incorporated and balanced in the ecosystem, and change the nature of the planet itself. Astronauts can now, for example, see evidence of strip mining, of deforestation, of ozone depletion, among other things, from their view of the earth from outer space.

Technology allows people to take advantage of the natural geography they face. If they are fortunate enough to live in a place with abundant natural resources, such as historically has been the case in the United States, for example, they will often develop technology to use those resources — it is not an accident that the United States invented the oil derrick, even though other places pump most of the crude oil at this point. But these adaptations, small at first, add up.

The problem comes in when there is historically a huge abundance of resources, and technologies are developed to take them. The culture then adapts, and technological growth ratchets up, tending to continue beyond the point the environment can sustain it. This leads to an inevitable collapse. The farther the ratcheting up of the technology beyond what is sustainable, the worse the eventual collapse. This pattern has been true since time immemorial. Burns and Rudel (2015) give a sustained example of this phenomenon in the 1840s in Ireland, and how it led to the devastating Potato Famine there. Yet, what makes it particularly risky now at the dawn of the third millennium, is the advanced technology making the ratcheting up easier without the temperance to keep excesses in check.

There have been parallels in U.S. history, to be sure, including the catastrophic Dustbowl in the American Heartland (Crane 2014; Egan 2005). The phenomenon is perhaps particularly challenging in the United States, precisely because the culture is so *enframed* (Heidegger 1932/1966; 2006) with technological innovation and material abundance, that those are taken for granted. By the time the cultural lag catches up, environmental problems created by such a combination will be even farther advanced.

This is more than an abstraction. Contrast the United States with much of Europe, which was more enclosed earlier, having fewer resources, in many cases (Crane 2014). This may be, at least in part, responsible for stronger environmental norms (and in many cases, the laws that flow from them) in many European countries than in the United States. The original technology for wind energy was developed in the United States, poising it for a leadership role. Yet, because it did not have the normative impetus to sustain it, the United States lost the leadership role to European countries such as the Netherlands and Germany, which now put the United States to shame in the number of green jobs they have in their economies.

Now, in the third millennium, we face truly daunting social and environmental problems. And many of those problems we can attribute to the invasive technologies that have been developed during and since industrialization. Technology also offers hope for addressing many of those problems, if we can bring our collective purpose and will to bear on them (Purdy 2015). Technology often requires expertise, and therefore dedicated professionals to manage it, and it does not take place in a normative or cultural vacuum. Green technology can only thrive in a culture that is organized around ecological principles and norms of sustainability.

Technological developments also bring forth a number of ethical questions and dilemmas that societies ignore at their peril (Moore 2009). Consider, for example, the advent of the technology to split the atom and thereby take its energy for nuclear power or an atomic bomb. What are the ethical uses of these technologies, if any? Are there some instances where their use would be warranted, and others where they would not? Even assuming people of good will develop them (which may be a fairly generous assumption to begin with), given the lessons of human history, what are the chances they will or will not fall into the hands of those who would use them for destructive purposes?

Technological Development and Cultural Lag

When there is a new scientific discovery, it is hard or impossible to know what the full ramifications of it will be. Consider that when Benjamin Franklin discovered electricity while flying a kite one evening, he could not possibly have known all, or even a significant part of, the effects electricity would have facilitated over the next decades and centuries. Life was changed forever with the advent of electricity, and those changes are still unfolding in our lifetimes, as they power computers, cell phones and small devices as well as major power grids. In fact, electricity's effect has been so profound that it would not be an overstatement to say that were the electricity grid to go down for even a day, social chaos would ensue.

There are several lessons here. Scientific discoveries tend to have the most social impact only when they are cast into technology. This technology transfer may take time, diffusing over weeks, months, years, decades or even centuries.

There is a saying that it is more than seldom the case with technology that "the leading edge is the bleeding edge." What Gerhard Lenski and other researchers have called "the advantage of backwardness" manifests itself when developing countries are able to take advantage of a technology that models itself after the leader. In such cases, without having to endure the dead-ends and cost associated with doing the research and development themselves, they can take advantage of the experiences and not make the mistakes that the original developers took.

One quick example, seemingly outrageous in hindsight, underscores this point. The very first freeway in the world, the Santa Barbara Freeway in Southern California, was way ahead of its time — so much so that they did not have the gradual on and off ramps that we now take for granted on freeways pretty much the world over, such as the U.S. Interstate Highway System. Rather, peo-

Figure 4.1 Genetically Modified Crops and the Precautionary Principle

May 2015, demonstration against Monsanto and its genetically modified crops in Toulouse, France.

Investors argue that the advent of genetically modified crops opens possibilities for new ways to grow food in quantity. While taken in the narrowest of terms, there is a strain of truth to this. There is also a plethora of potential problems unleashed by these genetically modified crops — potential new strains of drug resistant bacteria, for example, or new types of invasive species that could choke out the vegetation that is growing currently in some bio-regions.

Genetically modified crops and pesticide usage, particularly as they involve large-scale production, have become controversial topics worldwide. There are peasant movements in an array of areas, such as South America, Asia, and Africa (Lapegna 2014; Kim 2014; Lieberman and Gray 2008), who are pushing back against these forces of globalization, power and modernity. In such places, indigenous voices and others are calling for a much more widespread use of the precautionary principle, a lowering of pesticide usage, and a wariness toward the widespread adoption of genetically modified crops.

It is not always easy to know which way the precautionary principle points, however (Scott 2005). Sometimes it may be, for example, that the danger of an insect-borne disease is unknown relative to the danger of using a pesticide to stop an infestation of the insects carrying that disease. Further, how much of a pesticide is needed is not something that can be estimated precisely. It is often the case that it is overestimated and there is "overkill," or it is underestimated, or it is used but after waiting too long, in which case the worst of all worlds occurs — the infestation and the toxic effects of the pesticide that did not work to eradicate the pest.

As new technologies are developed, it will be important to cross traditional boundaries between academic and commercial research. In fact, some of the most fruitful endeavors in developing sustainable and viable "green" technology has involved partnerships, in which universities and businesses are able to cooperate when need be, in order to promulgate something that will benefit the common good (Vallas and Kleinman 2008).

Kenyans examining insect resistant corn.

While it is the case that, over time, a society can stress technologies that are more amenable to the natural ecology, this is something that is still much more a potential than a reality. If at some future point, there is a critical mass of these green technologies, the economy can come to organize itself around them, rather than invasive, more destructive technologies.

In developing alternative, or green technologies, it behooves a society to think them through carefully. Even when a technology seems green to people of good will, it still may prove to need adjustments over time. Work on culture and the environment finds that cultural processes flow from changes in technology, but they unfold over long periods of time, are subject to cultural lag, and diffuse from other areas (Burns 2009).

As society moves into the third millennium, many of the metaphors it will use to think about and evaluate new technology will be around risk and uncertainty (Petersen 2005). Recently reported issues such as genetically modified crops, cloning breakthroughs, embryonic stem cell research, and new genetic tests, for example, are characterized by contending metaphors (Pellegrini 2009). Those in favor of the new technologies characterize them positively, while those more skeptical lean more toward the precautionary principle.

As the exuberance and greed of investors push the envelope of research and development to devise ever more exotic and "efficient" genetic strains, they pay little, if any, attention to the externalities they create. If they are to be addressed at all, it typically will be with technology that is less powerful and under-funded, managed perhaps by well-meaning and public-spirited, but under-compensated technicians or volunteers. It will be important moving forward for people of good will to be aware and engaged, to stay abreast of these important issues.

Sources: Pellegrini (2009); Petersen (2005); Vallas and Kleinman (2008); Lapegna (2014); Kim (2014); Lieberman and Gray (2008).

ple would come to a stop sign and then enter the high-speed freeway. (Having the modern freeway pretty much enframed in your own thinking, at least since well before you were old enough to drive…), you can probably guess the results! It did not take the highway engineers for the *next* freeways to figure out not to do that — to give, as is now the custom in virtually all freeways throughout the world, the ability for people entering and exiting to get up to speed or to down-speed in a safe fashion.

This advantage of backwardness phenomenon is so ubiquitous, that we sometimes may not notice it, but people involved with technological development are well aware of it. Environmental sociologists and human ecologists can use this to make sense of an array of phenomena. A number of researchers have pointed out that some of the worst types of pollution are in developing countries — neither the most developed nor the least of all — but those rapidly developing countries somewhere in the middle. These countries include (but by no means are limited to) the so-called BRICS countries — Brazil, Russia, India, China and South Africa, and these countries have historically had access to resources and labor. They are at the higher end of the developing world, and as such, tend to have access to some fairly sophisticated technology. However, they tend not to have the pollution control and other sorts of breaks and governors on pollution that are found in more developed countries like the European Union.

Human ecologists note the differences between the technological environment and the natural environment. We can think of the technological environment as houses and office buildings, cars, roads, machines and such things, but also as the know-how that goes into making them — the engineering and mathematics, the ideas of the architects and engineers. Technology then is not just the material, tangible things like machines, but more profoundly, it is the way of thinking that goes into them. Here, the term of the philosopher Martin Heidegger is informative — certain ideas become "*enframed*" into the culture and, for all intents and purposes, cannot be "unthought." Once we have the details about how to solve differential equations as part of the culture, that will not go away (thank you, Newton and Leibniz!). As an underside of that, once a culture develops the details of how to make a bomb with sufficient power to destroy much of the life on the planet, that technology does not ever get unthought. As Garrett Harden pointed out so prophetically: *Technology can create problems it cannot solve*.

Since the dawn of the Anthropocene Age, and particularly in late modern times, the distinction between the natural environment, and the environment that is affected by humankind, is, in many cases, less than clear. Consider the forests that still do exist, or, in many cases, have regrown after human clearing or some other sort of human intervention. In modern times, the technological environment changes more rapidly than did the natural environment for most of the time of human evolution (Ogburn 1956).

Science and Technology as Tools of Progress, but Sometimes as Hubris

Beginning with the Enlightenment of the late seventeenth and eighteenth centuries, which then set much of the intellectual and social stage for the Industrial Revolution which followed, humankind has increasingly put its faith in science to understand its world, and to inform technologies to address problems. For its part, science has been, in many ways, spectacularly successful in finding breakthroughs in knowledge. It has also, along with the technology it informs, had inestimable and far-reaching effects on culture and society, as well as putting a permanent imprint on the planet.

Science, as we know it, came together over time as a series of events. Underpinning the discoveries, from the telescope, to penicillin, to DNA, to nuclear fission, was *a method*, and *a way of seeing the world* (Wootton 2015). Out of this came countless experiments, and a gradually honed sense of the laws of nature. The *concept of facts* became an important construct on which to build the enterprise of science.

Going back to the classical view of science, we notice that the word *science* itself comes from the Latin *scire*, meaning to know. Greek philosophers such as Aristotle sought to understand how nature worked, and saw science as a tool in that regard.

Following the lead of Aristotle, the philosopher and theologian Thomas Aquinas in Christendom, and his Muslim counterpart Averroes, saw science and mathematics as important studies because they believed their orderliness showed how the mind of God worked. While our current world has gone far beyond this view, in putting a premium on understanding ahead of manipulation, these early philosophers may have had some important lessons, even for those of us all these centuries later.

Aristotle studied many things. In addition to the sciences, he studied rhetoric, politics, and drama, among other things. In his study of drama, Aristotle noticed the protagonist tended to have a fatal flaw (*hamartia* — or literally, a missing of the mark). The tragic flaw that Aristotle identified, woven throughout tragedies such as the play *Oedipus Rex* by Sophocles, was *hubris* — an over-the-top arrogance, combined with a narcissistic confidence of invincibility. Despite whatever significant strengths the character brought to the battle (and in many cases, these were formidable indeed), the hubris would eventually be the undoing of the character.

As part of the Enlightenment philosophy, there was a division between science and religion. Yet, part of that scientific vision coming out of the Enlightenment still, to this day, has an unsettled quality. One of the early philosophers of science Francis Bacon articulated the vision of science as "torturing mother nature for her secrets." Despite his brilliance in other areas, Bacon's hubris has, to some extent, been transferred onto the science he promulgated. This view of science, in which the natural world is something to be subjugated and conquered, persists in some quarters to a large extent even today (Hard and Jamison 2005).

Contrast this with the ecological view of science, which seeks to understand the natural workings of the world, and to live in harmony with it. Moving forward into the twenty-first century and beyond, this ecological view may necessarily supplant the old Baconian view, if the planet is to survive and thrive.

Ecologically sound science does, over time, provide society with knowledge about what it studies that gels into a coherent picture. Science deals in probabilities, and at some point when there is a preponderance of evidence that has, over time and over a number of interrelated studies, been collected by well-trained scientists in research conducted in good faith, then it begins to come into focus as a coherent picture. At that point, science can say there is an overwhelming probability that a given phenomenon under study is to be taken seriously. People of good faith in the overall culture may be moved to act upon such knowledge, particularly if not doing so puts the society or the environment at greater risk than non-action. In such a case, denial of that science becomes hubris.

There is now, for example, overwhelming evidence of global environmental change having been caused by human activity (e.g., NRC 2006; Church and White 2006), and science has begun to systematically identify a number of the anthropogenic drivers of global climate change (Rosa et al. 2015). Research also indicates a strong countermovement, typically deriving not from mainstream science, but from well-funded lobbyists with ties to big businesses, particularly oil companies (Dunlap and McCright 2015; Antonio and Brulle 2011; Zehr 2000). While this is a topic better left to our chapter on governance, it does bear noting in this chapter, that it is sometimes the case that science, carried out in good will, can nonetheless be challenged by deniers. When such is the case, it is almost always worthwhile to ask where the funding sources are, and where the interests lie, for such deniers.

Science is not magic, and we do well in society to remember its tremendous power to yield answers when done in good faith. When it is, then the onus is on the society to act in good faith on its findings. In such cases, the denial of science becomes hubris. The fragile planet on which we all depend for life and sustenance can ill afford this.

Paradoxes of Technological Innovation

Science, as is true of any human endeavor, has up and down sides. To be sure, science has made great strides throughout the industrial period of the last several centuries. In fact, a good case can and has been made that the scientific discoveries and, more importantly, the method it laid down, were major legacies of the Enlightenment that led to the Industrial Revolution that came in its wake.

Yet, even in the face of its many discoveries and its indelible influence on technology and culture, we put science on a pedestal at our peril. But tempered with humility and wisdom, it can be an invaluable tool for understanding, wonder and discovery, and perhaps even helping to restore much needed balance to the planet.

It is important to distinguish among different types of technology. When thinking of technology, it is perhaps most typical to imagine leading-edge, or high-end technology. Thinking in a more hopeful way, technologies potentially help clean up after themselves. Yet, while there is also, at least in theory, the technology that trails behind and cleans up after itself, there, in fact, may be quite a difference between these two — leading-edge and cleaning-up technology (Schnaiberg 1980). As the prophetic Garrett Hardin (1968; 1993) observed, technology can create problems it cannot solve.

This conundrum posed by Hardin is one of the central paradoxes of the third millennium — the more advanced the technology becomes, the greater, other things held equal, the environmental displacement it causes. This is true in spite of the fact that, in theory, technology can be created (and in some limited instances have been implemented) to help defray or clean up environmental pollution. In fact, it is rarely, if ever, the case that technology is up to solving problems of the magnitude it is capable of creating. One of the challenges of the third millennium will be to engage technology in such a way that it (at least gradually) unwinds the environmental imbalances of the last two and a half centuries, even as it seeks to respect the principles of natural ecology moving forward.

This paradox is captured starkly in questions surrounding genetically modified organisms (GMOs), which raise a whole set of ethical as well as technological questions. As humankind learns more about genetics and the processes of how to control and manipulate them, the capabilities to generate different strains of species of all sorts goes up, but so do the risks. In a capitalist system, it is the case that investors are most likely to see the reward, while the risk is overlooked, or externalized, to others or to the natural environment (Shiva 2000).

Stanley Jevons observed over a century ago a curious phenomenon about social processes in the wake of new technological discoveries. When a new technology leads to a greater efficiency of a resource, it is, ironically, often the case that it leads to social processes resulting in so much greater consumption of that resource that, in aggregate, *there is a greater overall consumption of that resource than had the discovery never been made in the first place.*

He used the example from his day of coal consumption, but we see more recently the advent of fuel-efficient automobiles resulting in more automobiles being sold, more roads being built, longer commuting times, which in aggregate have resulted in a lot more gasoline being consumed after the fuel-efficient car was introduced than before. We are *not*, of course, arguing against

Figure 4.2 Jevons Paradox: Where Technology Meets the Unintended Consequences of the Free Market

Nineteenth century English economist W. Stanley Jevons.

Over a century ago, a keen social observer, Stanley Jevons, was interested to see what happens when a new technology is developed before the culture has time to adapt to it. His findings are far-reaching and telling, even more about human nature than about the technology it creates.

The *Jevons Paradox* points out that often, when a new technology leads to greater efficiency in the use of a given resource, the usage rate goes up. As a result, the gains are not only negated, but the overall use of the resource goes up higher than it was before the advent of the new technology. The use of coal, for example, tends to increase in the wake of developing new efficiencies in coal driven engines (Alcott 2005). This reality is in stark contrast to the belief systems that typically motivate governments, political parties, and even many non-governmental organizations (NGOs).

In fact, the Jevons Paradox can be found in a shockingly wide array of circumstances (York 2006). Examples include fuel-efficient automobiles leading to even greater use of automobiles, as families go from one car to 2-3 or more cars, more freeways are built and commutes become longer. The aggregate effect of all of this is to burn more fuel than before the fuel efficient cars were introduced. In the bureaucratic realm, the advent of "paperless office" measures, originally thought to replace paper memos with the Internet, for example, led to greater numbers of memoranda being written than before. Although many of these memos are, in fact, confined to the Internet, it is also the case that in absolute numbers, significantly greater amounts of paper are now consumed for memoranda that, while they may have originated in the Internet, are nonetheless being printed out.

So what is to be done about the Jevons Paradox? Some researchers advocate for imposing caps on consumption, such as quotas or limits (Alcott 2005). While that may work in the short run, it seems clear that over the longer haul, there must be *adaptations in the culture itself* that go beyond the logic of price equilibrium dictated by supply and demand. This is because as efficiency goes up, a given supply (of coal or gasoline, for example) effectively is increased because of its being able to provide more energy. This virtual increase in supply, assuming demand does not change, tends to drive the price down (remember the "invisible hand" of the market articulated by Adam Smith and taken as a cultural default in capitalist systems). This lower price, in turn, tends to increase buying.

This is not to say that societies should not strive to use the most efficient technologies possible, for these efficiencies can, at least in theory, lead to a slowing of environmental degradation. However, because of the social dynamics associated with Jevons Paradox, it not enough to increase technological efficiency. There must be adaptations in the cultural realm that are not based on ever-increasing use of resources.

Sources: Alcott (2005); Butts (2009); Polimeni et al. (2008); York (2006).

fuel-efficient cars — rather, the larger point here is that no problem can be solved with technology in isolation, however efficient, without some concomitant social and cultural changes as well. Those types of changes are more challenging.

One of the paradoxes of technological innovation is that there is often a mismatch between the technology that develops and uses resources on the one hand, and of the technology that cleans up on the other. This mismatch can be particularly pronounced in situations where investors are removed from the local ecology of where the technology is applied and where the resources for that technology are extracted. This is particularly problematic in late industrial society, where there are complex supply chain issues, where resources may be gathered from not only multiple locales, but from different continents, assembled in large-scale assembly plants using poorly compensated labor in high-risk conditions ("sweatshops"), often in developing countries.

Increasingly in global manufacture, mining and harvesting, ever greater scales of production and consumption threaten the resources of the planet (Downey and Strife 2010). Work on the global fishing industry as well, indicates that in fisheries in marine systems in different parts of the world, off different continental shelves, we see similar processes — overuse of technology to take fish, from salmon in the Pacific Northwest of the United States to the tuna off the coast of Sicily in the Mediterranean Sea, where those fish stocks that have supported peoples there, literally for millennia, already in a few decades with "hi-tech" have been fished to the state of collapse (defined as a decline of 90 per cent or more of their original levels, if not to the point of extinction).

This combination of conditions is spoken about in a number of writings, including those going under the names of *unequal ecological exchange* (Jorgenson 2006), *recursive exploitation* (Burns, Kick, and Davis 2006), *metabolic rift* (Moore 2015; Foster 1999; Foster et al. 2011), and the *ecological footprint* (Jorgenson 2003; Jorgenson, Rice, and Crowe 2005; Jorgenson and Burns 2007; York, Rosa, and Dietz 2003b, Kick and McKinney 2014). In each case, there are some commonalities that bear noting. Social actors such as corporations or investors, governments or militaries with money and / or power are able to leverage the situation to garner more resources (Horne 2015; Gould 2007; Fisher and Freudenburg 2004), most notably *natural* resources. They then are able to use those resources as inputs to technological production. Those processes often have a number of negative externalities on the people and ecologies coming into contact with them. There is evidence, for example, that much of the current boom in biotechnology development is increasingly targeted towards commodity-dependent consumption among people with high levels of affluence. It tends not to help the poorer, or the middle classes even in developed countries (Bowring 2003), let alone in the poorer countries on the planet.

Just to be clear, the technology already exists that could reduce carbon emissions by 90 per cent or more (Haszeldine 2009; Rubin 2008). The impediment in this case is not the technology itself, but the organizational will and the market driven expense of implementing it (Perrow and Pulver 2015; Pulver 2007). Put another way, the technology has moved beyond the ability of the culture to accommodate it.

Technology and the Economy in Advanced Capitalism

Increasing, technology ups the ante for what can be done, both in terms of extracting and using resources, but also in terms of the impact on the environment. Much of this idea can be characterized by the idea of the *treadmill of production*, which was first introduced by Allen Schnaiberg (1980), who finds major impacts of production processes upon ecosystems. While these date back to the start of the Industrial Revolution, the effects of technology on the natural environment began to grow exponentially in the post-World War II era.

Researchers find that economic considerations remain the primary criteria for the decision-making about production and consumption processes. To this date, economic expansion is seen as a necessary component of developed societies (Schnaiberg, Pellow and Weinberg 2002; Foster 2005).

In the chapter on Economism, we considered questions about scale. A process that may work fine in a small ecosystem, may be catastrophic when done in large-scale. It is crucial to keep in mind that it is often some form of advanced technology that makes these large-scale processes possible. In late modernity, large-scale production has become such a matter of course that it has become enframed in the culture and often goes unquestioned. New technologies are developed against this cultural backdrop.

These processes can have catastrophic consequences for the environment. Consider one such example. Ecosystems are able to replenish themselves in cases where they have large degrees of biodiversity. However, in situations where there is a huge scale such as "*mono-cropping*," or planting the same crop in huge swaths of land, the consequences for the ecosystem can be devastating. This often leads to problems such as soil degradation, biodiversity loss, and crop vulnerability to various pests and fungus infestations. Technologies attempting to head off these problems, such as pesticides and fungicides, lead to other problems, particularly when used in large scales, and often hit hardest people, animals and ecosystems living downstream of those using them (Steingraber 1998).

Developing a technology thus ups the cultural and ecological ante for its usage. The more far-reaching a technology (e.g., strip-mining equipment that, working in tandem, can literally move entire mountains), the more devastating the consequences can be. It may be used responsibly or irresponsibly, but the assumption that technology is neutral — that developing a technology in itself will not necessarily have any social or ecological implications — is a dangerous and highly naïve assumption (Braverman 1974/1998; Burns and Jorgenson 2007; Burns 2009). Particularly in late modernity, technological considerations are tied to economic decisions, often based on the interests of those with entrenched interests in money and power (Zuckerman 2013; Gold 2014).

As we saw in previous chapters, ideologies develop to support and bolster the material interests. These are based in the economy and the technology to which it is wedded. Here, the Marxist idea of class interests is important to keep in mind. It is, at least in the short run, typically in the interests of the people developing new technologies to be in favor of them politically, because it keeps those people employed and often, as it turns out, doing interesting work. Given some of the alternatives, it can be easy to justify.

Likewise, people working, for example, in the fields in the fracking industry, will go to great lengths to rationalize that what they are doing is justified. There are several points here. While a job or industry may start with technology, there are entire systems of interrelated social processes stemming from that technology.

History is also replete with examples of technology taken to extremes. Those extremes are an example of how volatile the technology is potentially, but more importantly, it is dependent on the social and political forces, as well as individual motives, which cross its path. These may, of course, vary in the extreme, but are rarely, if ever, contemplated along with the original vision of the ideal uses of the technology. And a technology, once developed, like Humpty Dumpty broken and not able to get back to a state of wholeness again, does not go away. Once the atomic bomb was invented, for instance, it was only a short time until it was deployed.

Technology becomes intertwined, not only with large economic interests but military ones as well. Environmental sociologists Andrew Jorgenson, Brett Clark, and Jennifer Givens (2012) find that across the world, there is a strong relationship between militarization and environmental degradation. There are a number of reasons for this. It is often the case that when militaries develop or adopt a technology or resource, it does a poor job of cleaning up after themselves. There may be a warrant for this, as in the case of an all-out war. However, so many military operations are carried out in secret, that oversight and accountability become problematic at best. Recall as well, that we have discussed the problems associated with largeness of scale at some length. Jorgenson, Clark, and Givens consider the tendency for militaries, which historically have placed a low priority on environmental concerns, to expand. This can have serious environmental consequences, as they sometimes reach and exceed the boundaries of ecological tipping points in the course of their technological development.

An ominous finding from the administrative science literature is that one of the main reasons companies adopt some new technologies and discontinue others is not environmental considerations at all. Rather, it often largely is a function of the ego dynamics among the chief executive officer and his inside circle. More specifically, there is research to show that the level of narcissism of the CEO is often directly involved with such decisions (Gerstner et al. 2013). It is little wonder, in such a business climate, that the natural environment becomes such an orphan issue.

One of the central features—indeed, some researchers (e.g., Lenski 1966; 2005) make a compelling case that it is *the* driving force — of social develop-

Figure 4.3 The Scale of the Fishing Industry: Technology and Ecosystems

Unloading frozen tuna from a commercial fishing trawler in Indonesia. Our technology enables us to harvest natural resources at unsustainable rates.

A key component of technological innovation revolves around how to make a process more widespread. Take, for example, the age-old activity of fishing. If the goal is to catch more fish, then a net is a technology that is more efficient than using a single fishing pole. Even a casual reading of the Gospels tells us that fishing nets were being used at the time of Jesus — 2,000 years ago, as some of Jesus's first disciples, including St. Peter himself, used these nets for fishing.

Yet, contrast that practice with some of the technologies of now, in which trawlers can "clean catch" or may use practices such as "longlining," in which a fishing line can be as long as 50 *miles*; "midwater trawling," in which ships pull nets the size of five football fields that can catch entire schools of fish. "Purse seining" surrounds huge areas with nets that are pulled progressively tighter to catch schools of fish.

There are other technologies that are even more efficient in catching fish (at least in the short run), that tend to disrupt ecosystems to the point that many fewer fish and other marine life are able to survive and reproduce, so that within a few generations, those stocks are permanently decimated, if not depleted. Some of these practices include "bottom trawling." In attempting to make large catches of bottom-dwelling fish like sole and halibut, as well as to get shrimp, fishing boats pull huge nets across the sea floor. To catch shellfish such as scallops, oysters and clams, "dredging" involves dragging huge baskets across the sea floor. Both of these practices are particularly damaging, as they often disrupt or kill much of the rich marine life along the floor of the sea that serves as an integral part of the ecosystem. Another related problem is that many of these practices, particularly dredging and trawling, result in large "by-catches," in which other fish or marine life that they were not necessarily trying to catch (such as dolphins in tuna nets), but that are mixed in, may be thrown back into the water, severely wounded or dead (Monterey Bay Aquarium 2015). Over time, this can wreak havoc on marine ecosystems.

In their book *The Tragedy of the Commodity*, Stefano Longo, Rebecca Classen, and Brett Clark (2015) delve into how the widespread adoption of large-scale technologies, in combination with economic practices such as the commodification of marine systems, can have catastrophic consequences. Focusing on two particular fishing operations from different parts of the world

— the Pacific salmon industry and the bluefin tuna from the Mediterranean Sea, Longo, Classen, and Clark find practices and social processes that already have led to dramatic declines in fish stocks and the marine systems that support them.

Dredging for mussels in the Menai Strait. Commercial dredging operations scour the sea floor, doing enormous damage.

The authors find evidence of the collective selfishness articulated by Garrett Hardin (1968; 1993) in his classic essay *The Tragedy of the Commons* and follow-up work. In trying to meet incessant and increasing demands for fish such as tuna and salmon, suppliers have adopted increasingly large-scale technologies, not just for fishing itself, but for making ships for catching and transporting fish larger, as well as making storage facilities, larger. Also, the use of advanced technologies such as sonar, as well as global positioning systems, aid in locating schools of fish. These lead to greater "efficiencies" to the point that the old metaphor of "shooting fish in a barrel" is not far removed from the actual reality. The aggregate of these technologies and practices, embedded in a culture where virtually unlimited removing of resources is often rewarded economically and socially, has taken the planet to a precarious place.

This brings on a vicious cycle — as fish get more depleted and demand continues to increase, there is an escalating pressure to find and develop ever more intrusive technologies. Taken together, these practices are quickly leading to the decline of fish stocks. A study in the prestigious journal *Science* projects that even with practices and technologies as they currently operate, global fish stocks will have reached a *state of collapse* (which ecologists define as a depletion of 90 percent or greater, including extinction of some species) by the year 2050.

What are the lessons here? The rise of a culture of sustainability would seem to be the best hope. Even though the technology exists to overfish, it is important to engage hard questions — and soon — about the ethics and advisability of using those technologies. Moving to smaller-scale operations, and away from some of the intrusive technologies and practices we have just read about, is necessary if the situation is to be stepped back from the brink of collapse.

Sources: Longo, Classen, and Clark (2015); Monterey Bay Aquarium (2015).

ment, is technology in one form or another. It was technological innovation that allowed people to stay in one place and grow crops, making the gradual transition from hunting and gathering beginning about twelve thousand years ago in what has been characterized, among other ways, as the Neolithic Revolution.

More recently in global time, the Industrial Revolution took place in a series of increasingly rapid technological changes beginning in the middle of the eighteenth century CE. In each case, technology was the catalyst for what were broad cultural, social, and economic changes, and humankind's relationship with the natural environment was profoundly changed. We are not so naïve or craven to contend that these changes were completely, or even primarily, negative in and of themselves. That said, the cultural norms of the nineteenth century, many of which are with us still, did not fully prepare us for the onslaught of technological development and its externalities.

Sociologists and historians may not necessarily agree on what aspects of technology are most crucial, and yet, as we saw in the last chapter, some major trends cannot escape notice. Many of the technologies developed over the course of industrialization have not taken full account (or in some cases, any significant account) of their environmental externalities.

The Effect of Technology Is Best Understood as It Interacts with Other Macro-Level Variables

Impacts on the natural environment tend to occur in countries at all levels of development, and technology plays a role, to be sure. That said, the effects differ across levels of development (Burns et al. 1994; 2006; Jorgenson and Burns 2007). Also, tropical nations, for example, tend to have different sorts of impacts on the environment than do non-tropical nations, particularly when controlling for population and affluence (York et al. 2003).

It is also worth considering that many of the developing nations of the semi-periphery experience even greater degradation than do the most developed core countries (Burns et al. 1994; 2006). There are several factors that contribute to this phenomenon. For one, population growth is much greater there. Also, although they are not as affluent as the most developed core countries, their rate of change, particularly in terms of growing wealth and consumption tend to be greater than either in the richest or poorest countries. Put another way, while the developed United States has a higher GDP in absolute terms than rapidly developing countries like China, the rate of *growth* of GDP per capita is greater in such countries than in the United States (Jorgenson and Burns 2007).

Also, developing countries often have access to some of the most invasive technologies — close to or equaling those available in developed countries. Combined with the fact that the level of oversight and regulation that sometimes keeps the worst abuses of these technologies from occurring in some developed countries, and we can start to understand how some of the most quickly degrading areas in the world are in the rapidly "developing" semiperiphery (Burns et al. 1994; 2006).

Standards of Knowledge and Proof

The Impacts of Technology and Environmental Assessment

Shortly after the founding of the Environmental Protection Agency in the United States in 1970, then President of the United States, Richard Nixon, approved the Technology Assessment Act (TAA) of 1972. It was charged with estimating what were the probable impacts of new technologies. The drafters of the TAA pointed out that, while those impacts could not necessarily be known in advance, it was still prudent to make good faith attempts to try. Technology, the drafters pointed out, was gaining complexity and growing in scale and, therefore, was likely to have extensive and poorly understood impacts on the environment. At the time, members of Congress on both sides of the aisle saw the critical nature of understanding the applications of technology. It was thought that such considerations should be part of the deliberations over public policy and national priorities (Brooks 1973). This built on earlier work, particularly the National Environmental Policy Act, which created the Council on Environmental Quality. It was at this point, that environmental impact statements began to be required for public actions which were likely to affect the quality of the human or natural environment.

It was clear at the founding of the EPA that technology assessment would be a central one of its functions. As society moves into the third millennium, it is virtually a sure bet that increasingly complex and potentially risky and dangerous technologies will continue to be devised. It will become increasingly important for society to mature in its ways of assessing them. A step in that direction will be to develop a set of measures up to the task. For lack of a better term, we might call them *New Ecological Measures*, or *NEMs*.

Developing New Ecological Measures: Coming Full Circle

Technology speeds up time, borrows against the future, and ups the ante for its consequences for good or ill.

If you ask me what is the most important thing I have learned… it's the idea that we are connected to community…that transcends time…we're connected to first who walked this earth [and] who aren't even born, yet, who are going to walk this earth. Our job in the middle is to bridge that gap…so that the future can enjoy the benefit… .

Rick Hill, Tuscarora Nation and Chair of Haudenosaunee Standing Committee on NAGPRA

In moving toward a solution, it is always helpful to see the problem clearly and to approach it with a degree of precision. This is an ideal that gets complicated in real live systems, and is particularly true in complex ecologies. Nonetheless, the development of a new set of ecological measures, suitable to the task of making sense of the problems of sustainability, would be a boon. Measuring things is an activity already integral to the culture of modernity. What we are proposing is a set of measures focused on some of the most daunting of ecological problems that would serve to put the gaze on crucial aspects of the ecosystem and life in it.

There are analogies here to previous breakthroughs in thinking, such as the Newtonian Revolution. Among other things, Newton developed mathematical techniques to address ways of conceptualizing and estimating phenomena previously beyond the grasp of science, such as estimating instantaneous change. The calculus of Newton and Leibniz has subsequently become so *enframed* in the culture, that we sometimes forget how powerful a truly innovative set of *ideas,* replete with their own vocabularies and measures, was the calculus. It facilitated widespread technological development by providing a framework with which to think through many challenging and otherwise overwhelming problems — not just at the time, but subsequently unto the present day.

Any change that occurs on the human cultural level involves innovations in ways of *thinking,* and typically develop new concepts and vocabularies. Consider, for example, the technological transformation that the advent of electricity has made possible, and the ways in which the culture has adapted. We now have words and ideas, not only for electronics, but for entire aspects of how we live and view the world that have come into being and into the way people think about their lives as a result (e.g., phones, computers, and lights).

Developing a set of *new ecological measures* (NEMs) could help us think through some of the aspects of the anthropogenic effects on the natural environment. These NEMs could help give us a more precise sense of the viability of a program or technology. The NEMs, for example, might take into account how long something will take to biodegrade, or the change in biodiversity a large-scale action such as the construction of a transnational pipeline over a major aquifer would be likely to cause. It would account for what the risks are in such a project, and what the potential for catastrophe could be if there were an unexpected leak in the system, for instance. These could build on existing ideas, such as radioactive half-life and environmental impact statements, but would be more proactive and forward thinking, tempered with some of the lessons of the past (Burns and Rudel 2015).

Mother Earth can recycle virtually anything, but she does so in her own time and in her own ways. Those ways may not be particularly friendly to human life, especially when the imbalances (many, but not all of which may be created by human social and cultural patterns) are extreme. A glass bottle, for example, might take 10,000 years to break down of its own accord. While it typically does not take as long to break down a plastic container as it does glass, in the meantime that plastic container can cause much disruption to the natural environment, in turn leading to *further* imbalances.

Consider as well, the phenomena of *bioaccumulation* and *biomagnification*, discussed in the chapter on health and the environment. Measuring exposure to persistent organic pollutants and the bioaccumulation of them and the increased probability of cancer or birth defects in an individual or a people, for example, is so complex that doing so *at the current level of knowledge* may not be conclusive. Yet, as the measures are developed in conjunction with other related areas of exploration, there is real hope of developing precision. Ideally, such measures will help to facilitate thinking about the environment the way, say GDP or supply throughput measures help economists think about and operationalize various aspects of monetary theory and practice. They should not be seen as an end in themselves, but rather as heuristic devices to facilitate ecological thinking and stewardship.

Likewise, as we develop new technologies, it will be increasingly important to also develop parallel technologies to measure what they are doing. Put another way, the old days of just developing the technology and then hoping for the best in terms of externalities, should be a thing of the past. The more complex the technology, the more complex the measures it is incumbent upon the technologists to develop to keep track of it.

Over and above the processes themselves, there are *scale* problems that the NEMs would need to take into account. Critical mass and tipping points are important as well — huge quantities of glass bottles massed together, for example, are not the same as one glass bottle taken thousands of times. Both are serious problems, but they present different sorts of challenges to the ecosystem.

Conclusions: Take-Away Lessons on Science, Technology, and the Environment

Technology is a crucial element in social and environmental change. It contains many paradoxes. Technologies have allowed us to heal diseases and to use resources that otherwise would have been unavailable. Technology can also cause problems, as we have seen. It is perhaps most accurate to say that technology ups the ante for many things. It allows us to use more resources, but then it places on us the cultural and personal responsibility to steward those resources and use them wisely.

Technology allows us to "borrow against the past and the future." In cutting down a redwood tree, for example, consider that it might be as old as 2,000 years. The dinosaur on the logo of one of the oil companies reminds us that the term "fossil fuel" is literally true for the gasoline we put into our cars, as it is for the coal we burn, and even for some of the natural gas that comes from the earth, via fracking or other less violent means.

The Great Law of the Iroquois is instructive here: Could it be done unto the seventh generation? If, for example, your ancestors, seven generations ago, had the technologies we now have available, and people had used resources as we do now, would the planet have survived thus far and, if so, in what shape? In confronting technology, honest people—people of good faith—are thus left with serious ethical questions.

One thing that is clear is that technology is not "neutral." Technology is intertwined with everything we do. It makes a huge difference in how we live our lives and in how we impact the planet. It interacts with other important variables such as population, affluence, and particularly culture, to produce tremendous effects on the natural environment and on the life it sustains.

An important lesson of human ecology is that no variable, however important, works in isolation. While laboratory work can, at times, lead to tremendous insight and sometimes opens avenues for further inquiry, it is crucial to keep in mind the key difference between laboratory work, which takes place in isolated, controlled conditions, and the way things operate in conjunction with the countless other factors that occur in actual ecosystems.

It is particularly important to consider this when attempting to bridge environmental science and policy. As York, Rosa, and Dietz (2002) point out, sound social policy depends on a regular and steady flow of rigorously conceived and executed science that then is competently articulated and disseminated; that process can break down at a number of places along the way. There is a desperate need for more scientific knowledge about the driving forces behind environmental change. Recently, a panel of social scientists led by Riley Dunlap and Robert Brulle (2015) have brought together much of the research to date looking at the human drivers of global climate change.

As York, Rosa, and Deitz (2002) point out, there is a great deal of "plasticity" among population, affluence and technology, in terms of their effects on the natural environment. By that, they mean that each of these key variables works in complex ways, and in conjunction and interaction with other variables, to produce environmental outcomes. Thus, while it may be impossible to say what the precise effect of another human being (or another billion human beings) may be on the planet, it is still important to keep in mind that population is an important driver of environmental change *when considering it in conjunction with the types of technology people are likely to be using themselves and causing to be used by their affluence and consumption patterns* (Hunter 2000).

This has been true in particular in the Anthropocene Age. Since the Industrial Revolution began in the late eighteenth century and profoundly changed ways in which humankind related to the earth and its resources, new technologies occurred at a great rate then, and technological innovation is very much still with us even today. New technologies can be a double-edged sword. They offer control over externals and efficiencies in garnering resources for livelihood and for luxuries, and in so doing, they tend to offer easier ways of extracting resources that can be detrimental to the environment. New, cleaner technologies do offer hope of balancing out some of the extreme incursions into the earth, but thus far, extractive and destructive technologies have tended to outstrip any green attempts to balance them.

One of the very important lessons from the research considering combinations of variables leading to environmental outcomes, such as population, affluence and technology (York et al. 2002; Burns et al. 1994) and the overarching effects of culture in which they are embedded (Burns 2009), is that those variables do have huge effects, but at the same time, almost never work in isolation. Rather, they work in complex arrays of combinations. It is important to keep this in mind and, rather than saying that one factor is more "important" than the others, acknowledge this complex, ecological relationship.

Chapter 4 Summary

- Technology has, over time, afforded ever greater mastery over the planet. At some point, the "mastery" over the planet becomes so profound, that those effects go beyond what can be simply incorporated and balanced in the ecosystem, and change the nature of the planet itself.

- Now, in the third millennium, we face truly daunting social and environmental problems. Many of those problems we can attribute to the invasive technologies that have been developed during and since industrialization.

- Green technology can best thrive in a culture that is organized around ecological principles and norms of sustainability.

- Human ecologists note the differences between the technological environment and the natural environment. We can think of the technological environment as houses and office buildings, cars, roads, machines and such things, but also as the know-how that goes into making them—the engineering and mathematics, the ideas of the architects and engineers.

- Even in the face of its many discoveries and its indelible influence on technology and culture, we put science on a pedestal at our peril. But tempered with humility and wisdom, science can be an invaluable tool for understanding, wonder and discovery, and perhaps even helping to restore much needed balance to the planet.

- One of the challenges of the third millennium will be to engage technology in such a way that it (at least gradually) unwinds the environmental imbalances of the last two and a half centuries, even as it seeks to understand and harmonize with the principles of natural ecology.

- We now have words and ideas for entire aspects of how we live and view the world, which has come into being and into the way people think about their lives as a result. This process is referred to as the *enframing* of technology in culture.

- In late modernity, large-scale production has become such a matter of course that it has become enframed in the culture and often goes unquestioned. New technologies are developed against this cultural backdrop.

- Technology "ups the ante" for many things. It allows us to extract and use more resources, but then it places on us the cultural and personal responsibility to steward those resources and use them wisely. Absent that wisdom, technology allows us to degrade the planet more quickly and efficiently than ever before.

- We intertwine technology with everything we do. It makes a huge difference in how we live our lives and in how we impact the planet. It interacts with other important variables such as population, affluence, and particularly culture, to produce tremendous effects on the natural environment and on the life it sustains.

- In order to come to grips with new technologies and their effect on the environment, it will be important to develop new ecological measures and vocabularies with which to think and communicate about as we incorporate them into the culture.

Chapter Five: Economics - The Capitalization of Everything or Natural Capital?

The economy is an institution that has, particularly in modern societies, brought incredible prosperity to some people. At the same time, it has led to wildly uneven distributions of wealth, so that now in a world with 7 billion people and rising, fewer than 400 individuals control more wealth than the poorer half (or 3.5 billion people) of the world. We look into some of the processes of the economy here, noting at the outset, that unchecked activity with a strictly economic focus can cause, and in fact in countless instances has caused, serious ecological damage.

The Discipline of Economics and How It Came About

In the opening chapter, we examined briefly the phenomenon of the Industrial Revolution and the tremendous social and environmental changes that came in its wake. The academic landscape was transformed irrevocably as well by the Industrial Revolution. Most of what became known as the social and behavioral sciences were spawned in the eighteenth and nineteenth centuries to deal with issues and problems that came up as a result of the social changes stemming from industrialization. The early sociologists and related thinkers were focused on problems of modernity, such as alienation (Marx and Simmel), egoism and anomie (Durkheim), narcissism (Freud), and the iron cage of rationality (Weber).

But early in the Industrial Revolution, Adam Smith (1776) published what was destined to become one of the most influential books in the history of humanity. In *The Wealth of Nations*, Smith (who ironically saw himself as a moral philosopher) spawned what was then the new discipline of economics.

Understand that when Smith wrote his work, there were still fewer than a billion people in the entire world; many natural resources (e.g., water and air) were still seen as virtually limitless. He envisioned a new science of economics that was, it seemed, brilliant for the time. However, as we will see, a number of his ideas became modified into truisms that have, to a large degree, outlived their usefulness without a good deal of reworking.

What Is the Value of Nature?

Virtually every equation in the discipline of economics has a variable for money. Money is, literally, the common denominator, or "bottom line" of economic thought. Seeing things primarily, or perhaps exclusively, in terms of money, leads to a number of social problems (Simmel 1907/1978; Poggi 1993;

Marx 1867/1967), including alienation and a cynicism that everything and everyone has a price.

Increasingly, in the culture of late modernity, monetization is seen as normal. It is just the way things are. Much as the rights of private property come to be seen as natural in a system of capitalism, aspects of nature come to be seen as something that can be owned by someone, and others excluded from its use.

Yet in the logic of ecology, some things are irreplaceable. How much is a drink of water "worth" to a dying person? What is the value of fresh air for someone dying of emphysema as they dwell in a place with heavily polluted air?

Even a green economics puts a price on such things. And yet, from an ecological perspective, to place a monetary value on such things makes about as much sense as would imposing the language of sight (such as color) on the sense of smell or hearing. There is a mismatch.

Economic Truisms and Their Limits

The central ideas of any discipline can come to be dumbed down by common usage and unquestioning belief. The language of disciplines can, not unlike religious belief that gets handed on from one generation to the next, come to reach a status of revealed wisdom.

As the discipline of economics seeped into the common consciousness in the culture of modernity, a number of ideas came to be accepted as truisms. Students in business schools in the United States and, by extension, the world over, write these ideas into their notes and give them back on tests, semester after semester. As they take on a life of their own, their meaning comes to outstrip their original usefulness, when they were first conceptualized over two centuries ago.

This has led to some mismatches between the economistic way of seeing the world and an ecological understanding of how the world works. In the words of process theologian and green economist John Cobb Jr., there is a fundamental mismatch between "economism" on the one hand, and "planetism" on the other.

Economies of Scale

There is a principle in economics that large-scale production is more efficient than small-scale production. This is a principle that has been put to tremendous use in things such as assembly lines. In fact, with the possible exception of the most expensive and rare cars, automobile manufacturing takes place in large assembly plants. Cars would not be affordable to the average consumer otherwise, and this is not to be taken lightly.

Large-scale agricultural production often follows similar principles. **Con-**

Figure 5.1 Perversities of Scale: Desertification of the American Breadbasket

Large-scale hog feeding facility.

The U.S. Environmental Protection Agency has long been concerned about Concentrated Animal Feeding Operations (CAFOs). These have numbers of animals such as cows or pigs confined in a small space that does not itself produce vegetation, for significant amounts of time. A number of organizations have pointed out the inhumane treatment of animals in these operations. Why do CAFOs exist then? From an economy of scale standpoint, they are able to produce large amounts of beef or pork in shorter amounts of time than is often the case with free ranging animals. A tractable workforce of people can feed large numbers of animals.

CAFOs require huge amounts of concentrated resources, such as corn and hay for feed and, in many cases, antibiotics used to keep animals from spreading contagious diseases to each other in such a small confined space. The most precious resource for this, as for virtually anything involving life, is water. Recent estimates of groundwater use from southwestern Kansas, for example, shows that about 97 percent of the water goes to livestock directly or indirectly through irrigated crops used for feeding (Sanderson and Frey 2014; U.S. Geological Survey 2005). In many ways, it is another instance of the *tragedy of the commons*, writ in large letters.

Researchers Matthew Sanderson and Scott Frey point out that many of the CAFOs in the United States are over just one very large source of water. This source, the Ogallala (or High Plains) Aquifer, runs under and in the southern part of South Dakota, the western parts of Kansas and Nebraska, and the Oklahoma and Texas Panhandles, and ranges into the very eastern parts of Wyoming, Colorado and New Mexico.

This naturally dry area, with irrigation from the aquifer, has been able to sustain the CAFOs. However, the Ogallala Aquifer is being depleted by this activity much more quickly than it can be replenished.

The High Plains Aquifer is considered "fossil water," in the sense that its primary sources were millennia of winter runoff from streams from the Rocky Mountains. Today, the Aquifer is recharged only by rainfall from a large area that is going through desertification and the rainfall will not nearly be enough to replenish it. The Ogallala Aquifer is down by about 30 percent from its original volume, just from over-pumping that has taken place in the late twentieth and early twenty-first centuries; by some projections, if these trends continue, the Aquifer will be down an additional 35-40 percent over the next 50 years. In the words of Sanderson and Frey: "The 'breadbasket of the world' appears to be on the verge of again becoming the Great American Desert. Formed over millions of years, the Aquifer is being depleted in the span of one human lifetime."

Cattle feedlot operation.

Huge economies of scale may work well in economics and business textbooks, but they can be catastrophic in real life. The tragic tale of the Ogallala Aquifer is a case in point. The CAFOs could arguably have made sense at some point from a narrowly economistic view (although that was never the case ecologically), but that time is already gone. The Aquifer cannot sustain the scale of use that it has over the last several decades.

What is the best hope? Ratcheting back on huge scales of production may be a saving grace. That would appear to be the case with the areas around historically magnificent resources that are being depleted faster than they can replenish themselves. Learning to live with the abundance that nature does provide, while at the same time being aware of and respecting natural limits, will be crucial as society moves into the twenty-first century.

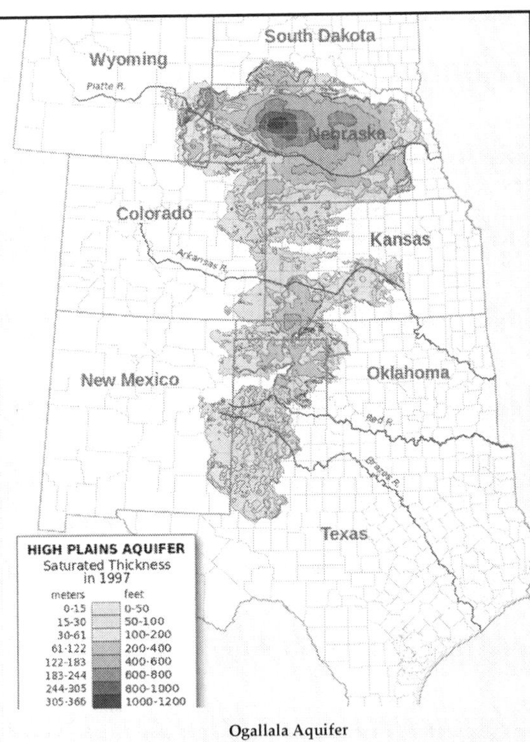

Ogallala Aquifer

Sources: Sanderson and Frey (2014); United States Geological Survey (2005 and 2011).

centrated Animal Feeding Operations (CAFOs) can be found where there are abundant sources of water. Here, cattle and other livestock are concentrated in small areas. It makes the feeding more efficient and the cattle more manageable. However, with concentrations of waste and the runoff into nearby streams, the natural ecology can easily become overwhelmed (Steingraber 2010).

Externalities

On one level, an **externality** is a variable that is left out of an equation. In a statistics class, all the externalities get lumped into a category of "residual (or unexplained) variance." But in the natural ecology of things, the fact that someone neglects to account for something in their humanly created model does not mean that the planet does not suffer the consequences. It may be, for example, that fresh water is required to cool the reactors in the nuclear plant. What is the actual "cost" to doing that? It may not enter into the equation at all if the people involved see the water as a "free" resource.

Often, the externalities are borne by the planet at large, and by the most vulnerable people. Consider the world trade of bottled water, for example. Those able to afford the water have the privilege of drinking relatively clean, healthy water, while those who cannot are forced to drink from a common pool that often is increasingly polluted and containing toxins (Hacker 2008; Harvey 1996). Those who live downstream of CAFOs and other heavily polluting sources are at increased risk for all sorts of diseases, including cancers, even while those causing the pollution enrich themselves and do not pay the full cost of the resources they monopolize.

Comparative Advantage

The principle of **comparative advantage** (often referred to by economists as the law of comparative advantage) assumes a division of labor in which there are numerous specialty tasks (such as assembly line work, mining, transportation and management, for example), and each task is assigned in a way that creates the greatest efficiency at the least overall cost. While this works well in principle, there are a number of perversities in actual practice, many of which redound into serious environmental problems.

Particularly in the current geo-political climate, where environmental laws differ greatly between (and within) nation-states, the way comparative advantage works, is that firms have incentives to move their business to places with the cheapest overhead costs (Leonard 2006). This, in turn, leads to a situation in which much of the consumption takes place by people in affluent regions, while the pollution and full costs of production are offlaid to poorer regions (Jorgenson 2003, 2004). There also is some evidence that this trend, rather than evening out, is getting more extreme over time (Jorgenson and Burns 2007).

Perpetual Expansion

About a generation after Smith, Thomas Malthus (1798) sounded the alarm for what he called **over-population**, a term with which he has become identified. Malthus saw that with the new methods of modern production brought on by technology, the food supply would continue to increase, but would do so "arithmetically," or in a gradual linear fashion. Population, on the other hand, would increase much more rapidly, in a "geometric" (or what we might now term exponential) fashion.

A number of modern-day human ecologists and environmental sociologists take inspiration from Malthus, in calling for limits to population expansion. Malthus thought the increasing mismatch between the growing population, and the society's (and planet's) ability to feed and provide necessities, much less luxury goods, for that population, would increasingly put the world at risk for a number of calamities. He postulated these as the **Four Horsemen** of an apocalyptic future: War, Famine, Pestilence and Plague.

In the post-World War II period, some of the shortages and problems associated with these disasters have been severe enough to inspire a new generation of thinkers to question the limits to growth (see, for example, Meadows 2004; Heinberg 2011). A common theme is that continual growth of the economy necessarily depletes the planet. At some point, that depletion becomes unsustainable.

The Invisible Hand of the Free Market

Malthus and more recent theorists who sound the alarm about the limits to growth have not been without their detractors. Most notably, the twentieth-century economist Julian Simon (1983) thought that exponential population growth would be sustainable because he counted on increasing human ingenuity to solve the problems of crowding and competition over scarce resources.

However, Simon fails to account for the fact that the planet is finite, and its resources are not unlimited. In fact, much of mainstream economic thought externalizes resource problems entirely, with an assumption that they will be available. When one resource runs short, Simon believed that the invisible hand would lead people to adapt by finding a new resource. Yet, Simon does not account for the fact that at some point, resources are not interchangeable. Alternatives have tradeoffs, and some of the consequences of those are severe (Burns et al. 2014).

Figure 5.2 The Harsh Reality of Externalities: Living Downstream of Moneyed Interests

Shipyard, Rio de Janeiro, Brazil.

Earlier, we looked at Concentrated Animal Feeding Operations (CAFOs) from the standpoint of economies of scale, and how those scales can overrun the natural ecological cycles (that in some cases may run in the time frames of millennia). In this box, we look at some of the externalities of the CAFOs. In addition to drying up a long-term source of water, which has ramifications for all life forms, including humankind, some common externalities of CAFOs include serious pollution, disease, and birth defects for the people living downstream.

Economists use the term **externality** in a couple of different, albeit related, ways. On one level, an externality is something not accounted for properly. In an econometric regression equation, something that affects the outcome that is not measured as an independent variable in the equation (and therefore contributing to "residual" variance) is referred to as an externality. We focus here on its second usage—an economic decision made by one person or group that extracts a cost on another person, or group of people, where the affected group is not involved in making the decision. After giving a formal definition, economics texts typically go on to cheerily assert that an externality can be either positive or negative, as though the two were even remotely equally likely.

People who live downstream of CAFOs are exposed to toxins and pollution, and are at greater risk for a number of negative outcomes, including certain kinds of cancers and birth defects.

People exposed to the "second hand smoke" from other people, are at greater risk for a number of things, including cancer, DNA damage, emphysema, asthma and other lung and vascular problems.

Living in the area of, and downstream from, fracking operations has created an array of problems.

These include aquifer and groundwater contamination, exposure to chemicals the effects of which are not fully known, and increased earthquakes, among other things. In some cases, there have been flash flames and other sorts of fires.

A number of toxic activities have aspects about them that are not yet fully known. For example, in the case of fracking, a substantial number of rock and shale formations contain millennia-old deposits of substances that become toxic when stirred up—radium is one such substance. This is not to say that a given formation will or will not have radium. It could have any one of a number of substances that may or may not be tested for and, even if found, be deemed "safe" by people with a vested interest in doing the fracking.

In instances where someone with money and power finds themselves downstream of a toxic operation, the outcome can offer ironic twists. In one such instance, the CEO of Exxon, Rex Tillerson, and Dick Armey, a retired congressman noted for his anti-environmental voting record, joined neighbors from a local upscale housing development to attempt to stop fracking in their area. This is a prime example of the NIMBY ("Not in My Back Yard") phenomenon. In situations of toxic activity with significant effects for those living downstream, combined with concentrations of wealth, one of the chief uses of money then, rather than trying to promote a healthy environment for all, becomes offlaying the negatives of living downstream to someone or someplace else.

Moneyed interests often are able to get the public to allow them to do dangerous or harmful activities because they are able to influence elected officials through lobbying and campaign contributions, among other things. Another common strategy is to use lobbyists to promote the idea that since all the facts are not in about something (e.g., fracking), they should be allowed to go ahead with it.

As Steingraber (2010) points out, societies can address this dire "living downstream" phenomenon in some positive ways. A cancer survivor herself, as well as a scientist, she makes a compelling case that societies should take the precautionary principle much more seriously. Rather than the people who are affected by something they had little or no choice in promulgating, Steingraber makes a good case for the burden of proof being put on would-be polluters to show in advance that what they are doing is not harmful to the people and life downstream from them.

Sources: Steingraber (2010); Centers for Disease Control (2015).

Individual and Collective Interests: The Drama and Tragedy of the Commons

Adam Smith thought that each person acting in their own self-interest would lead to the optimal system, in which there was a balance of individual interests and the collective good.

However, it has been pointed out by a number of observers, particularly by Garrett Hardin (1968, 1993), that the aggregate of many people placing their own selfish interests above those of the collective can, and typically does, lead to a **tragedy of the commons**. Hardin saw quite clearly that a common area, such as a grazing land or forest, could become depleted rapidly and irretrievably if individuals believed it was in their best interest, in the short run, to take more than they put back.

Elinor Ostrom (1990) believed that the tragedy of the commons could be avoided under certain circumstances. In her Nobel Prize winning work, Ostrom advocated for a situation in which there was communal ownership of common areas, in which stakeholders felt a common bond of stewardship toward the resource. They would internalize, and in turn be bound by, a common normative system that discouraged, either formally or informally (or, ideally,

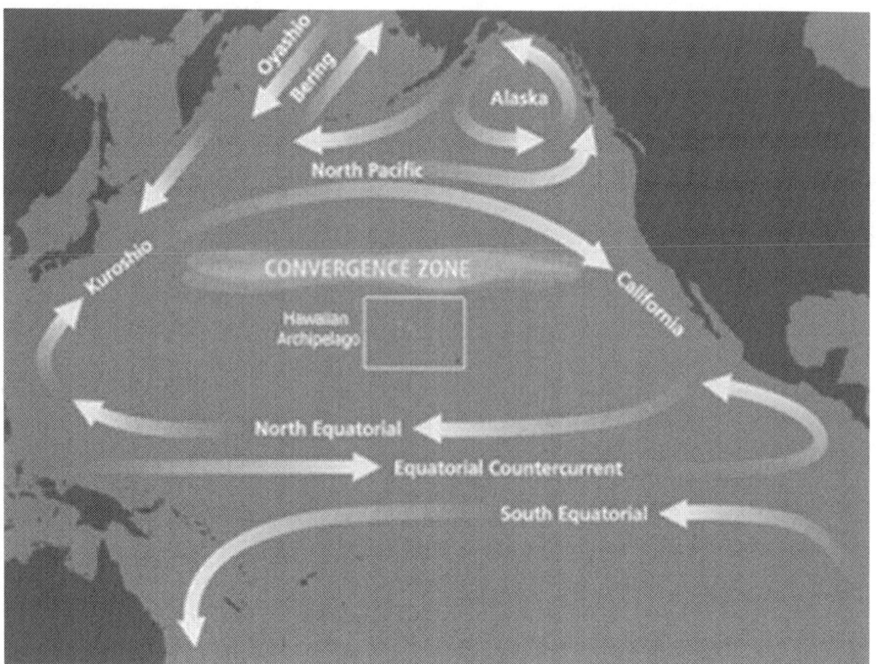

Pacific Trash Vortex.

with a combination of both) being a "free rider" and taking more than one's fair share.

This is facilitated by being part of a social network that is somewhat "closed," in the sense that, rather than people coming and going without constraint, they would be known in the community. As Ostrom and others (e.g., Boyce 2013) have pointed out, however, this becomes more problematic as the scale of common resource increases.

In other words, stewarding a lake, in which people are local to the lake, make their common livelihood on the lake, and feel a sense of responsibility in keeping it healthy and pristine, is oftentimes easier than stewarding an ocean. This is because there are so many other people involved, and there are so many ways to degrade the ocean (e.g., by putting toxic waste into it), that there is an unfortunate tendency among many people to see the ocean as limitless and not needing stewardship. It is this kind of thinking, aggregated across time and numbers, that lead to situations like the Pacific Trash Vortex.

Distributions of Wealth and the Environment

Even Karl Marx fell into this trap. Marx (1867/1967) saw value coming from two major sources: labor and capital. According to Marx's famous "labor theory of value" formulation, it is labor that gives true value to something, with capital being a false, fetishized component. But here, Marx falls into the trap of economic thinking. Unlike the conservative economists of his and our day, Marx saw very clearly the tremendous social problems that concentrations of wealth in a few hands causes. However, very much like his more conservative counterparts, Marx did not acknowledge that all value, whether it be food, water or energy, ultimately is rooted in the earth. The "raw materials" that people invest in, and which people transform and recombine through their labor, come from nature.

This is not to say that Marx ignored nature. In processes of **metabolic rift**, resources indigenous to one place are brought to another (for expansion of this theme, see Moore 2011a and 2011b; Foster 1999; Foster et al. 2011). Marx, however, did not develop these ideas nearly as much as he did ideas about labor and capital. Sociologists in the critical tradition have extended Marx's analysis considerably, focusing in particular on contradictions in capitalism that cause it to use resources in ways that far outstrip the planet's ability to sustain itself (O'Connor 1998; Antonio 2009).

As a general rule, the larger the scales of production and consumption, the greater the level of metabolic rift. The use of ever larger scales of operation would, one might conjecture, at least lead to bigger incomes for people who work in connection with them. But that turns out rarely to be the case. Looking at personal income over the four decades spanning the late twentieth and early twenty-first centuries, Sanderson and Frey (2014:529) discover something quite telling when they look at scales of production in agriculture and livestock. While the income of people living in other areas of Kansas saw their incomes nearly triple over that period, the figures for the counties where there are CAFOs and large-scale agriculture flatlined over the same period. Put another way, already poor incomes became relatively even poorer. While the benefits of increased revenues go to large-scale investors and the largest agribusiness operations, the smallholders and workers are left behind. Economies of scale, it turns out, often have serious drawbacks, both in terms of the economy for all except the already privileged few, and in terms of the natural ecology.

The Treadmill of Production and Consumption

As we saw, one of the central tenets of mainstream economics is that economies can continually expand. While they may go through boom and bust cycles, the ultimate trajectory is constant expansion. A growth in the GDP of 2.5 to 3 percent per year is seen as what a normal healthy economy does.

Yet, the expansion cannot take place without resources to fuel it. On a planet with finite resources, this constant expansion is unsustainable.

Allan Schnaiberg (1980) has coined the term **treadmill of production** to refer to this constant upping the ante of what is produced. Entire sectors of the economy then are given over to marketing and advertising, to ensure that people consume what is produced. To fuel the growth, the production and consumption cycle gets bigger as time goes by.

This creates a number of perversities in the economy, particularly around the margins of very rich and very poor people. Put another way, virtually every resource, from the most vital for life (e.g., water) to the more luxurious (e.g., prime redwood for hot tubs), is differentially accessed by rich and poor (Gould et al. 2008). The market for luxury goods may include endangered species or resources which, following "normal" laws of supply and demand, drives the price up precipitously, which in turn, encourages people with little to lose because of their poor and precarious situations, to poach scarce resources to virtual extinction (Schnaiberg and Gould 1994).

Contributions and Limitations of Environmental Economics

A number of economists have tried to grapple with the questions we are raising in this chapter. While the details vary among them, green economists do center on a number of principles. These include working toward a robust economy, but one that is not beholden to the perpetual growth model (Heal 2000; Jackson 2011).

In addition, green economists must come to terms with each of the economic truisms that have come to haunt contemporary society and plague the natural environment (Daly 1996; Daly and Cobb 1994; Daly and Farley 2011). In addition, they must deal with issues of *transition* from the old ways of doing business to the sustainable ones (Boyce 2013; Baker 2013; Heinberg 2011).

Economic Incentives: When and How Do They Work?

One of the latent effects of any economy, is that there are built-in incentives and disincentives for certain kinds of behavior. For example, giving a tax break for some kinds of activities tends to skew a number of people in the direction of doing those activities (e.g., the ability to deduct the interest on mortgages for home loans, gives somewhat of an incentive to many people to buy a house rather than rent).

In a landmark article, Ridley and Low (1994) pose the provocative question: *Can Selfishness Save the Environment?* They make a compelling case that many of our environmental problems can be addressed economically, by giving proper incentives. If gasoline consumption pollutes the planet and causes greenhouse gas emissions, Ridley and Low argue that a way to address it is to tax gasoline consumption heavily, and use those funds to help defray the costs of cleaning the environment and to pay for the medical costs of those who suffer most from pollution-related diseases. This line of thinking is not without critics. Also, not all environmental problems can be addressed that easily. Nonetheless, Ridley and Low offer some intriguing food for thought.

More profoundly though, in a time when distributions of wealth are so unequal, those with ready access to wealth can make decisions that may be framed as "rational" for them (although perhaps selfish or short-sighted would be more appropriate terms), that have devastating consequences for the environment. There is often a fundamental mismatch between the workings of natural ecological cycles, and those of the economy (Burns and Rudel 2015), particularly when it carries the assumptions of "neo-classical" economics that we have reviewed in this chapter.

While economic incentives can, in some limited instances, have positive results, it is important to make sure that, when they are put into place, they do not exacerbate the problems of economism, but rather work to ameliorate them. That is best done by being aware of the problems we have discussed, and gearing any incentives in such a way as to minimize their negative impacts.

One such example is a tobacco tax. Since the positives of not smoking far outweigh those of smoking for everyone involved (not just for the smoker engaging in self-destructive behavior, but for everyone exposed to the second hand smoke), a good case could be made for such an anti-smoking economic incentive (Becker et al. 1984).

What Can Societies Do Now? Adapting Old Ideas to Contemporary Problems

Adam Smith promulgated ideas such as the invisible hand, economies of scale, and (combined with later influences) comparative advantage[i]. These have morphed into central organizing principles of the global market economy. If anything, the ideas have picked up momentum, and in one form or another are perhaps more influential than ever in the contemporary era.

As we saw earlier, one of the *other* ideas of Adam Smith, largely forgotten in the unbridled leap of faith in a relentlessly growing global market economy, is that of the viability of a progressive tax on certain aspects of the economy, particularly where the well-being and life of the planet are involved. This would have the potential to offset, at least partially, some of the imbalances of an economy misshapen by huge concentrations of wealth and luxury on the one hand, but of even larger concentrations of immiseration, risk and degradation on the other.

Societies that wish to take environmental problems seriously can begin to unwind some of the excesses of the "neo-classical" economics that have ensued in the wake of Adam Smith's thinking. While huge scales of production may work well and be "efficient" in sophomore economics and business textbooks, they often create havoc in real ecosystems. Moves toward smaller, local scales are something that communities and societies will do well to engage seriously as we move forward into the third millennium.

In a related vein, it makes sense to have a progressive tax on economies of scale, particularly where they use critical resources and/or concentrate waste that takes considerable time to bio-degrade, or which facilitates other unhealthy consequences. How long is too long? One crucial aspect of the New Ecological Measures would be their potential utility in illuminating this and related issues. To build on a previous example, a bottle that takes 10,000 years to return to its natural state, does put a strain on the ecosystem that is orders of magnitude greater than a container that bio-degrades in a season or a year[ii].

More broadly, a society can put together incentives for positive change. Those incentives can sometimes be through tax structures. In a vacuum, this will do little, but as part of a comprehensive set of norms, values and goals, could be quite beneficial.

Similar considerations can and do need to be addressed for things we use and take for granted. Gasoline and the vehicles based on them and plastics are other examples that come readily to mind. More broadly, a sustainable economy would reassess the efficacy of money as a yardstick for well-being. Access to clean air and water, trees, and walking trails, for example, are vital concerns[iii]. Money, of course, is an important general medium of exchange. But it is important to move beyond the notion that everything, including life and the natural environment, can be reduced to its terms.

Conclusions: Take-Away Lessons on Economics and the Environment

In order for us to reach a sustainable planet, it will be necessary to reconsider many of the truisms of economics that have reached the status of revealed wisdom in developed societies, as well as in most of the developing societies that wish to emulate them (which is to say, at this point, virtually throughout the entire world). And yet, robust economies that move beyond the perpetual growth model and which question the revealed truths are possible with some imagination and wisdom (Heal 2000; Jackson 2011).

Independent of any changes we do make, are questions about *how* we make those changes, and on what trajectory of time. There are several ways to stop a runaway bus. The quickest and most precipitous is to simply crash it into a concrete wall. This, of course, has huge negative consequences, and it makes more sense, if it is at all possible, to slow the bus gradually and to turn it onto a safer and saner route.

Perhaps this is a metaphor we could keep in mind in facing the future (c.f. Lakoff and Johnson 2003). As Baker (2013) points out, the social and ecosystems have been driven to the point of impending collapse. The choices that make sense now include how to collapse "consciously" in such a way as to transition to alternative fuels, sustainable living, and a robust and stable, but not growing, economy. We can do that, but the ability to do it gracefully diminishes every day we continue with the profligate use of nature in a way that is extravagantly beyond our means, or the planet's means, to adapt.

The best hope lies in a transformation of the way we think about the planet. In the terms of process theologian and green economist, John Cobb Jr. (1991), there is a fundamental divide between thinking of the planet as something to be taken from and used, or to live with cooperatively in a spirit of good will and stewardship. Cobb characterizes this fundamental choice, that we all must make as individuals and collectively, as between **economism** on the one hand, and **planetism** on the other. For Cobb, it is the most fundamental and important choice we make in our lifetimes, and in the life of the planet.

Endnotes:

[i] See Smith (1776/1937; 1759/1976).

[ii] While it is not necessarily an end solution, the technology already exists to make bottles that biodegrade in less than one year. This and other promising ideas should be explored, but with a sense of humility that any new technology is likely to have unintended consequences. This is not a counsel against pursuing these technologies, but it should only be done with broader ecological principles in mind. Such technology would not be an end, but rather part of a process of moving in the direction of living in harmony with nature.

[iii] There is an important movement among some economists to attempt to

come to grips with these realities. Herman Daly and colleagues, in particular, have made some good faith attempts to balance ideas from economics with those of sustainability (see Daly 1996; Daly and Cobb 1994; Daly and Farley 2011). See also Heal's (2000) *Nature and the Marketplace* for an attempt to come to what is sometimes characterized as 'ecological economics.'

Chapter 5 Summary

- The economy is an institution that has, particularly in modern societies, brought tremendous prosperity to some people. While inequality waxes and wanes, it has generally increased over the course of the last forty years. With rises of wealth and inequality, there has been a concomitant ratcheting in the "*treadmill of production*," with greater extraction of the earth's resources and degradation of the planet as a result.

- The resources on the planet are finite. As Garrett Hardin pointed out in *The Tragedy of the Commons*, selfish utility maximizing behavior may benefit certain members of the society and provide profit to them as individuals; yet it increases the overall strain on the resources of the collective whole. This can have local, regional, and even global significance.

- Adam Smith and his work, *The Wealth of Nations*, brought about a new economic outlook, bringing forward the ideas that framed principles of global market economics. Some of the ideas that have been with us ever since include a belief in the "invisible hand" of the market; hyperspecialization and the law of comparative advantage; the efficacy of large-scale production; externalization of the costs of production, particularly those associated with the environment, and discounting the future.

- Each of these economic truisms, when examined more carefully, present significant mismatches with the natural constraints of actual ecosystems. Particularly when pushed to extremes, they cause significant environmental harm and compromise the well-being of those dependent upon the natural environment for their livelihood.

- Concentrated agricultural feeding operations (CAFOs) such as huge feed lots for cattle or pigs, for example, tend to have vast impacts on our planet and on the life (including humankind as well as the animals) coming into contact with them. Whether it is the accelerated drawing down of major aquifers or pollution, disease and birth defects, CAFOs' negative impacts, when looked at from an ecological or health standpoint for the many, tend to outweigh whatever benefit there is for the few.

- Huge economies of scale, such as those commonly taught in economics and business classes make sense on one level, but present problems on a multitude of others. There are limits to what our planet can provide, and those limits must be carefully weighed when considering economic gain.

- In particular concentrations of capital there can be perverse effects on many levels. Moneyed interests often are able to get the public to allow them to do dangerous or harmful activities because they have the ability to influence elected officials through lobbying, campaign contributions, and manage public perception through the selective promulgation of information manufactured by biased "think tanks," media outlets, and other artifacts of cultural management.

- Especially in the age of globalization, the larger the scales of production and consumption, the greater the level of *metabolic rift*. Most of the increase in profit goes to larger stakeholders and business owners who do not pass on that increase to those who do the labor. Additionally, with large-scale production and metabolic rift, there is a greater tendency toward ecological degradation.

- A century and a half ago, Karl Marx articulated a fundamental contradiction of *bourgeois society*: Capitalism would continue with the owners (*bourgeoisie*) accumulating wealth, and the workers who produced that wealth (*the proletariat*) becoming increasingly impoverished, until the system imploded under its own weight. Capitalism, for Marx, thus "...[p]roduces its own grave diggers..."

- An ecological Marxist of the late twentieth century, James O'Connor, added to this a "second contradiction of capitalism..." In late modernity, the appetite for resources would continue unabated, and, in fact, become ever greater in the quest to produce ever more material things (c.f. what Allan Schnaiberg has characterized as "*the treadmill of production*"). In this way, capitalism would become ever more heated until the resources became so degraded that the system would collapse.

- As an alternative scenario, in order for us to reach a sustainable planet, it will be necessary to reconsider many of the truisms of economics that have reached the status of revealed wisdom in developed societies, as well as in most of the developing societies that wish to emulate them (which is to say, at this point, nearly the entire world).

- There is a fundamental divide between thinking of the planet as something to be taken from and used, or to live with cooperatively in a spirit of good will and stewardship. John Cobb, Jr. characterizes this fundamental choice, that we all must make as individuals and collectively, as between *economism* on the one hand, and *planetism* on the other. Cobb's articulation of planetism may offer the most coherent alternative vision to the run-away economism that so characterizes the contemporary culture of late modernity.

Chapter Six - Governance, Policies, and Institutions

In democratic societies, political institutions are the sites where potential solutions to social problems are adjudicated and public policy is created. This chapter will review the relevant political institutions involved in environmental policy making. Specific challenges arise when faced with environmental problems that cross national boundaries and/or defy the ability of a single nation to protect its people from unwanted environmental degradation. Recent trends in national, regional, and global environmental governance will be evaluated from a distinctly sociological point of view. We examine cross-cutting axes of power, which complicate environmental governance. We also examine the mismatch that often occurs between the scale of environmental problems and legalized solutions. Finally, we will consider the question of legitimacy in governance.

Background: Ways in Which Political Systems Work and Don't Work

The actions of industry, governments, and citizens toward the environment are regulated by a web of formal and informal policies, norms, and institutions. Regulating environmental harms has always posed a problem for authorities because waterways, smog, and other environmental problems often cross or transcend county, state, and national boundaries.

What Is Governance?

Governance is the process by which social groups create, institutionalize and enforce social norms. Some scholars define governance more narrowly, however, and emphasize the ways a community of interested and affected parties comes together to manage or solve particular social problems. This more specific conceptualization of governance has resulted in numerous studies of specific types of governance, such as water governance, environmental governance, and international trade governance.

Traditional models of governance focus on the role of the state, which is thought to be the primary governing and enforcement body. Under this definition, scholars examine "a government's ability to make and enforce rules, and to deliver services, regardless of whether that government is democratic or not" (Fukuyama 2013:3). In this scenario, good governance is measured as the extent to which the rules are executed. Sociologists examine governance in more complex ways. To sociologists, "Governance is not the same as government" (Lemos and Agrawal 2006). We examine the informal pathways of norm/rule creation, which include public perception of social problems and power relationships that determine who can participate in rule-making. We also examine the organizations and mechanisms of governance, such as environmental ministries, environmental laws, and international environmental treaties.

Sociologists have a long history of examining governance. Weber, Marx, and Durkheim each offered perspectives on the structural and cultural characteristics that hold societies together, solve shared problems, and maintain order. The structure of the economy, the role of rules and organizations, and the importance of moral and cultural frameworks each take their place in these classical explanations of the ways nations govern. These frameworks have been expanded by contemporary theorists to account for the ways globalization has impacted the methods that countries use to govern in the context of deteriorating sovereignty, permeable borders, the rise of global culture, and interdependent economies. In this section, we address these classical and contemporary theories of governance.

Classical Sociological Theories of Governance

During the Industrial Revolution, Karl Marx and his colleague, Frederich Engels, wrote extensively about the ways capitalism, as an economic form, structured the governance of societies. To begin with, capitalism structured people into three basic social classes; and which class people belonged to determined their power to participate in societal decision-making. The capitalist class or *bourgeoisie* consisted of those who owned the means of production, such as factories, natural resources, and land. Their resources were the foundation upon which the capitalist economy depended, which made them the primary architects of the ways decisions were made in modern nation-states. Members of the *proletariat* or labor class only possessed their own labor to sell; therefore, they really had no influence over societal decision-making. Instead, they were the workers who did the will of the capitalist class. The final class, the *lumpenproletariat* or underclass, was made up of those who were unable to participate in the capitalist system, including the marginally employed, the elderly, women, and the sick. And, due to their inability to participate in the production and consumption system, Marx considered them to be the least able to exercise self-determination or influence over the decisions of their countries. Marx believed that capitalism was incompatible with democracy by and for the people, which is why he advocated for revolution and the institution of communism as an alternative form of economic system.

Max Weber agreed that social class was an important determinant of the ways countries governed; however, he also argued that rationality and fairness were determined by rules and laws, which were designed and implemented by the political and economic institutions of society. In *Economy and Society* (1978), he laid out several criteria of bureaucracy that are designed to secure rational decision-making in government. The primary features of a rational government include offices: (1) organized into a clear hierarchy of positions that are (2) filled by candidates based on their technical skills and credentials, (3) free of conflicts of interest, and (4) overseen by strict discipline and control. Weber's belief was that clear rules and strict oversight would ensure that policies were implemented consistently and efficiently, which would introduce fairness and a semblance of equality into societal decision-making.

Rather than formal laws and institutions being the glue that kept order in society, Durkheim argued that a shared moral underpinning established a foundation from which governance takes place. Durkheim based his theory of moral authority on his examination of traditional societies, where populations were smaller and where the good of one member of society was tightly connected to the good of everyone. In these societies, or what earlier theorists had characterized as Gemeinschaft societies (see Tönnies [1887] 2001), cooperation was built upon shared perspectives on the world. Shared systems of beliefs, traditions, rituals, and routines served to organize daily life into predicable actions and clear divisions of labor that gave everyone a secure place in the social order. Seeing that societies had grown larger and more complex than traditional societies, Durkheim postulated that shared values still played a critical role in ensuring cooperation, but recognition of interdependence was also required to maintain civility. When people come to see themselves as different or more important than others in these *Gesellshaft* societies, conflict and competition would replace solidarity and cooperation in societies; therefore, a shared moral order that had at its base recognition of the value and mutual benefit of each member of society was a basic requirement to the maintenance of social order.

In the 1960s, Talcott Parsons offered a theoretical synthesis that bridged the moral and rule-based approaches of Durkheim and Weber. Parsons argued that the primary functions of society are performed by institutions, whether those functions are formal rule-formation or informally socializing members of society to share a moral orientation toward the world. In Parsons's theory, rule-formation is performed by the institutions of the government, such as the Senate; rule implementation and enforcement are handled by the courts, the police, and local authorities (e.g., mayors, city councils); and the job of socializing and enforcing shared morals, values, and beliefs are the purview of civil society, the family, churches, and the educational system. When each of these institutions is operating successfully, smooth functioning of society would endure. In addition, Parsons argued that the most successful societies created a certain amount of duplication of duties across their institutions, which would ensure the continued functioning of society if one of the institutions failed.

Contemporary Sociological Theories of Governance

Giant container ship loaded with products bound for far-flung ports. Globalization and multi-national trade have changed the governance role of nation-states.

Globalization has made governance much more complex than classical sociological theorists conceived, which has led to a considerable need to revise classical governance theories to account for today's contexts. The times that the classical theorists lived in were characterized by a global order where individual nations were relatively self-contained. National trade was a source of luxury and exotic goods, but nations primarily relied on their own resources to create the goods that filled the needs of their own people. Likewise, nations were self-contained in their forms of governance. Globalization has drastically changed the nation-state from a self-contained, relatively homogenous population into a very loose network of organizations and social groups marked by an incredible diversity of values, beliefs, and ethnic and religious backgrounds. Imports and exports make up larger and larger portions of consumer goods. Phrases like "assembled in America" indicate the complex and international character of contemporary production processes, where various parts of a product are made in different countries before they are shipped to a centralized assembly plant. Similarly, as we will see in great detail in the next section of this chapter, many of the problems nations experience today are neither local nor solvable by national governments alone; instead, problems such as international terrorism, climate change, and the stability of markets result from complex interdependencies among nations, and they require cooperation across nations to solve them. Sociological theories of governance have evolved to recognize these complexities.

Ecological Modernization Theory

The ecological modernization perspective precipitated from observable environmental improvement that spread across Europe in the late twentieth century (Buttel 2000a). Countries like Germany, the Netherlands and Sweden had successfully obtained support from industry to reduce packaging, decrease pollution, and generally improve their environmental impact. Ecological modernization scholars were eager to extract generalizable lessons from these European experiences to facilitate similar advances abroad. Their quest began with questioning why environmental policies were so successful, and the logic that emerged is roughly as follows: environmental reform has uniquely overcome the resistance of nation-states and industry, first, due to its ability to affect people of all classes; second, due to the increasing scientific evidence linking pollution to human health problems; and third, due to environmental pollution's ability to transcend national borders.

Although the exact formulation of ecological modernization theory differs slightly among its primary proponents, lessons from the European experience resulted in a core set of arguments. First, in contradistinction to the position of more eco-centric environmentalists (Mol 2003), ecological modernization scholars propose that the solution to contemporary, technology-induced environmental problems is *more* technological development, not less (Buttel, 2000a; Carolan, 2004). Increased environmental efficiency in production processes can reduce ecological impacts and ultimately create a net proenvironmental effect. A restructuring of the modern nation-state that facilitates a partnership between industry and governments, and delegates further environmental responsibility to the market, can free industry to create innovative solutions from cradle to grave. Such a strategy would necessitate more flexible regulatory regimes, which provide space for voluntary initiatives by industry to be implemented, monitored and evaluated.

Shortly following Buttel's (2000a) challenge to ecological modernization, Spaargaren, Mol and Buttel (2000) joined forces to collaboratively examine the theoretical strands of ecological modernization. The key distinction made by Spaargaren and Mol in their introductory essay argues that the uniqueness of ecological modernization theory lies in its assumption that ecological rationalities exert influences on production and consumption cycles that are independent of other rationalities, such as economics (a point to which we will return below). The spread of concepts such as the polluter pays principle (PPP) and environmental management systems is promulgated as evidence of environmental reform à la ecological modernization. They specifically state: "It is these kinds of concepts that establish a link between ecological modernization as a general theory of societal change on the one hand and ecological modernization as a political program or policy discourse on the other" (2000: 7). While this conceptual clarity addresses earlier critiques that ecological modernization lacked solid empirical support, it does not overcome the long-term prospects that the theory itself will avoid the fate forewarned by Buttel in *Geoforum* (2000b).

In other words, the central explanatory narrative evoked by most ecological modernization scholars is that the environment is somehow unique among social problems due to its scientific and biophysical nature. This tenet is best summarized by Buttel (2000a: 61): "…an ecological modernization perspective views the environment as in potentiality or in practice being an increasingly autonomous (or 'disembedded') arena of decision-making (what Mol refers to as the 'emancipation of ecology')." Not only are ecological problems considered unique because of their biophysical character, their tendency to threaten higher and lower strata persons alike and their ability to transcend national boundaries are thought to situate them high on both national and international political agendas.

World System Theory

World system theory provides an explanation of contemporary governance that is based on the classical perspectives of Karl Marx. However, rather than examining social classes of people within nations, world system theory examines the world in terms of classes of nations. The fundamental categories used in this theory to describe the classes of nations include: (1) the core nations, (2) the semi-peripheral nations, and (3) the peripheral nations. In this framework, the core nations include the most central countries defined by their importance to international trade, military power, and general strategic significance. Most world systems scholars include the United States, Japan, Australia, and the European nations in the core; some also consider Russia and China among the core nations (or members of a semi-core). Semi-peripheral nations are those which are strategically very important, whether because of their centrality in their region, such as Israel, their size, such as India, or their possession of strategically important natural resources, such as South Africa because of their possession of uranium. These nations emerge as powerful actors in certain international governance debates, while they recede to the background in others. Finally, the peripheral nations are those that possess small economies, lack significant strategic resources, and generally have little clout at the tables of international policy making.

In the world system theory model of international governance, the core nations generally set the overarching guidelines that organize trade, terrorism, environmental, and other international policies that require multi-lateral cooperation. The semi-periphery countries are consulted, and their approval is required in their primary areas–whether regional policy considerations or on issues pertaining to their fields of strategic importance. And, in most cases, the peripheral nations are forced to go along with the policy arrangements preferred by the consensus formed between the core and the semi-periphery. You can see the similarities between Marx's classes and world system theory's classification of nations. The general argument is the same: those with the most power in the military-industrial complex (C. Wright Mills) have the most power in all decision making. The important difference to highlight between world system theory and Marxist approaches to governance is that Marx gave great power to the proletariat, whose members he thought should join together and fight for a more equal society; however, world system theory generally relegates power to nation-states, ascribing no real power to citizens.

World Polity Theory

World polity theory offers a slightly more complex view of international decision-making and begins with an emphasis on global culture as the source of authority. While world system theory still holds that national sovereignty underpins the ways nations interact in the context of globalization, world polity theory proposes a messier global context where people, ideas, and organizations float more freely in a soup of global exchanges. These exchanges are not limited to the economic markets of nations, rather individuals from many nations travel to distant countries; some move permanently to another continent, speak a variety of languages, and acquire tastes for exotic foods, for example. The Internet has opened lines of communication and information-sharing that were formerly limited only to elites who could afford to travel. However, now citizens in relatively isolated nations like China and North Korea can get glimpses into more democratic societies, and, likewise, those of us living in more open societies can see and relate to environmental injustices around the world. In this context, nations have become more similar. McDonalds can be found around the world; sushi is a favorite food in the United States; Native American rug patterns are duplicated in textile factories in China for sale in European markets.

Some scholars argue that this type of exchange of cultural goods leads to an overall homogenization of society in ways that squelch local identities. But others, including world polity theorists, argue that the large-scale exchange of people, products, and ideas across national boundaries has produced a shared value system, which makes up the core of a global culture. Boli, Meyers and their colleagues, for example, have argued that shared global cultural values are carried by international organizations, like Amnesty International, Green Peace, and the World Council of Churches. These organizations possess a moral authority in international policy arenas, according to world polity theory, and nations–whether core, semi-periphery or periphery–are often forced to listen to these non-governmental organizations, because they represent the will of civil society. In this model, we see a kinship with Durkheim's arguments that governance is based on shared values and beliefs among members of society; however, unlike in the days of Durkheim, those members of society are no longer isolated from the members of other nations and continents. Instead, world polity theory recognizes that civil society is a force that influences countries during their international negotiations.

Figure 6.1 The Tragedy of the Commons

Plastics that are disposed of on one side of the world often end up as pollution an ocean away.

When an individual acts selfishly, without taking responsibility for the costs, and those costs are borne by the collective or the natural environment, this is known as *The Tragedy of the Commons* (Hardin 1968 and 1993), or simply as the *commons problem*. Put in terms of *rational choice theory*, people tend to maximize their own utility based on their own individual interests rather than the interests of the collective or the overall ecosystem, and this has unintended consequences for the overall larger system (Boudon 1982), whether the social system or the ecosystem.

Manufacture of plastic that does not biodegrade, combined with the "convenience" of throwing old containers and other trash in the water by enough people in various places throughout the world has, in combination with natural oceanic currents, led to what is now known as the Pacific Trash Vortex. In fact, almost all of the plastic ever manufactured is still in existence. Our civilization has yet to come to grips with this truly ominous situation.

A number of social observers have pointed out that individual and group priorities often come into conflict. Individuals make choices that "maximize their own benefits and minimize their own costs" (Coleman 1986). Put another way, they make decisions based on their own selfish interests. This has problems when relating it, not only to larger social collectives (Olson 1965), but to the natural environment as well (Burns 2009). In an increasingly competitive world, the commons problem becomes something more, well, common—and this causes resources to become depleted. Unfortunately, there is a feedback effect. As resources become exhausted and therefore scarcer, the competition over them tends to intensify. This, in turn, causes the probability of the tragedy of the commons occurring in the future, other things held equal, to increase.

While Hardin envisioned the tragedy of the commons as a problem, juxtaposing the individual against the collective, we could see this in broader terms, as collective interests on one level opposed to collective interests on a larger level. In any situation in which more than one entity has an interest in a resource, there is a potential for that resource to be abused.

The consequences are virtually endless, but one extended example here will suffice as an illustration. In his book *Earth in the Balance*, Al Gore (1993) discusses the tragic case of the Aral Sea, which once was the fourth largest land-locked body of water in the world. It had provided a living for generations of people there who made a modest but sustainable living from fishing and related work. In the political fallout of the breakup of the Soviet Union, the Aral Sea now found itself bordering on the foundering nations of Kazakhstan and Uzbekistan. Both nations sought to draw maximally on its rich resources. In attempts to make the most of a cash crop, water-intensive cotton was planted. This required huge draw-downs in terms of irrigation into the naturally dry area. For a few years, the cotton did grow, and a few people made what looked like a promising amount of money. But it was bound to fail. The Aral Sea could not sustain that amount of irrigation, and eventually its water table lowered.

Then something even more ominous seems to have happened. The hydrological cycle of the region appeared to have changed, perhaps from a combination of the over-irrigation, or perhaps from more macro-level changing weather patterns as a result of more global environmental change, or some combination thereof. In any case, the Aral Sea had permanently changed. There were now, as Gore characterized it, "ships in the desert"—fishing vessels that had been permanently beached because of changing climatic conditions that no doubt was caused by some combination of human activity and natural patterns. Thus, the tragedy of the commons rears its ugly head at all levels of analysis—not just at the individual vs. the collective level, but at the level of one collective vs. another.

We conclude this box with a look at the implications of the work of two Nobel Prize winners who thought long and hard about these issues: James Buchanan, Jr. and Elinor Ostrom. Buchanan (Buchanan et al. 1980) was a political scientist particularly concerned with how selfishness affects the process of governance. Buchanan saw that, regardless of the platform on which a politician was elected, s/he almost immediately went to work on their own selfish interests. One of the central political processes was "log-rolling," in which a politician was likely to deal away support for issues s/he may have campaigned for, even vigorously, if those were not among their true top 1-3 highest priority issues. Burns (1993; also see Coleman 1986) has shown that in the underside of this process, the issues that do *not* receive priority treatment (even though they may get plenty of positive spin and lip service), run the risk of becoming what amount to "orphan issues" that lose resources in the ensuing governance process. While Burns and LeMoyne (2001) look more explicitly at the implications of this for environmental issues, suffice it to say here that the implications are significant, particularly in political climates where people see environmental issues having a lower priority than other issues such as terrorism, gay marriage or gun control. Burns and LeMoyne find these processes go a long way toward explaining the lack of effectiveness in promoting environmental issues in governance processes in a broad array of circumstances and levels of analysis.

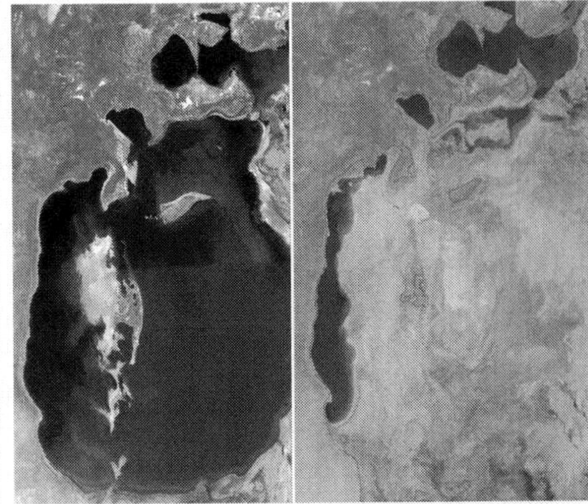

A comparison of the Aral Sea from space–on the left, in 1989, and on the right, in 2014. Formerly, one of the four largest lakes in the world, the Aral Sea has been shrinking since the 1960s when the Soviet Union began diverting its source waters for irrigation. The area's eco-system has, essentially, been destroyed.

Elinor Ostrom and her colleagues (Ostrom et al. 2012; Committee on the Human Dimensions of Global Change 2002) take a decidedly more optimistic tone, and envision the possibility of a "drama of the commons," in which people of good will pitch in and take care of common resources and impose penalties or sanctions on the selfish "free riders" who want to take more than their fair share. The conditions under which the drama of the commons can operate best include a situation where there is a relatively "closed loop" where people feel like they are accountable to someone (such as a neighbor, community or team), and people cannot just take resources from somewhere other than where they live. As a note here, this would exclude what Marx characterized as metabolic rift (or the taking of resources from a place or ecosystem other than one's own). Rather, people would have to live in the ecosystem on which they draw their resources. Combine that with a system of shared governance and accountability among equals, and the system begins to approach something that might actually work sustainably. In such instances, Ostrom and others have pointed out, the tragedy of the commons would become rare, replaced by the drama of the commons.

Sources: Hardin (1968, 1993); Olson (1965); Boudon (1982); Burns (2009); Burns and LeMoyne (2001); Gore (1993); Coleman (1986); Ostrom et al. (2012); Buchanan et al. (1980); Committee on the Human Dimensions of Global Change (2002).

Private Property and Market Mechanisms of Environmental Governance

Rational choice models of governance are based on several important assumptions. First, they believe that the actions of individuals are based upon calculations of personal economic gains and losses, rather than altruism or other moral/ethical calculations. They also hold that the profit-motive is the primary organizing feature of industry, requiring governance to provide profitable outcomes in exchange for compliance with the rules of law. Many scholars argue that international law has become increasingly focused on the priority of neo-liberalizing trade, which takes precedence over governing the common good, such as environmental protection and human rights.

These arguments also characterize discussions of governance at the more local scale. In these cases, the emphasis is on the ways that social orders based on individualism cultivate selfishness. This selfishness draws us away from emphasizing the common good and the intrinsic value of nature toward a focus on personal gain. Below, we elaborate this perspective.

Who Should Govern the Commons?

One of the earliest sociological questions about environmental governance addressed the use of *the commons*. The commons refers to land for which shared responsibility is held by a community of users, typically by a group of livestock grazers, farmers or hunters. Historically, these lands were often the shared settlement territories of extended families, ethnic communities or tribes. While the commons is a rare arrangement among farmers and ranchers in the United States, fish stocks in the ocean are often considered a common-pool resource, and farmers, families, and tribes share common lands in developing countries around the world.

Garrett Hardin–a professor of biology, rather than sociology–wrote extensively about how difficult governance of the commons could be (1968). In his highly cited article, "The Tragedy of the Commons," Hardin argues that resources held in common are at severe risk of overuse and depletion as population growth continues. Even if there are enough resources to share among all users, Hardin argues that people will be motivated to use more than their share. Positing the thoughts of a herdsman, Hardin writes: "What is the utility to *me* of adding one more animal to my herd?" Any person who is driven by what Hardin calls *utility maximizing behavior* will calculate an answer to this question that concludes that their personal gain outweighs collective loss, since the herdsman will earn all of the profit from the additional animal, while the cost in grazing will be spread among all of the users of the commons. The tragedy that ensues is that Hardin expects every member of the community to draw the same conclusion and graze additional animals, ultimately resulting in the commons being depleted for everyone.

The commons was originally an area of land that was a shared responsibility and resource of a community of users. It typically entailed the right to graze (such as the pigs in this photo), farm, hunt or gather. Today, the world's fisheries are considered a common-pool resource.

Hardin's work has been critical in discussion of whether common-pool resources can be governed in ways that protect resources. Much of this literature addresses common-pool resources shared by the community of nation-states, such as oceans, migrating fish stocks, or the quality of the atmosphere (Hardin 1968). A second literature focuses on the common-pool resources of the poor in developing countries (Beck 2001, Kumar 2002). And another group of scholars uses Hardin's work as a jumping off point for discussions regarding privatization of common-pool resources as a means of protection (Ostrom et al. 2002, 2012).

Private vs. Public Land Ethic

According to Geisler (2000: 54), "More than any other facet of American culture, the dialectic between ... public and private ownership perspectives drives conservation policy today." Geisler argues that two distinct subcultures influence America's land conservation approaches. The private land subculture, developed during the nineteenth century, is described by Geisler as a subculture characterized by "possessive individualism"–a view that land will be improved "for the greater good of the nation" if it is privatized (2000: 55). The public land subculture, on the other hand, is characterized by a belief that "America's seminal greatness is found in its appreciation of wilderness as an end in itself" (Geisler 2000: 55).

Although Geisler names the private land subculture "possessive individualism" and the public land subculture "the conservation movement," a review of Brulle (2000) suggests that Geisler's land conservation subcultures correspond to the manifest destiny frame and a hybrid of the preservation and conservation frames in the United States environmental movement. Each of these traditions in the United States environmental movement espouses unique arguments regarding human-environment interactions and the value of nature. The private land subculture, as described by Geisler (2000), closely corresponds to Brulle's (2000) description of the manifest destiny frame. The belief in abundant natural resources and the need for humans to transform wilderness into "useful commodities" fit with Geisler's exposition of a private land ownership ethic focused on the improvement of land for the greater good. On the other hand, Geisler's (2000: 55) public land subculture assigns responsibility to the government to protect the environment "from the excesses of private enclosure" and "put reservation on equal footing with disposition in public land policy." These views correspond to Brulle's (2000: 146) description of the conservation frame, which maintains that "nature can be managed by humans through the application of technical knowledge used by competent professionals." It also echoes his description of the preservation frame, which places a priority on the "protection of wilderness and wildlife for the current and future generations..."

In their analyses, both Geisler and Brulle refer to "possessive individualism." For Geisler (2000: 55), possessive individualism captures the ethic of the private property subculture and favors privatization of land over wildlife refuges, national forests or preserves. Brulle's description, on the other hand, reveals a central dilemma for the functioning of a democracy under the ethic of possessive individualism. Brulle (2000: 41) (2000) states:

> Possessive individualism manifests itself in narcissism, leading to a life divorced from civic involvement and to a single-minded careerism that exalts the satisfaction of personal ambition as the preeminent value. The individual is left apart from society and alienated from any notion of a larger moral order. With the atrophy of the lifeworld, the development of human interactions based upon a shared moral vision becomes more difficult to form and sustain. (P. 41)

The implications of such a worldview for land management become much clearer in light of this comment. In turn, the dilemma presented for the coexistence of private and public land subcultures might be presented in Freyfogle's (2003) words as one between "private property and the common good."

Clearly, however, membership in Geisler's subcultures and espousal of Brulle's frames do not neatly correspond to an individual's status as a landowner. Particularly in the American post-industrial economy (Gilbert 2002), where approximately 3 percent of Americans derive their primary income from agriculture, individuals often purchase land with the intention of stewardship and recreation, rather than an intention to till the soil or run livestock. Scholarly accounts present us with the argument that droves of conservation-oriented landowners have joined the private property movement due to the land-use limits that resulted from passage of federal environmental laws, such as wetlands legislation during the first Bush administration (Pollot 1993; Minter 1994). Likewise, the strategies often utilized by the manifest destiny/private property movement, especially the use of constitutional or state takings legislation during court battles, are employed to protect the right to degrade property as well as the right to protect property from degradation (Freyfogle 2003).

The complex interrelationship between the existence of distinct land ownership subcultures or frames and the hearts and minds of individual land owners is important to explore, particularly in states where the majority of land is in private hands. As stated by Freyfogle (2003):

> The more fragmented a landscape becomes, the harder it is to make sensible, large-scale plans. Externalities increase. Market imperfections rise. Transaction costs escalate. It becomes ever harder to identify sources of problems and trace their ripple effects. It becomes infeasible if not impossible to pursue goals that require coordinated action. (P.177)

This challenge is even more poignant in light of the relationship between private property ownership and resources management. In states where the proportion of privately owned land is high, individual property rights can govern the majority of resources. Groundwater is a useful example. While wildlife and surface water are classified as commonly owned in America and are governed by state and federal agencies, groundwater can be privately owned. Unlike mineral rights, which are often retained after land is sold, groundwater rights in most of these states typically transfer with the sale of property (Freyfogle 2003). In many states, laws regarding the amount of groundwater a landowner can withdraw annually were codified without sufficient scientific understanding of hydrogeology. Even when new groundwater law is created in light of improved scientific understanding of local aquifers, permits that were issued prior to the new law are often renewed at their original levels through "grandfather" clauses. Thus, we might presume that the overuse of groundwater resources could occur in such regimes, especially if land ownership patterns are relatively stable over time.

Optimists in the Commons

In contrast to those who believe privatization is the only way to protect common-pool resources, a rich literature exists that examines a series of factors that make shared governance of the commons a very rational alternative. Elinore Ostrom (2009, 2010), Argarwal (2006) and others have extensively studied the predictors of successful collectivist governance schemes in local common-pool resources systems, such as forest and grazing management systems. These scholars suggest that "adaptive co-management," a place-based participatory governance system, provides local communities with the flexibility to apply shared natural resource management responsibility based on collaborative learning, trust, and common principles (Folke et al. 2005).

Institutional Mismatch and Adaptive Approaches to Environmental Governance

Institutional Mismatch

Environmental problems manifest at levels from the local (e.g., a polluted pond) to the planetary (e.g., global warming). At least in theory and sometimes in actual practice, there are institutions in place at *some* of these levels that can work to counteract an environmental hazard. In many instances though, the scope of an environmental problem does not match the reach of an institution that would address it (Cash et al. 2006).

In an ideally functional system (Parsons 1951), each level of organization could be expected to have its own institutions to adapt to challenges that occur. One of the failures of functional analysis is that actual processes virtually never work this way in practice. One of the key reasons for this is precisely this mismatch between social problems and institutions that would address them. The mismatch between the global economy and institutions that would keep it in check has been noted by students of political economy (e.g., Robinson 2004; Sklair 2002). This is reflected in work by environmental researchers (e.g., Pellow 2007; Roberts and Parks 2007a; Speth and Haas 2006).

Fragmented governance is "the allocation of responsibility for governance among multiple actors and/or agencies, with relatively little or no coordination" (Hill et al. 2008:316). Fragmented governance structures are common among water regulating agencies. Scholars have found that fragmentation of water governance is a "persistent challenge in solving complex water problems" (Cook 2011:25). However, water governance is not the only natural resource governance structure that consistently experiences regulatory fragmentation; researchers have found that in all areas of environmental law there is evidence of overlapping and redundancy (Buzbee 2005). Researchers have also discovered that different types of fragmentation exist at different levels of the governance structure. Some different forms of fragmentation are: jurisdictional fragmentation, territorial fragmentation, and biophysical fragmentation (Bakker and Cook 2011; Cash et al. 2006; Cook 2011). Territorial fragmentation refers to fragmentation caused by political boundaries, and biophysical fragmentation refers to the fragmentation of watersheds and ecosystems through the creation of states or countries. Jurisdictional fragmentation can be defined as "the fragmentation created by the interaction of political and legal institutions that hold or assign authority to a territory" (Cook 2011:26). As such, jurisdictional fragmentation has a negative impact on natural resource governances because "too many separate actors and actions can become dysfunctional" which leads to inefficiencies or inaction in solving resource issues (Cook 2011:33). Jurisdictional fragmentation is the type of fragmentation most significantly affecting natural resource governance.

Jurisdictional fragmentation has a potent effect on resource governance. One way to observe jurisdictional fragmentation is to analyze institutional policies such as: "constitutions, statutes, regulations, common law rules, international treaties, and policies" (Cook 2011:28; Ostrom 2010). The outcome of jurisdictional fragmentation is a "governance gap," meaning that there is uncertainty between agencies or actors as to who has jurisdiction over a resource (Cash et al. 2006; Cook 2011). The "governance gap" can lead to multiple problems, the first is inaction because "where social ill is juxtaposed against multiple potential regulators all will be tempted to ignore that social ill and free ride on the anticipated actions of others" (Buzbee 2003:21). In addition to agency inaction, another issue that arises is over-action. Over-action occurs when multiple agencies attempt to take control of and address a resource situation without a clear understanding of which agency is actually responsible. Thus, when governance becomes fragmented, it ineffectively regulates that which it is trying to govern. Despite being ineffective, it is often not clear that fragmentation is occurring until either it is determined through analysis, or it is exposed through a shock or disturbance to the system. This is connected to resilience because vulnerabilities within a system are often not exposed until that system experiences a shock or disturbance and is incapable of responding to, or adapting to, the shock (Caniglia et al. 2014). As climate variability is likely to worsen in unpredictable ways, it is now more important than ever to analyze natural resource governance structures so that governance structures can become prepared before the system is exposed to a shock or disturbance.

When a problem occurs at a given level or set of levels, and its institutions fail, an institution organized at a different level may come in as a stopgap. This is less than optimal, but can, in some cases, at least partially address a problem. Consider for example, the failure to ensure civil rights for minorities in the Southern United States. During the civil rights movement of the 1960s, the federal government was able to step in to challenge some of the extreme practices like exclusion of blacks from access to higher education. The construction of "states' rights" was countered with an alternative and more universal logic from a larger collective (Kerner 2015).

Yet , many environmental problems occur and go largely unaddressed because the problem can be "externalized" to a level unmatched by an appropriate governance structure (York, Rosa and Dietz 2003). A factory in the Great Lakes region of the United States, for example, may comply with local regulations by raising a smokestack so that emissions go higher into the sky, thereby rendering its discharge levels within the letter of "compliance." But this, in turn, results in a greater load for Canada, resulting in acid rain hundreds of miles north in the Hudson Bay. As the recipients of that particular set of "externalities" are part of a different polity, there is little that can be done to directly address the problem under current (human organizational) conditions.

Increasingly, with processes of global "integration," the mismatches potentially become worse. This is attributable to a number of reasons, but particularly to a cascade of mismatches between and among actors at various levels of organization, and their respective relationships to the natural environment. The integration that does occur is in terms of economic and market exchanges, but not in terms of non-market needs.

Macro-Level Environmental Problems and Nation-States

The global economic market system is, at least arguably, the strongest, most robust social institution to date, establishing a worldwide reach, and affecting virtually every aspect of human and planetary life at multiple levels. As various authors have pointed out (e.g., Mandel 1998; Robinson 2004), the global market system that has evolved, has far outstripped the logic of the nation-state. While transnational corporations still typically are headquartered in core states and enjoy the protection of the military and political apparatus of those states, their reach is not constrained by the nation-state, and many argue that core states prefer short-term profits over environmental protection (Bonnano 1996; Foster et al. 2011; Robinson 2004).

As Marx ([1867] 1967) foresaw, capital could move quickly between places and polities, finding its most advantageous place, exploiting the exchange, and then moving on to the next opportunity. This was one of the competitive advantages of capitalism over feudalism. As has been noted by a number of scholars in the Marxist tradition, this led to wildly unequal ecological exchange (Foster 1999; Foster et al. 2011; Moore 2000, 2003).

The nation-state arose over time in response to material conditions (Tilly 1992). It is ill-suited to deal effectively with some classes of environmental problems. No small part of the failure can be attributed to cultural lag (Ogburn [1932] 1961), in that many of the problems have evolved and morphed over time. Material conditions, most notably anthropogenic environmental changes, are accruing faster than pre-industrial institutional structures can catch up (Burns 2009).

Environmental problems do not necessarily match the nation-state level. When they do, they often compete for attention with other priorities. Even when there is a will to address them (which, of course, is far from given), the focus and resolve can be deflected with infighting that often makes what eventual action that is taken less effective than it would optimally be (Burns and LeMoyne 2001; Olzak and Soule 2009).

In sum, moving into the third millennium, the logic of global capitalism threatens to overwhelm the natural ecology, even as it overpowers and engulfs the institutions that would keep it in check (Burns 2009; Foster et al. 2011; Gould, Pellow and Schnaiberg 2008; Hornborg 1998; McNeill 2000; O'Connor 1994; Schnaiberg and Gould 1994).

Civil Society and Hybrid Governance

The most recent innovations in environmental governance focus on the inclusion of non-state actors in policy arenas and as participants in the implementation of policy decisions. "Stakeholder participation" or "hybrid governance" approaches bring the subjects of governance (e.g., citizens, industry, trade unions, and indigenous peoples) to the table as equal partners with government officials. The argument for this type of approach is that policies are more effective if those who are accountable to them understand them fully, including the goals they are meant to achieve and why the mechanisms included in the policy were chosen over other alternative approaches.

Participatory governance models take a number of forms. For example, citizen juries can be created to adjudicate certain details of policies about which officials are ambiguous. In this case, government officials have identified a natural resource challenge that requires regulation (e.g., increased wildfire danger). Mitigating this threat requires cooperation among property owners, a variety of state agencies, local fire departments, and members of the government. When a problem requires collaboration among so many sectors of society, government officials often winnow the policy options down to a few that they think will work and ask representatives of the relevant sectors to get together and comment on the options. Although this approach is much better than excluding nongovernmental groups from the process, many still complain that the sector participants are often hand-selected from a group of people who are expected to go along with what the government wants, regardless of how the majority of sector participants feels.

Another very popular hybrid governance approach is to bring together sector participants for a multi-stakeholder dialogue. The underpinning argument for hosting dialogues is that collaborative learning and empathy develops when people from a variety of different sectors get to know one another and understand each other's concerns and preferences. One of the best examples of this form of dialogue was very successful at the United Nations Commission on Sustainable Development (UNCSD), now known as the High Level Forum on Sustainable Development (HLFSD). For five years, the UNCSD brought together representatives of nongovernmental organizations (NGOs), industry, trade unions, scientists, farmers, youth, women's groups, indigenous peoples, and governments North and South to discuss policy approaches to the achievement of sustainable development. The representatives were chosen from within their own sectors, and the positions presented by the representatives were extensively negotiated among the diversity of sector members. Collaborative learning and increased trust were exhibited over the five years these dialogues took place, illustrating that stakeholder dialogues are a productive approach to solving complex environmental problems (Jasanoff 2004).

Of course, hybrid governance is subject to a great deal of criticism. Bringing together representatives from such a diversity of sectors often serves to amplify the conflicts and misunderstandings that exist. In the field of climate change, for example, simply bringing together members of the United States Congress to discuss climate change illustrates a range of conflicts: (1) Does climate change even exist? (2) Can we really afford financially to curtail our development in order to lower emissions? (3) Isn't God the only power in control of the planet? While these questions disappear when we bring together farmers, native communities, and citizens who are faced with the outcomes of climate change, such as severe drought, flooding, wildfires, and species migration, the diversity of our world today is characterized by conflicting and converging ideas about how to protect people, animals, and resources from environmental problems. Persistent inequality–both within and between nations–also raises suspicion across sectors and erodes the trust needed for successful shared governance (Lewis 2000).

Regardless of these challenges, environmental ministers, social movement activists, industry representatives, and others appear to have adopted hybrid governance as a method of collective problem-solving. Farmer's cooperatives meet with park managers to devise collective predator management regimes; landowners come together with local fire departments to create prescribed burn associations; and local production plants join forces with surrounding neighborhoods to improve wetlands and provide space for community gardens. Scholars in sociology argue that these types of solutions are often more successful than natural resource management programs that are created in isolation of the communities they are meant to protect.

Conclusions: Take-Away Lessons about Environmental Governance

Sociologists examine governance from a variety of perspectives. In the case of environmental problems, governance systems are complex, because there are often mismatches between the scales of environmental problems and the ability of government agencies to respond. Adaptive governance is viewed as a way of embedding environmental governance in agencies with overlapping jurisdictions, so that when solutions fail to come at one level another institution can step in. Transparent organizations with clear lines of authority and rational rules based on science can help to ensure that environmental problems are addressed effectively. However, regardless of how rational the rules are, conflicting interests across different sectors of society can lead to conflicts that get in the way of effectively implementing environmental policies. Governance processes that include representatives from the community members who are affected by environmental problems can increase the legitimacy of those policies and increase the likelihood they will be implemented effectively.

Sociological theories of governance suggest that large-scale inequalities that exist within and between nations impact whose interests are emphasized within environmental policies. Concerns related to the interests of industry over the interests of the poor or communities of color can receive undue weight when the processes of creating policies do not include participation from the diversity of communities of affected parties. Hybrid governance systems, like the multi-stakeholder dialogues at the UN Commission on Sustainable Development, can increase the extent to which the needs of underrepresented groups are considered in the halls of government. The role of nongovernmental organizations and civil society more generally is critical to counter the individualism and market interests of the core nations and those for whom profits outweigh the common good.

Chapter 6 Summary

- Sociologists tend to view governance as broader than just government per se; it includes the impacts of rule-making and norms on the broader culture.

- Regulating environmental harms has historically posed a problem for authorities, because waterways, smog, and other environmental problems often cross or transcend county, state, and national boundaries.

- Each of the classical theorists had a particular perspective on governance. Marx emphasized the structure of the economy; Weber focused on the role of rules and organizations; Durkheim saw the importance of moral and cultural frameworks.

- These perspectives have been expanded by contemporary theorists to account for the ways globalization has impacted the methods that countries use to govern.

- Karl Marx's view of governance focused on problems of capitalism. In the classical sense, the *bourgeoisie* owned the means of production (e.g., factories, natural resources, and land), and exploited the *proletariat* (the labor class) and the *lumpenproletariat* (a "reserve army of the unemployed").

- Max Weber wrote about *rational governance*, which was comprised of a clear hierarchy of positions, filled by those who had the skills and credentials to hold office, ideally holding no bias or conflict of interest and overseen with strict adherence to rules lined out by those in office. While he believed that if these guidelines were followed then fairness and equality among all groups could be achieved, there was also the possibility of an "iron cage of rationality," in which the rules would become so constrictive that human agency would be crushed.

- Durkheim argued that a shared moral underpinning established a foundation from which governance takes place. In these *Gemeinshaft* societies, cooperation was built upon shared perspectives on the world. Shared systems of beliefs, traditions, rituals, and routines served to organize daily life into predicable actions and clear divisions of labor that gave everyone a secure place in the social order.

- As societies modernized, this moral order became more problematic. Durkheim saw the rise of what he characterized as *organic solidarity*, based on a more elaborate division of labor, and the rise of cultural values that we discussed in earlier chapters.

- Talcott Parsons argued that the primary functions of society are performed by institutions, whether those functions are formal rule-formation or informally socializing members of society to share a moral orientation toward the world.

- Globalization has made governance more complex than classical sociological theorists conceived, which has led to a considerable need to revise classical governance theories to account for today's contexts. Globalization has drastically changed the nation-state from a self-contained, relatively homogenous population into a very loose network of organizations and social groups marked by an incredible diversity of values, beliefs, ethnic, and religious backgrounds.

- When governance becomes fragmented, it ineffectively regulates that which it is trying to govern.

- Increased efficiency in production processes can reduce ecological impacts and ultimately create a net pro-environmental effect. A restructuring of the modern nation-state that facilitates a partnership between industry and governments and delegates further environmental responsibility to the market can free industry to create innovative solutions.

- As individualism increases, promulgating what Geisler calls *"possessive individualism,"* less emphasis is placed on the collective view that sees resources needing to be preserved and cared for. There arises a subculture around this, which rises to the point of selfishness. It becomes even more complicated when private and public land arguments are added to the discussion of who decides what happens to the limited supply.

- This feeds into the *tragedy of the commons*. When there is an overriding culture of possessive individualism (or what otherwise might be called *"collective selfishness"*), there is an increased risk for a tragedy of the commons, in which collective resources, including the natural environment, are degraded.

- There can, under some circumstances, be a *"drama of the commons,"* in which environmental stewardship and responsibility become shared cultural values. This tends to be when there is a common normative system that people feel a part of, that is promulgated widely, and that discourages free-riders through some combination of formal and informal sanctions. Ultimately, environmental stewardship works best when it has become a central part of the culture, bolstered by a strong normative base.

Chapter Seven - Health, Well-Being, and the Environment

Public Health and the Environment

Human health has a direct relationship to ecological health, and areas of environmental degradation are linked to increased instances of human health problems. This link between environment and health has been known for quite some time. Yet, only recently have we turned our attention to the question of health and sickness by looking at adaptation and natural selection. In this chapter, we explore how natural processes and the degradation caused by human activity interact, and the consequences for human health.

More broadly, healthy living necessarily involves harmonizing with the natural environment. Illness, on the other hand, comes about when the natural balances have been thrown off. When there are imbalances in the natural environment, there cannot help but be an effect on those dependent on that environment.

Why We Get Sick: A Darwinian Approach to Health

Although the study of biology relies heavily on Darwinian theory, only recently has the field of medicine used a Darwinian approach to the study of health and disease. This new way of looking at why we get sick takes an evolutionary view of human health and disease and has been termed *"Darwinian medicine"* or *"evolutionary medicine."*

Darwinian medicine theorizes that our bodies are governed by the evolutionary principle of adaptation by natural selection that takes place over millennia. In their book *Why We Get Sick: The New Science of Darwinian Medicine* (1994), authors Randolph M. Neese and George C. Williams cogently make the case that human health and disease is affected by the back and forth struggle of the body's evolutionary adaptation to pathogens and the counter adaptation of those same pathogens to human evolutionary processes that play out over long periods of time. Neese and Williams explore the evolutionary underpinnings of the body's functioning and malfunctioning. Darwinian medicine looks beyond the how people (as well as plant and animal life) get sick, to find a deeper why that disease occurs in the first place. Environments vary and an organism that has adapted to one may be maladapted to another. When taken to extremes, adaptations that confer fitness in one environment may be detrimental and confer "unfitness" in another environment. To minimize this tendency, given a stable environment, organisms will naturally avoid extremes by seeking an optimal *balance point* between them. Examples of the balance principle are numerous and help to explain the evolution of both physical characteristics and diseases.

The distribution of height in the population is familiar to all of us and can be explained with the balance point principle. On the whole, height is a normally distributed trait. Most people are of moderate height while a few are on either end of the curve tending towards short or tall height. On the one hand, tallness maximizes, among other things, the ability to gather food from high trees and bushes. While, on the other hand, smaller people require fewer calories—shortness being optimal for surviving periods of food scarcity. Nature has balanced out the extremes by selecting for the optimal balance point between maximizing food gathering and maximizing the ability to survive on fewer calories. We can also gain important insight into illness and health processes with the balance principle.

Sickle cell anemia is a blood disorder that is most prevalent among people of African origin. Sickle cell anemia occurs when a person inherits two recessive genes—one from each parent. The result is a relatively rare occurrence in which the blood cells fold in such a way that they become deformed and resemble a sickle. The disease is painful, debilitating, and can lead to complications such as severe infections and stroke; and can sometimes cause death. Despite the grim results of inheriting a set of the genes, the benefits of inheriting only one of the genes—the most likely scenario—are substantial. One recessive gene produces an immune response to malaria—a debilitating mosquito-borne illness common to sub-Saharan Africa. This protection from malaria is an adaptive strategy that allows the majority of the population to survive to reproductive age. Once again, the balance principle proves useful in maximizing a trait that, when taken to the extreme, can be detrimental.

So, too, we see the balance principle at play in the case of allergies. Over a long period of time, humans have developed a finely tuned immune system and assorted defenses (e.g., sneezing, coughing, vomiting) to combat the ill effects of toxic substances, germs, bacteria, and other microscopic marauders. Most often, the tiny antibodies that act as sentry and defense forces do an admirable job of protecting us; however, in some instances, the immune system becomes hyper-vigilant and overreacts. These overreactions can do more harm than good, and, in these cases, the result is an allergic reaction that can incapacitate or even kill. Once again, for most people, the balance principle minimizes the extremes so as to maximize the benefits of a robust immune defense. Yet, we see that the extremes do exist, and the result is over-sensitivity and the development of allergies.

Curiously, the pervasiveness of allergies has increased in modern times. Respiratory allergies, for example, are ten times more prevalent now than one hundred and fifty years ago (Neese and Williams 1994:170). We now know that allergies arise from an imbalance of certain parts of the immune system. If

Figure 7.1 Supernormal Stimulus

Hyper-green, weedless lawns and golf courses that are not found in nature, and can only be acheived with the aid of toxic herbicides and fertilizers, now seem "normal" and are preferred over natural environments by many people.

Ethologists, or biologists who study animals in their natural habitat, have discovered an interesting phenomenon. Sometimes birds will sit on their best looking, roundest eggs, even to the point of kicking the less round eggs out of the nest and breaking them.

Ethologists noticed this and substituted the birds' real eggs with artificial eggs that were rounder and more "perfectly" shaped than their own natural eggs. What do you think happened? In many cases, the birds were fooled, to the point of nurturing the fake eggs, which were really made out of plastic, even to the point of kicking their own real eggs out of the nest where they broke on the ground.

You might say that this is pretty silly for a bird to do. This is a behavior that ethologists came to call responding to a "supernormal stimulus." The fake egg that looked so good that it captured the bird's best behavior—this *supernormal stimulus*—holds a number of lessons for humankind.

Deirdre Barrett (2010) finds applications of the supernormal stimulus in a wide array of human circumstances, from the use of silicone breast implants to weedless green "healthy" looking lawns made that way with the aid of toxic herbicides, to white sugar and high fructose corn syrup that gives food a taste sweeter than anything actually found in nature. Meanwhile, "diseases of civilization" (Neese and Williams 1994) such as type II diabetes, obesity, and certain kinds of cancers are at historic highs and continue to rise.

As Neese and Williams point out in their work in Darwinian medicine, we have evolved over eons to be attracted to sweetness in, for example, fruit. It gave a survival advantage to eat sweet fruit rather than bitter fruit, because the sweet, ripe fruit was very likely healthier, and therefore provided better nutrition and better survival value. The bitter fruit was perhaps more likely to be less healthy. So, over time, humankind developed something of a sweet tooth.

That worked well, until the advent of the supernormal stimulus of white sugar, which concentrated sweetness with very little nutritional value. This is taken to an even more extreme level with high fructose corn syrup, which is the common sweetener now in many, if not most, canned sodas. The intense and prolonged exposure to these supernormal sweeteners put more strain on the body, particularly the pancreas to produce insulin, than the body was able to handle.

To be sure, there are genetic differences as well, that interact with these processes. Not everyone who consumes large amounts of canned sodas, for example, comes down with type II diabetes. However, in the aggregate, we can see these trends, and attribute significant portions of them to unhealthy environmental or lifestyle factors, some of which come back to the supernormal stimulus.

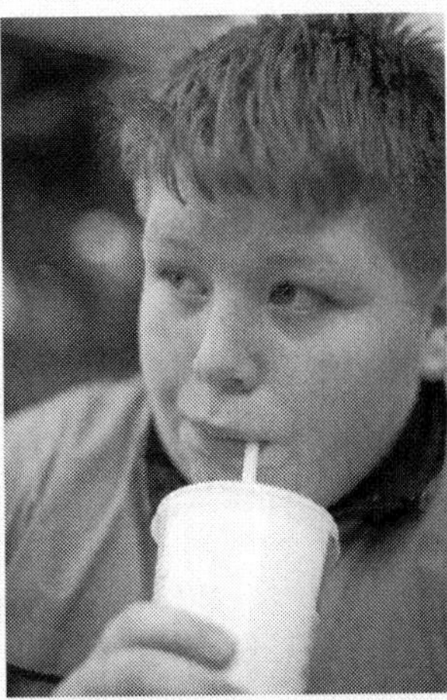

High fructose corn syrup makes things taste sweeter than anything found in nature. Meanwhile, "diseases of civilizaton" like type II diabetes and certain cancers are at all time highs.

Sources: Barrett (2010); Neese and Williams (1994).

the imbalance occurs during important developmental periods, the likelihood of developing an allergy increases. For instance, infants who are not breastfed are more likely to develop allergies later in life. This may be due to the inability of the nursing mother to pass on some important substance in mother's milk that establishes a proper balance in the infant's immune system; or conversely, an increased exposure to toxic substances during critical developmental periods may disrupt this delicate immune system balance.

We come now to one of the curiosities of the biosocial world: the *supernormal stimulus*. A number of diseases of civilization can actually be attributed to this phenomenon, and so it is worth examining in a bit more depth.

Our bodies are sensitive and finely tuned organisms that require balance. As a species we have evolved and retained balance by adapting gradually over a long stretch of time. One of the principle characteristics of modernity, however, is the speed with which change occurs. No longer are humans able to adapt to the stresses and strains of modern life on a time scale that our bodies are designed for. With the supernormal stimulus we respond to strain by reaching for what may appear to be healthy, but which increases the imbalance.

Sickness as a Function of an Environment Out of Balance

The geographical expansion of the human race occurred over a long period of time. Therefore, people were constrained to a relatively small area of the world for extended time spans. The result was that adaptation and natural selection processes to disease and other threats became indigenous to the place in which they occurred. As we discussed earlier, the body's response to malaria is unique to a particular group of people living in a distinct location where malaria is prevalent. This response took many generations and over time became a genetic adaptive trait that was passed on because a person was less likely to survive to reproductive age without it.

Likewise, people have adapted to breathing a mixture of gases such as oxygen and nitrogen in the air that through natural selection was optimal for human health. Again, keep in mind that this process took place over a very long time frame. Today, the air that we breathe—due to the Industrial Revolution and the increased burning of fossil fuels—is different from the air that was present in earlier times. Higher levels of methane and carbon dioxide became the norm in a relatively short period of time. The result is an environment out of balance that, in turn, becomes a catalyst for human disease. To a limited extent, the immune system can cope with pollution, but eventually it becomes too extreme, and maladies such as asthma, emphysema and cancer result.

The recent propensity of mankind to congregate in cities has exacerbated the problem of an environment out of balance. Urban settings expose us to greater numbers and varieties of toxins and microbes and pose serious problems of waste disposal. In fact, cities tend to be "microbe heavens" (Garrett 1994:235).

That is not to say, however, that those who live in rural settings are in balance with nature. Indeed, the modern rural inhabitant has in many ways eclipsed the city dweller in terms of pollution and an imbalanced existence. Modern agricultural practices, in particular, are responsible for the introduction of herbicides, pesticides, toxic fertilizers, and untreated animal waste into the environment. Rural dwellers also tend to have high rates of obesity, tobacco use, and other lifestyle obstacles. It was once the case that disease rates were higher and life expectancy lower in urban areas, but today rural inhabitants have "caught up" to, and in some cases have surpassed, urban brethren.

Immunities that develop after repeated exposure to toxins pose a problem for those people outside of our industrial and post-industrial societies. Over time, antibodies have developed in populations to combat common illnesses such as measles, mumps, and chicken pox. Someone with these antibodies can spread disease to someone without the antibodies, even though the antibody possessor is not sick. This has happened many times in the past, and some scholars believe that a major factor in the subjugation of the New World by Europeans is the incapacitation and decimation of indigenous populations by these very antibodies (Crosby 1986; also see McNeill 1976); (Diamond 1999).

The balance principle also applies to other living organisms. When species that have not previously come into contact begin to interact, there is the possibility that they will exchange diseases. Immunities have not had a chance to develop to the introduction of new pathogens. Many human diseases developed when humankind evolved from hunter-gatherer societies to agricultural societies that practiced animal husbandry. A number of previously unknown diseases were introduced to humans in this way (Crosby 1986:31).

The transfer of diseases from animal species to humans is called zoonosis. Zoonosis is responsible for such varied ailments as influenza, rabies, anthrax, bubonic plague, and Lyme disease, to name a few. Evidence grows that HIV/Aids and even Ebola are due to zoonotic transfer. For instance, it is theorized that residents of remote African villages came in contact with apes that were infected with the simian immunodeficiency virus (SIV) and that the villagers, in turn, became infected when the virus "jumped species" through blood. As roads such as the Kinshasa highway through central Africa developed, and towns and industry encroached upon once remote areas, it became more likely that the new mutated disease (HIV) would be transmitted to a larger human population.

The increased use of chemicals in modern society is also responsible for an environment out of balance. The use of synthetic pesticides, fertilizers, and herbicides has increased immensely since World War II (e.g., Carson 1962; Steingraber 1997; Cordner et al. 2013). At the same time there has been a comparable increase in many diseases, especially cancers. While, it can be argued, that the use of such products dramatically expanded agricultural yields, the question must be asked—at what cost?

Pesticides, for example, are not very efficient when you consider that insects only ingest about 0.1 percent, and the remaining 99.9 percent becomes part of the ecosystem (Steingraber 1997). To make matters worse, it is extremely difficult to contain pesticides to the crops that they are intended for. Colborn et al. (1997), have shown toxic chemicals can travel thousands of miles—from Alabama north to the Great Lakes where they are consumed by eels, and then to the Sargasso Sea in the Atlantic Ocean. The journey continues when other fish eat the eels and, in turn, the fish are eaten in the Arctic by polar bears.

Of course, the greatest human risk for diseases and maladies that arise from an environment out of balance lies with the poor and the undeveloped countries. These people have little money or power with which to protect themselves. The rich can oftentimes "buy their way out" of environmental problems while the burdens of environmental degradation fall disproportionately on the poor and minorities.

Ultimately, however, we are all at risk. The effect of a world out of balance is becoming a global calamity that respects no political or social boundaries. No one really knows what the true risks are. Rachel Carson pointed out the disastrous consequences of DDT use and it was eventually banned. Yet, today, the number of chemicals in use that may be even more harmful than DDT is a thousand fold greater. Little is known about the associated risks of their use. The chemical industry produces new agents faster than they can be adequately examined.

Air and water pollution, diseases and cancers, and global warming are the most noticeable signs of an environment out of balance and are immediate threats to the health and life of every individual. But what of the effects on societies? What are the social outcomes?

Inequality, Scarcity, Marginalization, and Societal Breakdown

We know that an environment out of balance is detrimental to human health individually and collectively. Expanding this line of reasoning reveals a link between environmental degradation and social unrest as manifested in such ills as violence, ethnic clashes, political instability, and a generally diminished societal well-being. Some scholars believe that there is a relationship between environmental balance and societal well-being.

In his book, *Environment, Scarcity, and Violence*, the author, Thomas Homer-Dixon, writes of an array of physical trends of global change that affect social stability and well-being. These trends—human population growth, rising energy consumption, global warming, ozone depletion, cropland scarcity, freshwater depletion, declining fish stocks, and biodiversity loss—can individually and collectively cause violent outcomes.

A familiar pattern precipitates the journey towards violence. Two interactions serve as the catalyst for this path. The first of these, "resource capture," refers to situations in which societies experience a large population growth and a simultaneous shortage of a renewable resource. In response to this situation, the elites in society hoard the scarce resource. In other words, they capture the resource for themselves. The second interaction is called "ecological marginalization" which occurs when population growth combined with vastly unequal access to land forces the poor to migrate into environmentally fragile areas.

Both of these scenarios can lead to violence within society. Homer-Dixon cites two examples as illustration. In the case of resource capture, he looks to the relations of Arabs and Israelis on the West Bank of the Jordan River. Chronic water shortages and overstressed aquifers led the Israeli authorities to place limits on the number of wells that Arabs could drill and the amount of water that could be pumped from them. This, in turn, led to a drop in Arab agriculture and an angry Arab population. It is a small leap to hypothesize that resource capture by the Israeli elite contributed to the unrest on the West Bank.

Ecological marginalization leads to serious social problems, which, in turn, drive serious environmental problems. In the early 1990s, the local elites in Chiapas, Mexico exerted control over more and more of the best land just as the indigenous people and peasants were experiencing a growth in population. The poor subsistence farmers were forced to claim increasingly marginal land. The competition for land eventually led to violence and paved the way for the Zapatista insurgency.

Although the previous two examples have been rural in nature, urban areas also have experienced civil unrest. Instances of riots and violence can be linked to the competition for jobs, housing, education, and other resources. Additionally, as life in rural areas becomes increasingly difficult, rural to urban migration increases and makes urban stresses more acute.

Thus, as we consider outcomes of environmental degradation, certainly compromised health is a serious consideration. More broadly, it is important to consider a wide array of negative outcomes, including risk of violence.

It is also important to consider many of the items that we encounter every day, and become more aware of the multiple risks they impose. Second-hand smoke, the noise pollution from industrial machinery and even aggressively loud, downbeat music, can take their toll. Exposure to heavy metals, pesticides, herbicides, and even some compounds found around the house, can pose significant risk.

Environmental Justice and Health

A number of researchers have shown that environmental risk tends to excessively affect disenfranchised populations—the poor, people of color, and indigenous peoples (Crowder and Downey 2010; Hooks and Smith 2004). It is, for example, often the case that hazardous waste sites tend to be located where the local people are not politically engaged or connected enough to effectively keep them from coming (Pellow 2007; Bullard 2000). Thus, these toxic activities tend to be sited in places where there are marginalized people (Brown 2007; Pellow and Brulle 2005).

In what is sometimes referred to as the "not in my back yard" (or NIMBY) phenomenon (Mix 2009), people with power and means can transfer environmental risk away from themselves, either through access to financial or political resources, or because they are able to frame what the issues are in the first place (Freudenburg 2005; Myers and Kent 2001). These processes go a long way toward understanding why sociologists have found an inverse relationship between social class and power on the one hand, and risk of all sorts on the other—including risk of being a victim of a violent crime, risk of exposure to environmental toxins and, relatedly, risk of greater morbidity and earlier mortality (Beck 1995; Bell and York 2010).

On the most macro level, well-connected and politically powerful nations enjoy a high ecological footprint at the expense of the poorer, less-connected, and dependent nations (Jorgenson 2003; Jorgenson and Burns 2007). Yet, these processes replicate themselves at virtually all levels of social organization (Burns et al. 2006).

Many, if not most, human interactions involving the environment involve social inequalities as well. This is true at virtually every level of analysis. In the United States, for example, blacks, Latinos, and poor rural whites are more likely than affluent suburban whites to live in close proximity to environmental hazards (Crowder and Downey 2010). Native peoples in rural areas on and off reservations are also at elevated levels of risk (Hooks and Smith 2004; Shriver and Webb 2009).

In sum, whenever there is environmental degradation leading to health disparities, there are typically complex issues of social inequality surrounding it (Brown 1997; Brown 2007). This is true at all levels of analysis, from the local, to the national (Steingraber 1997), to the global (Gould, Pellow and Schnaiberg 2008; World Health Organization 2014).

Close to Home, Far from Safe

Some common, close to home aspects of our lives can contain more toxins than we might imagine. For example, the air you breathe, particularly if people around you are smoking, or if there are paint fumes carrying volatile organic compounds (VOCs), or estrogen-mimicking chemicals and other cancer-causing elements. The commercial meat and poultry available at the supermarket is pumped full of hormones and additives that can disrupt the body's natural processes, and this is particularly true of meat raised in concentrated agricultural feeding operations.

Bovine growth hormones are genetically engineered and routinely given to industrially raised cattle, poultry, and other livestock to increase their growth. In fact, these can be dangerous to human beings. They have been linked to prostate and colon cancer. This is good to keep in mind when buying meat at the supermarket. Range fed is a better option for a number of reasons, chief among them being that they are not dependent on these toxic hormones.

Genetically modified organisms (GMOs) are foods that can, as their name implies, be genetically modified in a number of different ways. One of the common ways this happens is to have an insecticide gene implanted into their very DNA. This may allow them to be resistant to dying from pesticides. However, it then gives farmers (who may be contractually obligated to a larger agribusiness operation, with interests in some combination of large-scale production, and the GMO and/or pesticide industry) the ability to use more pesticides without killing the crop.

GMOs, which may include corn, soy, canola, cottonseed oil, and sugar beets, among others, accumulate these pesticides, and then are consumed directly, or the pesticides are washed downstream into the watershed.

Some common problems associated with the consumption of GMOs include gastrointestinal problems such as cancers, but also immune disorders. The regular consumption of genetically modified foods has also been shown to be toxic to certain aspects of the reproductive process, including lowered testosterone levels and throwing imbalances into the estrogen cycle.

Phthalates are a family of chemicals, typically used industrially to make plastics like polyvinyl chloride (PVC) more flexible and resilient. They are found in products as widely arrayed as detergents, plastics, certain kinds of soap (particularly industrial grade), vinyl flooring, shampoo, hair spray, nail polish, plastic bags, processed food packaging, garden hoses, and blood storage bags. These are some of the most pervasive of endocrine disruptors, leading to problems in the reproductive cycle, including incomplete testicular descent, reduced sperm count, and testicular atrophy in males, and estrogen cycle disruption in females.

Bisphenol A (or BPA) is a common ingredient in many plastics such as reusable water bottles, resins lining food cans, and dental sealants, and is also used in canned foods and plastic baby bottles and food storage. It is now so ubiquitous that traces of BPA can be found in the umbilical cords of about 90 percent of the newborn infants in developing countries. BPA mimics estrogen, and so it can lead to a number of issues such as early puberty, infertility, elevated rates of certain kinds of cancers, diabetes, and heart disease.

Girls now, for instance, tend to reach puberty a full two years earlier than their grandmothers and great-grandmothers did. This is largely because of so much free estrogen in the environment, available through products containing BPA, but also because there is estrogen in the wastewater from concentrated agricultural feeding operations (CAFOs)—particularly those raising poultry—flowing downstream.

A number of hormone disruptors are found in plastics and pesticides, which cause various problems with human and animal and plant life. Glyphosate, for example, is the active ingredient in some widely used pesticides, particularly in connection with genetically modified crops. It has been found in the gastrointestinal tracts of people ingesting the genetically modified foods on which it was used, putting them at a higher risk for certain kinds of cancers. Also, over time, this bioaccumulates in human and animal bodies. This is to say that rather than extruding it, human and animal bodies tend to accumulate it, particularly in fatty tissue. Thus, it is difficult to say what a safe level is, if any. Over time, even "safe" levels become toxic, because of this bioaccumulation effect.

Parabens are a class of chemicals commonly used in the cosmetics and pharmaceutical industries. They are also widely used in shampoo and hair dyes, food additives, moisturizers, and shaving gels. Much is to be learned about this class of chemicals, but concerns have been raised about their being possible endocrine disruptors. Grapefruit seed extract has been used successfully as a healthy alternative under the precautionary principle. That said, parabens still remain in widespread use.

Fluoride has an interesting history, particularly in developed countries. It is an industrial waste product expelled into the atmosphere in places where there are poor environmental protections. In fact, chlorofluorocarbons are one of the greenhouse gases—less common than methane or carbon dioxide, but far more potent than either. While it is true that fluoride *in the water, in very small and controlled amounts* can help to strengthen the teeth and therefore help decrease cavities in peoples' teeth, entire communities in the United States have put fluoride into the drinking water in attempts to keep cavities down. This may be something akin to shooting rats with a machine gun. It may indeed get rid of a few rats, but is the stray fire worth it? In addition to the few cavities it may avert, fluoride exposure can lead to many health-related problems such as immune disorders, lowered fertility rates, and hormonal imbalances, and probably interacts with other chemical disruptors already in the environment in complex ways that we are only, at best, beginning to understand.

One such interaction of fluoride with other chemicals is found in perfluorooctanoic acid (or PFOA). PFOA is a chemical that makes foods and other things resistant to leakage, and is used, for example, to keep grease from leaking through fast food wrappers and microwave popcorn bags. It is commonly used, as well, in nonstick coatings like Teflon pans and water resistant fabrics such as Gore-Tex. But, for all these positives, PFOA has some serious downsides. It is an estrogen compound that can disrupt, not only the estrogen cycle, but other hormone cycles as well. It has been linked to certain kinds of cancers including breast cancer. In addition, it has been linked to thyroid disease, immune system problems, and increased LDL cholesterol levels. It also bears noting here that PFOA tends to bioaccumulate in the body, which, as we saw, means it tends to remain present for many years. A series of exposures, even though many years apart, and although seemingly benign by themselves, can combine into something more serious in the aggregate.

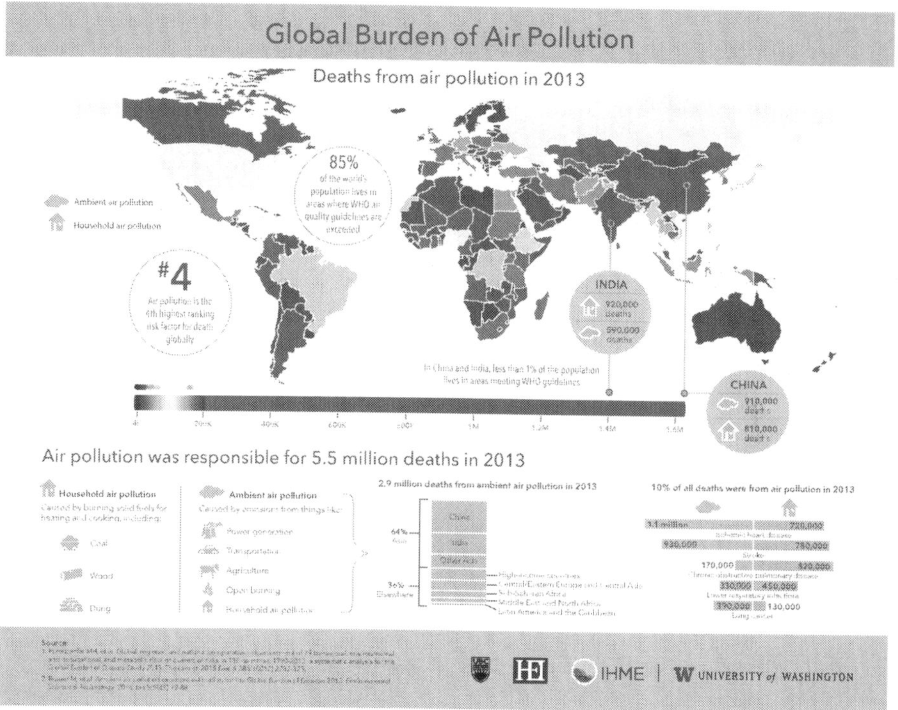

When economism trumps planetism, pollution manifests itself as a byproduct of the externality of industrialization. Air pollution is caused by the industrialization of the world's natural resources. The end result is the sickening and death of large numbers of people.

Poisoning and Premature Deaths from Pollution

According to the best estimates, from 5 1/2 to 7 million deaths per year are attributable to air pollution (World Health Organization 2014). Most of these are in developing countries, particularly India and China, which have tremendous pollution problems. Also included are Mexico, Ghana, Russia, Brazil, and other countries with large concentrations of population and lax emissions standards.

Much of pollution is a byproduct or "externality" of industrialization (Malin and Petrzelka 2012; Boudet and Ortolano 2010). When the culture carries the weight of what ethicist John B. Cobb, Jr. (1991) characterizes as "economism" over "planetism," or what environmental sociologists William Catton and Riley Dunlap (1980) characterize as the "human exemptionalism paradigm" over

Much of pollution is a byproduct or "externality" of industrialization.

the "new environmental paradigm," this tends to manifest in a number of ways, the bottom line being that the people do not steward the planet, using it for "resources" without regard to the imbalances this causes. Politically, there is an unwillingness on the part of those in power, to protect the earth's vital resources, which, in turn, places the health and well-being of the planet and the people in it in jeopardy.

Many of the same factors that lead to climate change, also constitute the worst pollutants for the atmosphere that make people sick and miserable, and cause them to die earlier than they otherwise would. These include compounds such as sulfur oxides, nitrogen oxides, carbon monoxide, volatile organic compounds, particulate matter from factory and vehicle emissions, persistent free radicals, toxic heavy metals such as lead and cadmium, ammonia, odors from garbage and sewage, radioactive pollution, radioactive particles, and persistent organic pollutants such as those found in commonly used herbicides like atrazine (NIOSH 2014; US HHS 2014).

A number of heavy metals pose significant dangers as well. Lead, in particular, has been in the news recently with reports of lead poisoning in the water of Flint, Michigan. Lead causes long-term damage to the nervous system of people, particularly young people in critical stages of development. Put another way, lead accumulation in the body causes lifelong damage. It stays in the system for years, sometimes decades, which is to say it *bioaccumulates*. In addition, it has affinity for calcium, which means that it stays in the bones sometimes for decades. For women going through menopause many years later, as they lose bone mass they may experience a "re-poisoning effect" as the lead that had been sequestered in their bones reenters their system, again causing problems (Markowitz and Rosner 2013).

We find outbreaks of lead poisoning in places where there are concentrations of minorities and poor people with little political power. Those people tend to live downstream from places where there are concentrations of pollution (Denworth 2009). In the case of the people in Flint, Michigan, one of the proximal causes of lead poisoning, was switching from a cleaner source of water to a lead contaminated source of water. The people in power perhaps thought they would "save" a small amount of money by doing so, and it appears that no small amount of negligence was present as well. Whatever they may have "saved" is overwhelmed infinitely by the amount of human suffering they have caused in the process.

Taking a longer view, it is incumbent upon us as environmental sociologists and citizens to ask the harder questions about what could have been done in the longer run to have avoided this in the first place. Automobile manufacturing and paint plants have been there for decades. They have been given "incentives" for much or all of that time, including lax environmental regulations. How much of the fact that there is now a lead poisoning crisis in Michigan, is attributable not just to mistakes of the last few years, but other patterns that stretch back for decades?

What is to be done about lead poisoning? Until the time that the Clean Air Act was signed in the United States in the early 1970s, there were lead additives routinely put into gasoline. Much of the lead poisoning that people experienced was from the fumes in the atmosphere because of that. Additionally, it was common to use lead-based paint, particularly in poorer neighborhoods. The outlawing of lead-based additives in gasoline and lead-based paint did have a salubrious effect and, in fact, they cut down on the prevalence of lead poisoning in the United States, which does have lower rates of lead poisoning than places which do not have such regulations (Markowitz and Rosner 2013).

Lead is but one of the heavy metals that cause poisoning. Aluminum poisoning causes problems in the blood, and can breach the "blood-brain barrier." Recent research indicates that some of the rises in Alzheimer's disease and dementia seen over the most recent decades may be, at least partially, due to aluminum poisoning in communal water supplies. Copper can cause brain and liver damage. Water that has been exposed to copper pipes can have effects,

Like these Japanese commuters, we have become used to pollution as a byproduct of modern life.

including increases in violent behavior among people with chronic exposure. A commonly used herbicide, outlawed in the European Union because it is thought to be even more toxic than DDT, and yet still used freely in the United States, has been linked to a number of kinds of cancers and birth defects. These are just a few examples of heavy metals and other compounds that are not uncommon in industrial society (Sanchez 2013; Ross 1994).

There are ways to address metal poisoning in mild cases. They are expensive, they are not perfect, and in fact, once heavy metal poisoning has gotten to a certain level, its effects are, for all intents and purposes, irreversible. Yet, there is promising research indicating that techniques of "chelation," in which certain compounds can be ingested that will bond with the heavy metals in the body rendering them somewhat inert, so the person will extrude them through their urine. This has to be done over a period of treatments in a controlled environment. It is expensive, and insurance companies tend not to cover it. Having doses of antioxidants such as vitamins A, C, E, and selenium can, in proper dosages, help to alleviate some of the problems in mild cases (Sanchez 2013; Ross 1994). However, in cases where the poisoning is severe, the stopgap measures tend to have little effect.

In late modernity, with between 5 1/2 and 7 million deaths from air pollution per year and rising, this already makes air pollution the fourth largest cause of mortality worldwide. When adding to the burden of air pollution, these other problems, including poisoning from heavy metals and chemicals, the toll of modernity indeed looms large. As society moves into the twenty-first century, it will be more critical than ever to face these head on.

Conclusions: Takeaway Lessons about Health, Well-Being and the Environment

As humankind has progressed from hunting and gathering to late modernity, we have impacted the environment in increasingly profound ways. Pollution, global warming, modern agricultural practices, urban life, and other hallmarks of modernity place stresses on the natural world. The world as it once was no longer exists, and bodies that adapted to that world are ill-suited to the modern world. As environmental balance spins out of control, it places new stresses on humans, and the result often is stress and disease. The wealthy are often able to "buy their way out" of the effects of environmental problems while the poor and minorities bear the brunt of the problems. Ultimately, however, we are all at risk (Beck 1995).

The science of Darwinian medicine explores the mismatches between human evolution and the stresses that an out of balance environment places on our immune and adaptive systems. In earlier times, change was slow enough that human immune systems had time to adapt. The balance principle posits that nature tends to maximize adaptive benefits by avoiding extremes. Balance is the guiding principle in the natural world as illustrated by such varied phenomena as height, the recessive gene that can prevent malaria, but also can lead to sickle cell anemia in extremes, and the causes of allergies. It is when balance is no longer possible that trouble occurs.

An environment out of balance is bad for societal health as well as human health. Thomas Homer-Dixon writes of a number of physical trends of global change that affect social stability and well-being. These trends—human population growth, rising energy consumption, global warming, ozone depletion, cropland scarcity, freshwater depletion, declining fish stocks, and biodiversity loss—can individually and in combination with other social variables, cause violent behavior that affects society in both rural and urban areas.

As societies continue to industrialize, and as the world continues to globalize, we see greater and greater concentrations of pollution in population centers around the globe. This is particularly true in rapidly industrializing societies such as India and China. In recent years, the best figures from responsible agencies such as the World Health Organization have found as many as 7 million deaths annually are attributable to air pollution. The preponderance of these are in developing societies, with India and China leading the way. It is also in these places where some of the worst pollution is found.

The problems are not just with air pollution though. The widespread use of fertilizers, herbicides, and pesticides in amounts way too heavy for the natural recycling capabilities of the environment to absorb, upset the natural balances, and increased risk for diseases such as cancer and other problems including birth defects. The bioaccumulation of heavy metals such as lead, aluminum, and copper cause problems that can have effects for decades to come.

As society moves into the third millennium, the complex linkages between environmental degradation and compromised health and well-being become increasingly important topics on which to focus, as they point to an increasingly pressing social problems, reaching a crisis state. While problems are particularly acute in developing countries, they nonetheless affect everyone worldwide.

Chapter 7 Summary

- There is a direct correlation between health and the environment. Environmental degradation has been linked to a decline in the health of humans and other species with which we share the planet. While negative outcomes are experienced most dramatically in developing countries with runaway pollution, it is a problem worldwide.

- Darwinian medicine and similar approaches suggest that disease is often the result of mismatches between the human adaptive mechanisms evolved over millennia, and the toxins posed by the environment. When there are pollutants or irritants in the environment that cause an imbalance that the adaptive response cannot handle, there is a decline in overall health.

- Particularly dangerous are chemicals such as DDT, herbicides, pesticides, and PCBs for which humankind has not adapted an immune response. When these come into the body, the immune system does not recognize them as foreign, and thus does not combat them. This very quality, which makes them so effective at killing unwanted life forms such as insects, inflicts concomitant damage on other life forms, including humans.

- The effects of a world out of balance include environmental problems at all levels, from the local to the global, which respect no political or social boundaries. While the complete extent of the risks is not yet fully known, there does appear to be more than enough warrant to apply the precautionary principle in cases where more knowledge is still needed, particularly when the ecological penalty for not doing so is potentially catastrophic.

- Many, if not most, human interactions with the environment involve social inequalities as well. This is true at virtually every level of analysis, from the local to the global. Where environmental degradation or exploitation takes place, someone typically is using a disproportionate share of resources, and "externalizing" the costs (not just monetary, but in terms of health and well-being) on someone poorer or less powerful. As a result, the burden of some of the most dreaded diseases, as well as risk of being the victim of violence and higher mortality rates, are borne disproportionately by the poor and disenfranchised.

- Humanly created imbalances—those associated with GMOs, phthalates and BPA, for example—were created to benefit some (typically advantaged) sector of society. The negative effects from the processes to create and use them, on balance, far outweigh any benefits they may provide. From cancer to infertility and other alarming byproducts, the burden typically falls most heavily on those living "downstream," or in the wake of the processes that benefit the privileged few.

- Many of the same factors that lead to climate change, also constitute pollutants for the atmosphere that make people sick and miserable and, in some cases, cause them to die earlier than they otherwise would. It is incumbent upon us as environmental sociologists and citizens to ask hard questions about what can and should be done in the longer run to avoid or minimize these pollution problems in the first place.

- An environment out of balance is bad for societal health as well as human health. A number of trends—human population growth, rising energy consumption, global warming, ozone depletion, cropland scarcity, fresh water depletion, declining fish stocks, and biodiversity loss—can individually, and in combination with social factors such as grinding poverty and inequality, lead to outcomes that include compromised health, and increased risk of violence, morbidity and mortality.

- The bioaccumulation of heavy metals such as lead, aluminum, and copper cause problems that can have effects for decades to come. These cause or contribute to a wide array of health problems, including certain types of cancers, brain and neurological problems, and compromised kidney, bladder, colon, and liver function.

- As societies continue to industrialize, and as the world continues to globalize, we see greater and greater concentrations of pollution, and pollution centers, around the globe. Though most of the concentration of pollution resulting in a decline in health are centered in developing countries, the overall effects are felt worldwide.

Chapter Eight - Collective Behavior and Social Movements

The environmental movement has been a major source of pro-environmental reform. In fact, some scholars believe that the environmental movement is the best hope for surmounting the myriad of environmental problems we face today (Buttel 2003). Most scholars argue that the environmental movement is far from a unified front. Instead, a diversity of movements is focused on environmental issues. Sometimes these groups converge around particular environmental struggles to support a common set of policies; other times, they conflict with each other over either the causes of, or solutions to, particular environmental problems and find each other at odds over which policies or actions are needed.

In spite of its diversity, the environmental movement has successfully mobilized to accomplish important outcomes. In the United States and internationally, the environmental movement is credited for convincing government officials that the environment deserves a prominent place on political agendas. This victory resulted in the creation of important legal institutions, like the U.S. Environmental Protection Agency and the United Nations Environment Programme. These institutions, in turn, provided a focal point for movement organizing, which ultimately resulted in important legal frameworks that reshaped human relationships with nature. While most scholars argue that the environmental movement's successes outweigh their failures, environmental advocates face a political opportunity structure that often results in setbacks, if not outright losses. In this chapter, we'll review both the successes and the challenges faced by the environmental movement.

Background: Who or What is the Environmental Movement?

Most people who study the environmental movement agree that the groups associated with the movement actually make up a collection of movements that work on environmental issues from a variety of angles. Generally, we can define the environmental movement as a loosely affiliated set of individuals, institutes, and organizations that promotes sustainable human-environment relations for political, social, moral, and scientific reasons. Unfortunately, little agreement exists regarding exactly how to categorize the diverse segments of the environmental movement.

One of the most basic distinctions made of the environmental movement is that it falls into a category called new social movements (Mertig and Dunlap 2001). Compared to traditional political movements, new social movements are loosely organized grassroots movements focused on lifestyle choices. Dickens (2004) argues that new social movements, like the environmental movement, focus predominately on civil society, rather than on political institutions, to create new values and indeed new forms of human identity. In this way, the environmental movement serves to distinguish those who respect and live in harmony with the earth from those who disregard and degrade it. In addition to identity politics, Dickens argues that the environmental movement responds directly to real environmental risks and works to build momentum to reduce such risks and reestablish a sustainable balance in human-environment interactions.

Such a basic distinction from more politically-oriented movements is not sufficient to describe the collection of different viewpoints embodied in the environmental movement, however, and two scholars in particular have promulgated complex taxonomies to describe this array. Robert Brulle (2000) conducted frame analysis on the I-90 forms submitted by U.S. environmental movement organizations and originally found nine (9) distinct articulations of the causes of and solutions to environmental problems. Based on environmental movement organizations' (EMOs) descriptions of their work, Brulle categorized discourses that articulate human-environment relations ranging from manifest destiny to deep ecology, with environmental conservation, green politics, and environmental justice in between. He finds that most organizational members of the U.S. environmental movement pursue relatively moderate goals focused on preservation and conservation of natural places and resources. A growing number of organizations emphasize more progressive goals, such as environmental justice and environmental health, but a consistent segment of the movement emphasizes the right of humans to consume the earth's resources and transform the planet according to human needs (See figure 9.1). Brulle's classification scheme emphasizes both the primary goals the organizations seek to achieve and a secondary concern with tactics and strategies used to achieve their aims.

Dryzek (1997), on the other hand, proposes a discursive framework that contrasts parts of the environmental movement to the dominant discourse of modernity. Derived from a 2 by 2 table designed to measure the extent they reject industrialization (reformist or radical) and the types of alternatives they propose (prosaic or imaginative), Dryzek's schema categorizes environmental discourses into four categories: problem solving, sustainability, survivalism and green radicalism. Dryzek's insights are drawn from a broader population of environmental organizations and describe the international environmental movement better than Brulle's framework, which by design best describes the U.S. segment of the movement.

Environmental Movement Strengths

It may seem surprising, given its diversity, that the environmental movement has such a positive impact on environmental reform. However, the movement has developed an array of strategies that enable it to be considered by some as *the* primary hope for the planet (Buttel 2003). One of its most effective tools is agenda-setting, which encompasses an array of tactics movement groups use to pressure governments and other decision makers to publicly acknowledge environmental problems and address how to solve them. Many argue that the environmental movement deserves credit for important institutional changes, such as the creation of environmentally friendly policies and educational curricula. As they recruit a cadre of people to take up their causes, movement groups awaken our hearts and minds to the many ways the environment supports our quality of life and mobilize us to bring our voices to bear—both through political institutions and our conversations with friends, family and acquaintances.

Figure 8.1: Brulle's Analysis of U.S. Environmental Movement Diversity

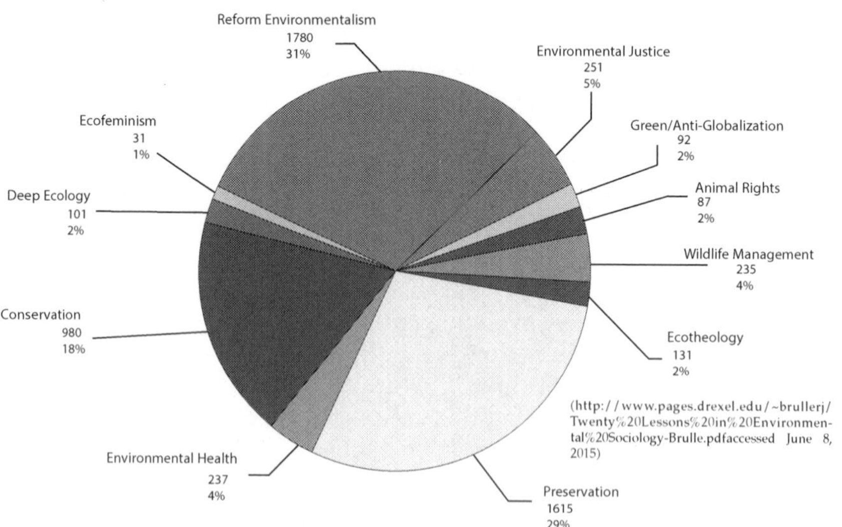

(http://www.pages.drexel.edu/~brullerj/Twenty%20Lessons%20in%20Environmental%20Sociology-Brulle.pdfaccessed June 8, 2015)

Institutional Change

The institutionalization of environmental reform is an enduring impact of social movements. Institutions reproduce themselves by creating processes, which systematically pass along knowledge and restructure the ways humans interact with the environment. Although this sounds very abstract, a closer examination of important environmental reforms illustrates just how central institutional change is to social movement actions.

In the United States, the modern environmental movement arose and achieved some of its greatest institutional successes in the 1970s—a decade that witnessed the first Earth Day, the largest environmental protest and teach-in of that era. Organized by environmental activist Denis Hayes, Earth Day turned universities around the country, the Mall in Washington, D.C., and communities around the nation into hosts of environmental awareness-building celebrations, which galvanized thousands to demand greater protection for the environment. The environment was not high on the U.S. political agenda before these events, and according to then Senator Gaylord Nelson of Wisconsin, Earth Day convinced the U.S. Senate that environmental issues should receive more attention on the nation's legislative agenda. Later that year, President Nixon created the Environmental Protection Agency (EPA), which still stands today as our government's central environmental institution. Most scholars agree that Earth Day—a social movement designed to draw the U.S. government's attention to the problems facing the natural environment, successfully galvanized the support needed to create the EPA.

This environmental movement victory marked a turning point that significantly improved America's environmental problems. In the decade following the founding of the EPA, an impressive array of environmental laws was passed, including the Clean Air Act, the Clean Water Act, the Endangered Species Act, and the Toxic Substances Control Act. In the 1960s and early '70s, American rivers were catching on fire due to toxic run-off from industrial processes. City air was thick with smog, causing asthma, emphysema, and aggravating allergies. Acid rain and other toxic side effects of unregulated industrial processes were contributing to poor quality of life and broad-scale species extinctions in the United States. The institutional reforms implemented by the EPA set standards that restricted emissions and run-off of industrial effluents into local streams and rivers, enabling the earth's natural recovery systems to reverse much of the damage (Johnson et al. 2010). Ecosystem recovery and the Endangered Species Act improved habitat and the rebound of some endangered species like the bald eagle, the gray wolf, the Florida panther, and the grizzly bear. Although today's EPA is often subject to political cuts and other pressures, the institution still stands as a central feature of America's environmental governance and ensures that environmental issues remain on the government agenda. And institutions like the EPA give activists and concerned citizens a place to go for environmental information.

The International Environmental Movement

Mirroring the environmental momentum of the United States, international law also experienced significant institutionalization in the 1970s. The first international conference on the environment, The United Nations Conference on the Human Environment, was sponsored by the United Nations in Stockholm, Sweden in 1972. Many consider this event to be the birth of the international environmental movement, which is credited for pressuring governments to set international standards on such issues as whaling, trade in endangered species, deforestation, and protection of the world's oceans. Prior to the Stockholm conference, the environment was considered "low politics," which, according to international relations scholars, comprises a set of minor issues requiring technical solutions rather than high-level international negotiators (Porter and Brown 1991). Similar to the U.S. case, government leaders did not feel environmental issues were high priority.

In the international arena, the major players in the creation of environmental law are governments, intergovernmental organizations (IGOs), nongovernmental organizations (NGOs), and corporations. Intergovernmental organizations are the primary institutions of international governance. In other words, when governments feel a problem requires international cooperation to alleviate it, they create an organization to focus on that problem. The most famous intergovernmental organization is the United Nations (UN), which was founded following WWII to facilitate international peace and security. However, the UN is an umbrella organization that is comprised of many sub-organizations—each assigned particular issues and/or problems to focus on. Prior to the Stockholm conference on the environment and development, the UN didn't have an environmental sub-organization, and filling this gap became a central theme of the international environmental movement.

The international environmental movement is even more diverse than the U.S. environmental movement, though we can still draw from Brulle, Dryzek, and Dickens to grasp the breadth of its members' interests. In addition to their diversity of interests, however, the international environmental movement also struggles to unify due to drastic differences that separate rich industrialized nations (the global North) from poor developing nations (the global South). The types of environmental problems most acute to developing countries include issues such as loss of cooking fuel due to desertification, poor farming conditions from deforestation, and severe health problems that result from lack of clean drinking water. Polluted water supplies contribute to high infant mortality rates and early death via cholera, diarrhea, and other avoidable water-borne diseases. Desertification and deforestation impact self-sufficiency by lowering soil quality and crop yields and forcing migration to find cooking fuels. It's easy to see that the environmental problems of the global South are quite different from those faced by industrialized nations like the United States.

Despite these differences, the global environmental movement has managed to come together and win a number of critical victories that institutionalized environmental protection around the world. The United Nations Environment Programme (UNEP)was established as an outcome of the Stockholm Conference on the Human Environment, which created a central institution for global environmental governance. This organization became a focal point for the international environmental movement, providing a target for regulating pollution and the use of natural resources. Just as the creation of the EPA opened the door for numerous environmental protection laws, UNEP resulted in a variety of international agreements regarding, for example, the hunting of whales, protections against oil spills, and preservation of the Amazon rain forest and the environmental rights of indigenous peoples. This institutional framework, while frequently tested, has expanded to include a complex set of international laws that govern how humans around the world relate to the environment. Most scholars argue that these laws would be much weaker and in some cases nonexistent if it weren't for the initiatives and continuous monitoring of the international environmental movement.

Changing Hearts and Minds

Despite these important institutional victories, many argue that the most profound impact that any social movement can make is to alter the hearts and minds of ordinary citizens (Tarrow 1998), and this is certainly a role the environmental movement has taken around the world. In his famous book *The Greening of America*, Charles A. Reich describes the importance of social movements in changing people's consciousness.

> At the heart of everything is what we shall call a change of consciousness. This means a "new head"—a new way of living—a new man [sic.]. This is what the new generation has been searching for, and what it has started achieving. Industrialism produced a new man, too—one adapted to the demands of the machine. In contrast, today's emerging consciousness seeks a new knowledge of what it means to be human, in order that the machine, having been built, may now be turned to human ends; in order that man once more can become a creative force, renewing and creating his own life and thus giving life back to his society. (1970:6)

This quote is illustrative of the consciousness changes that swept through America during the movements of the 1960s and '70s. A new awareness of the struggles between the pressures and opportunities of modernity fueled the American environmental movement. Aldo Leopold articulated his land ethic in *A Sand County Almanac* and provided a central piece to the consciousness of the American environmental movement: "All ethics so far evolved rest upon a single premise: that the individual is a member of a community of interdependent parts. The land ethic simply enlarges the boundaries of the community to include soils, waters, plants and animals, or collectively the land" (1949:204). A similar sentiment is found in the words of Sandra Postel, author of *Last Oasis: Facing Water Scarcity*: "For many of us, water simply flows from a faucet, and we think little about it beyond this point of contact. We have lost a sense of respect for the wild river, for the complex workings of a wetland, for the intricate web of life that water supports" (2003).

Many scientists were members of the environmental movement, and they brought their own insights and consciousness-raising efforts to the cause. For example, deep consciousness changes followed the first images of Earth from space—the pale blue dot, as Carl Sagan called it. He is often quoted as saying:

> Our posturing, our imagined self-importance, the delusion that we have some privileged position in the universe, are challenged by this point of light. Our planet is a lonely speck in the great enveloping cosmic dark. In our obscurity, in all this vastness, there is no hint that help will come from elsewhere to save us from ourselves. (*The Independent* 2009)

He and other scientists, like Rachel Carson, committed their lives and risked their professional reputations to raise awareness among ordinary citizens regarding the risks modern technologies posed to nature and human health. Carson's writings regarding the complex interdependence of life in the natural world are representative of the consciousness of the late twentieth century American environmental movement:

> The earth's vegetation is part of a web of life in which there are intimate and essential relations between plants and animals. Sometimes we have no choice but to disturb these relationships, but we should do so thoughtfully, with full awareness that what we do may have consequences remote in time and place. (2002:64)

Recent evidence suggests that environmentalism makes up a central part of the identity of the majority of Americans. According to a recent Gallup Poll, three out of four Americans recycle, buy environmentally friendly products, and have reduced household energy use (Morales 2010). Similar consensus has been documented across Europe. Movement groups have developed numerous ways to reach the public with their messages. For example, street theatre is a way movements dramatize environmental threats that aren't often in view. Greenpeace is especially known for dressing in chemical suits as a way to draw attention to the dangers of toxic chemicals. Such demonstrations make provocative news articles and encourage those who see them to consider more carefully the safety of their food and water.

In keeping with our focus on hearts and minds, scholars have recently highlighted the role the environmental movement plays to "reenchant nature" (Gibson 2010). Segments of the environmental movement especially work to

Figure 8.2: Representative Environmental Activist Bios

Charles A. Reich Reich was a professor at Yale during the student movement of the 1960s. Inspired by this movement, Reich wrote *The Greening of America*, in which he articulated a rising new conciousness–one that valued humanity, peace, and all living creatures over profits and the primacy of industrialization.

Bunyan Bryant Bryant is a professor at the University of Michigan. As an activist scholar he founded the Environmental Justice Initiative–an organization that galvanizes scholarly work to expose issues of injustice and follow the stream of waste disposal in America.

Lois Gibbs Lois Gibbs mobilized to relocate her Love Canal neighborhood when she discovered that it was built on a seeping toxic waste site. Her road as an anti-toxics activist led from her life as a housewife to her current position as director of the Center for Health and Environmental Justice in Washington D.C.

Julia Butterfly Hill When she learned about the destruction of the Redwood Forest in California, Julia Butterfly Hill climbed into a tree she named Luna and lived there for almost two years. Though Luna was eventually cut for lumber, Butterfly Hill still fights to bring environmental awareness to people around the world.

Wangari Maathai Founder of the Greenbelt Movement in Kenya, Wangari Maathai spent her life planting trees, restoring the environment of her native country and advocating for a healthier relationship between people and their planet. She was awarded the 2004 Nobel Peace Prize. Wangari Maathai died in 2011.

highlight the spiritual and moral sides of environmental stewardship. The animal rights movement, for example, often conducts fundraising campaigns to care for animals that are left behind during natural disasters, using pictures of adorable dogs and cats to pull at potential donors' heart strings. The eco-spiritual movement, too, strives to encourage people to conceive of plants, animals, and even bugs as God's creation and hopes to foster a sense of responsibility among people of faith to care for all creatures, great and small.

Perhaps the most powerful recent environmental movement to impact hearts and minds is the environmental justice movement (Čapek 1993; Norgaard 2006). This arm of the environmental movement focuses on the unequal distribution of environmental goods and bads (Agyeman 2005; Krieg 1998; Sbicca 2012; Gellert 2003; Sicotte and Swanson 2007; Harlan et al. 2007; Scanlan 2009). Their work, in collaboration with many scholars, has shown that toxic sites have a high probability of being located in neighborhoods populated by people of color, especially African-American, and Hispanic neighborhoods in the United States (Commission for Racial Justice 1987; Taylor 2000; Mohai et al. 2009). Studies have also shown that working-class families are far more likely to suffer health problems due to toxic dumping than their upper-class counterparts (Bullard 1994). And according to Greg Hooks and Chris Smith (2004), Native Americans, too, are subject to prejudicial environmental problems, due to the existence of unexploded munitions on lands adjacent to Native American reservations. The environmental justice movement draws our attention to these injustices and works to block the continued siting of toxic facilities in lower-income, black and Hispanic neighborhoods.

Members of the environmental justice movement galvanize lawsuits, the media, and often door-to-door campaigns to bring injustices to people's attention and to mobilize them to fight for equal environmental rights for all people. Scholars such as David Pellow, Robert Bullard and Bunyan Bryant have raised considerable awareness regarding discriminatory environmental behaviors by governments, developers, and corporations. Bunyan Bryant is particularly accomplished as an activist scholar and director of the Environmental Justice Initiative. His work helps to institutionalize environmental justice policies, and he was previously instrumental in convincing former President Bill Clinton to sign the Environmental Justice Executive Order that required all federal agencies to integrate environmental justice concerns into their mandates.

As with all environmental movements, however, one doesn't have to be a renowned scholar to galvanize a movement. The environmental justice movement is filled with average citizens who have dedicated their lives to overcoming the sometimes deadly hidden practices of the governments and corporations. Lois Gibbs, now known as the mother of the anti-toxics movement, was a stay-at-home mom in 1978 when she discovered that her child was attending a school that sat on top of a toxic waste dump. It was eventually revealed that Gibbs's entire Love Canal neighborhood was sited on the same dump, and Gibbs spent countless hours, over years, mobilizing to prove that local miscarriages and other health problems were caused by seepage from that waste dump. After successfully forcing officials to relocate her community, Gibbs moved to Washington, D.C. where she now runs the Center for Health and Environmental Justice—an organization that assists other average citizens who fear their neighborhoods are also toxic.

Professor Wangari Maathai, winner of the 2004 Nobel Peace Prize, with then U.S. Senator Barack Obama, in 2006.

Whether it is the environmental justice movement, or earlier Earth Day activists, environmental movement members have long drawn our attention to the importance of a clean environment for humans and other living beings. These efforts have mobilized support, changed government agendas, and led to the creation of federal institutions that protect the environment. As we will see in the next section, however, environmental movements come up against significant roadblocks. Recent years have seen a decline in progress toward environmental protection, and some have even tried to push back critical legislation like the Clean Air and Endangered Species Acts.

Environmental Movement Limitations

Despite the impressive mobilization and framing contributions of the environmental movement, the movement alone is not sufficient to accomplish the entire range of changes needed to ameliorate our human impact on the planet. Political structures and conflicting interests at the regional, national, and international levels form considerable barriers that are sometimes insurmountable. Environmental interests have to compete with an array of public concerns, such as economic crises, human rights, and reducing infant mortality (Burns and LeMoyne 2001). This is especially poignant in countries in the global South, where environmental problems are frequently subsumed under the rubric of sustainable development, emphasizing the acute need for stable governments and economic opportunities in many regions. Such competition with other pressing needs makes the availability of funds for the environmen-

Figure 8.3 Dimensions of the Political Opportunity Structure

"(1) The relative openness or closure of the institutionalized political system; (2) the stability or instability of that broad set of elite alignments that typically undergird a polity; (3) the presence or absence of elite allies; [or] (4) the state's capacity and propensity for repression." (McAdam 1996: 27)

tal movement and its corresponding causes uncertain at times. And, even though the movement has clearly affected the values of citizens and increased our concern about environmental problems, our attitudes toward the earth don't always translate into perfect pro-environmental behavior.

Conflicting Priorities and the Two-Party System in the United States

Countries and their leaders operate under the influence of often conflicting logics, and their variety of goals and/or responsibilities are difficult to meet to their constituents' satisfaction. In the United States, evidence highlights that pro-environmental reforms generally advance during Democratic administrations, while they lapse or even fall behind during Republican administrations. Even when a supportive administration is in place, social movements can fight the good fight and still fail. How the Obama administration handled climate change legislation during its first term is illustrative.

During the 2009 campaign, Republicans and Democrats advocated for the creation of a cap and trade system to regulate greenhouse gas emissions in response to climate change. In 2003, McCain co-authored climate change legislation to advocate cap and trade; he is also quoted as saying: "It is time for the United States government to do its part to address this global problem, and a discussion of mandatory reductions is the form of leadership that is required" (Revkin et. al., 2008). Shortly after taking office, on January 26, 2009, President Obama gave a speech about the economic crisis, energy, and climate change in which he said, "These urgent dangers to our national and economic security are compounded by the long-term threat of climate change, which if left unchecked could result in violent conflict, terrible storms, shrinking coastlines and irreversible catastrophe" (Whitehouse.gov "From Peril to Progress" speech accessed May 29, 2015). Several social movements geared up to support Obama's commitment to climate change legislation and the need for an international treaty to curtail climate change. Rallies were held in Washington, D.C.; bills were introduced, debated, and passed out of the House of Representatives; yet, by the midterm elections in 2010, the Copenhagen Conference on Climate Change had come and gone and the United States still had no policy to reduce greenhouse gas emissions.

While there are several narratives that attempt to explain why the movement to enact climate legislation by the midterm elections in 2010 failed, some illustrative lessons can be learned from this example. To begin with, social movements face what is known as the political opportunity structure, which is essentially a way to understand how certain characteristics of the political environment are more or less favorable to the goals and tactics of social movements. Regardless of consensus on cap and trade, America and the rest of the world were in a terrible economic recession at the beginning of the Obama administration; therefore, an economic stimulus was the first order of business, and climate change legislation was delayed. Further complications arose when political alliances in Washington shifted into three political factions: the Republicans, the mainstream Democrats and the so-called Blue-dog Democrats. Although Democrats held majorities in both the House and the Senate and Barack Obama was at the helm, many Blue-dog Democrats (primarily from the increasingly conservative South) faced constituents whose livelihoods depended upon the fossil fuel industries—a segment of the economy that would be impacted by climate change legislation.

In spite of the agreement that characterized the presidential campaign trail between McCain and Obama on the need for climate change legislation, President Obama's first term in office was confronted by a Republican minority that objected to almost every piece of legislation, regardless of whether there were points of agreement across the aisles. As Republicans geared up for the midterm elections, knowing they could regain important seats given the bad economy, the odds of a climate bill passing grew slimmer and ultimately disappeared. The political opportunity structure (See Figure 9.3), made up of the alignments, access points and priorities of leaders in the political arena, simply prioritized the economy over the environment and faced a deeply divided Congress unable to acquiesce to movement pressures.

Challenges to the Environmental Movement in the International Arena

The environmental movement faces similar limitations in the international arena, where hard and soft law institutions regulate who can participate in the articulation of international environmental standards. International institutions, like the United Nations, are often forced to mediate between the grievances of civil society and the sovereignty of nation-states. As civil society groups, like the environmental movement, grow more aware of and engaged in international institutions, it becomes more important to understand the limits those institutions grapple with and the circumstances under which such institutions incorporate the voices of non-state actors.

As we described in the last chapter on the role of political institutions, each sector of the United Nations is populated by particular agencies that are charged to address particular problems or enact particular programs under their purview. Formal international environmental governance is managed by the United Nations, particularly through the United Nations Environment Program (UNEP), the United Nations Commission on Sustainable Development (UNCSD), the United Nations Development Organization (UNDP) and a myriad of specific treaty secretariats, which oversee such issue areas as oceans, climate change, ozone, and whaling (Ivanova and Roy 2007). Advocates for the environmental movement clearly recognize that global environmental governance institutions provide important channels through which to effect change, both at home and abroad. Many are uncertain, however, of which institutions provide the most efficient avenues for change and whether engagement in intergovernmental institutions like the United Nations will ever result in significant reform.

Beth Caniglia's (2011) work in this area highlights that there are three broad forces in the global environmental arena that shape how effective social movement groups are at achieving their environmental aims. Hard law treaty organizations like the United Nations Framework Convention on Climate Change (UNFCCC) regulate social movement participation most strictly, inviting movement input early in the annual review cycle and closing them out as governments get together for negotiations. Soft law organizations like the Commission on Sustainable Development (CSD), on the other hand, tend to incorporate social movements throughout their negotiation process, as long as those groups are willing to follow political protocols.

Certain social movement tactics are off limits when working inside of UN agencies. For example, organizing protests during negotiating sessions is discouraged during official UN meetings. At the UN General Assembly (UNGASS) 5 year review of the Commission on Sustainable Development, for example, Nobel Prize winner and environmental activist Wangari Maathai organized a sing-in where activists linked arms, surrounded delegates and sang "Harambe, UNGASS, Harambe–PARTNERSHIP!" The activists were sanctioned and threatened with removal from the negotiations if they did not behave according to diplomatic protocol. A similar development occurred at the 2009 Copenhagen meeting of the UNFCCC when environmental activists and some official government representatives staged a protest and walk-out from the meetings as a way to draw media attention to the failing negotiations. Many delegates expressed outrage that environmental movement groups would violate diplomatic protocol, and access to the meeting site was restricted significantly after that event.

The third force involved in international environmental law negotiations is the World Social Forum (WSF), a loosely organized collection of social movement organizations from around the world, described in more detail in the previous chapter. Designed first as a movement against the World Economic Forum where the World Bank, International Monetary Fund, and the World Trade Organizations meet with governments, the World Social Forum now stands as a platform for progressive causes world-wide, including labor rights, protection against child trafficking and environmental justice to name a few. The World Social Forum has been a major force of global mobilization and information sharing; however, its diversity is a weakness when it comes to taking positions and lobbying governments. The WSF refuses to take strong stands on issues, arguing that it is a platform for diverse voices to be heard, rather than a position-taking organization. As a result, this site of progressive protest fails to actually pressure governments to change their behaviors. Most scholars argue that, in spite of its failure to take strong positions, the WSF is still a central player in the global justice movement, which sometimes focuses on environmental issues as well.

There is talk that an overhaul in international environmental governance is overdue. In the meantime, however, specific characteristics of the High Level Forum on Sustainable Development suggest that this organization is best poised to facilitate global frameworks that support environmental aims (Caniglia 2011). Treaty organizations like the UN Framework Convention on Climate Change (UNFCCC) also have an important role to play; however, NGOs, movement groups and other non-state actors are more limited in such hard law environments. In order to successfully navigate these diverse institutional venues, the most effective advocates for environmental concerns have charted an integrated strategy that includes targeting the UN Commission on Sustainable Development and the specific treaty organizations that are relevant to their interests.

Conclusions: Take-Away Lessons about Social Movements and the Environment

The environmental movement is a diverse collection of people and organizations focused on the alleviation of environmental problems. As noted, their diversity sometimes hinders unity due to their different views of which environmental problems are most critical and how those should actually be solved. The drastic lifestyle differences between the global industrial North and the developing global South is especially difficult to overcome, since movements in the global South are rightly focused on meeting basic sanitation and health needs. In spite of these differences, the movement—both nationally and abroad—has come together and pressured governments to create critical institutional frameworks that protect the environment. Out of those institutions have come important legal protections, like the Clean Air Act and the Endangered Species Act, the International Whaling Commission and the Kyoto Protocol. Therefore, the environmental movement is certainly a central protagonist in our examination of potential solutions to our currently imbalanced relationship with nature.

The environmental movement's successes have lessened some of the most severe impacts of industrial modernity, such as flaming rivers. They have also made important inroads by opening people's minds to the importance of nature both as a life support system for humanity and as a community of life in its own right. Still, the concerns of our modern life—concerns like unemployment, political battles, and even the lives of movie stars, can too easily distract us and our politicians away from the foundation of environmental resources that currently faces a grim and uncertain future. Clearly, the environmental movement can't fix the situation alone. Therefore, in the coming chapters we will examine additional actors and institutions—such as scientists, the educational system, industry and governments, which also can and do play a pivotal role in bringing our relationship with nature back into balance.

Chapter 8 Summary

- In spite of its diversity, the environmental movement has successfully mobilized to accomplish important outcomes. In some cases, it has been able to convince government officials that the environment deserves a prominent place on political agendas.

- Though some scholars argue that the environmental movement's successes outweigh its failures, others have noted the lack of success of the environmental movement relative to other social movements. In moving forward, it will be vital to keep the focus on the goal of actual environmental stewardship, and not lose sight of that while involved in the machinations of the political process itself.

- Environmental movements are loosely affiliated sets of individuals, institutions, and organizations that promote sustainable human environment relations for political, social, moral, and scientific reasons. Many scholars see them as grassroots movements focused on lifestyle choices as the predominant focal point of civil society rather than on political institutions.

- The environmental movement was in the spotlight, both in the United States and globally, in the 1970s, when a number of significant progressive events occurred. In the United States, the Environmental Protection Agency (EPA) was created with bipartisan support in both houses of Congress and signed into law under President Richard Nixon. On the global stage, the United Nations Environmental Programme (UNEP) came into being. It provided an entrée for numerous environmental protection laws and international agreements that have facilitated cooperation among nation-states and non-governmental organizations (NGOs) to help protect the natural environment.

- The environmental movement alone is not sufficient to accomplish the entire range of changes needed to ameliorate the human impact on the planet. That is best facilitated when government, organizations, communities, and citizens come together, acting in good faith, around environmental stewardship.

- Social movements operate within what social scientists characterize as the "political opportunity structure." This is a framework for understanding how certain characteristics of the political environment are more or less favorable to the goals and tactics of social movements. The political opportunity structure, made up of the alignments, access points, and priorities of the political arena, will act in opposition to the environmental movement when it prioritizes other issues, such as the treadmill of production economy, over the environment.

- Internationally, the environmental movement also faces similar issues to those found in the United States. International institutions, like the United Nations, are often forced to mediate between the grievances of civil society and the sovereignty of nation-states. In order to successfully navigate these diverse institutional venues, the most effective advocates for environmental concerns have found integrated strategies that include working with the High Level Forum on Sustainable Development and other specific treaty organizations that prioritize environmental stewardship.

- The environmental movement is a central protagonist in our examination of potential solutions to our currently unbalanced relationship with nature. As a diverse collection of people and organizations focused on the alleviation of environmental problems, important legal protections have been established through the efforts of environmental movement organizations; examples include the International Whaling Commission, the Endangered Species Act, and the Kyoto Protocol.

- Advocates and other environmental organizations cannot fix environmental problems alone. At best, they serve as a catalyst for broader action, involving people of good will at all levels.

Chapter Nine - Late Modernity and the Environment in Emerging Economies

While environmental problems present themselves in countless ways around the world, they manifest differently in different regions and different levels of development. Emerging economies often have access to the technology to make incursions into the environment, but tend not to have the level of environmental protections found in more developed societies. As a result, some of the worst environmental degradation is found in developing societies.

The Environment and the Modern World-System

World-systems analysis (Wallerstein 1974, 1989, 1999; Chase-Dunn 2000; Chase-Dunn and Hall 1994, 1997) looks at the world in terms of core-periphery hierarchies, in which the most developed countries, such as the United States, Japan, England, and Germany would be considered "core" countries; the least developed countries such as those found in sub-Saharan Africa, including Chad and Niger, and less developed countries in Asia such as Myanmar, are considered part of the "periphery." Countries at an intermediate level of development are considered part of the "semi-periphery." These countries would include, for example, Mexico and South Korea. Some researchers in the world-system tradition (e.g., Burns et al. 1997, 2003) have found it useful to break out the intermediate countries into the higher end, or "semi-core" countries, and lower end semi-periphery. In a related vein, countries lower in the order tend to have a dependent relationship with those higher, thus placing them at a disadvantage in exchanges (Frank 1978), including ecological exchanges (Bunker and Ciccantell 2005).

Research has shown that these three, or sometimes four, tiers of the world-system, have quite different profiles in terms of environmental degradation. Bearing in mind that we are speaking in ideal-typical terms, we nonetheless begin to see some patterns emerging around the world.

The highest consumption of energy and a wide array of manufactured goods and luxury items occur in the core countries. Yet, consumption levels are rising worldwide and are particularly troublesome in the semi-core countries, the most notable of which are known by the acronym BRIC, for Brazil, Russia, India, and China. The BRICs are abundant in natural resources (particularly in the case of Brazil and Russia) and/or population (as in the case of China and India). The former makes them especially attractive for exploitation of natural resources, while the latter makes them particularly good targets for exploitation of cheap labor.

Much of international commerce is controlled by multinational corporations (MNCs), most of which are headquartered in core countries (Sklair 1999). While they enjoy the protections of the military and navies of core countries, they are able to move capital around and are not necessarily committed to having their operations in any one country. In fact, one of the artifacts of a globalizing society is the advent of "commodity chains" where a complex product, such as an automobile or a computer, might have components that have been manufactured in over a dozen countries on a multitude of continents (Robinson 2004). As we saw in the chapter on economics, the law of comparative advantage has become a central idea in the capitalism of late modernity (Burns, Boyd, and Burns 2014; Prechel 1994). In these commodity chains, the cheapest resources or component parts are used, regardless of the environmental cost; the cheapest labor is used, regardless of the human cost. The product is manufactured efficiently, thus making a profit for investors, most or virtually all of whom are removed from the production process itself. The results are often daunting to everyone else, in terms of the burden on the environment and human well-being.

Some of the most polluted places on the planet are in the developing societies—neither in the richest, nor in the poorest countries, but in the middle. To be even more precise, countries toward the higher end of the middle—the BRICs in particular—are experiencing some of the worst degradation. As we saw in the chapter on health, illness, and the environment, slightly over half of the deaths attributable to air pollution occurred in just two (albeit the two most populous) countries—India and China (World Health Organization 2015).

Other countries, such as those in sub-Saharan Africa and in the poorest parts of Asia and Latin America are "catching up" rapidly, however. Consumption patterns are rising rapidly around the globe, and this includes even in the least developed countries.

The Recursive Structure of the World-System: Replicating Itself at Different Levels of Analysis

It bears noting that, while the core, semi-periphery, and periphery of the world-system were originally conceptualized on the nation-state level, these hierarchies actually occur at a number of levels of analysis, from the global, to the national, to the more local. Within a nation-state there are regions that are more core and those that are more peripheral, with a semi-peripheral buffer in between. Put another way, the core-periphery hierarchy can be seen as a recursive structure (Burns et al. 2006). In the United States, for example, researchers have shown how tribal reservations (Hooks and Smith 2014) have been, in many cases, relegated to periphery status, as has much of the Appalachian region of the eastern United States (Dunaway 1996). They are used to extract resources and to bear the brunt of the externalities of the extractive process by being exposed to disproportionate shares of toxins and other risks.

The Environmental Kuznets Curve

The considerations we have been discussing, led some observers to posit what they have called the environmental Kuznets curve, based on the work of the economist Simon Kuznets (1955), who saw a curvilinear relationship between economic growth and income inequality. The environmental Kuznets curve highlights the curvilinear relationship between the level of economic development of the country and its level of environmental degradation, with the highest levels of pollution in developing societies and lower levels in the least and most developed societies (Torras and Boyce 1998). In world-system terms, this would predict the lowest levels of pollution to be found in the periphery and in the core, with the higher levels to be found in the semi-periphery and the semi-core (Burns et al. 1994, 1997, 2003). Yet, the empirical support for this is mixed, at best (e.g., Seldon and Song 1994; Stern and Common 2001; Suri and Chapman 1998).

The Netherlands Fallacy and the Ecological Footprint

The environmental Kuznets literature tends to miss an important point, and one that is captured in the term the "*Netherlands fallacy.*" What is the Netherlands fallacy? We begin the discussion by acknowledging that it could just as easily, or perhaps even more appropriately, be called the North American fallacy, or even the United States fallacy. But since the Netherlands was the first country where people noticed this happening, it was the one that got the moniker, and since then the name has stuck. The Netherlands, as it turns out, has very low levels of pollution. Having few trees left to cut, it has negligible levels of deforestation. And so, the Netherlands does indeed fall on the far right side of the graph of the environmental Kuznets curve. It is a developed country, in the core on the world economy, and one that pollutes very little—or does it?

Here, it is important to consider the concept of the ecological footprint (Wackernagel and Rees 1996). This goes beyond how much pollution there is in one's own locale or even in one's own country, and asks a deeper question: how much of the pollution and environmental degradation—even though they may have been experienced in another country, perhaps on another continent, or out in the ocean—were *caused* by the consumption patterns in that country (Wackernagel et al. 1999)? The ecological footprint is a measure of consumption of an array of goods, including energy sources such as fossil fuels, food, and manufactured goods.

Empirical work has shown a roughly linear relationship between the level of development and the ecological footprint, with the footprint being highest in the most developed countries (Jorgenson 2003, 2004; Jorgenson, Rice, and Crowe 2005; York, Rosa, and Dietz 2003). This is exacerbated by a number of considerations, including economies of scale (Wackernagel and Silverstein

2000). It is also the case that the countries with the highest per capita footprints at the beginning of the last decade of the twentieth century, also tended to be those with the greatest growth in footprint size over that decade (Jorgenson and Burns 2007).

As the world becomes more globalized, which is to say it becomes more interconnected, there is much more interchange than ever before between countries and regions. In an ideal-typical sense, resources are extracted from peripheral countries, below market value, at rates that do not particularly benefit the average people in those countries. While it may enrich a few people at the very top, it mainly benefits those people in the extraction industry itself. It is often the case that there is a high degree of inequality in these countries already, and these patterns of *unequal ecological exchange* exacerbate those inequalities (Austin 2012; Jorgenson 2006; Jorgenson and Burns 2007).

In addition to taking the resources from poor countries, there are often serious externalities, or "dark value" left in the wake (Clelland 2012; Frey 2006). These include the drawing down of water on aquifers that hurt local farming and pollute drinking water. In the mining of heavy metals, as we saw in the chapter on environment and health, the chronic exposure to these heavy metals can cause cancer, nerve damage, lung, kidney, and liver damage as well. In some cases, where there is radioactive material, such as uranium, the risks can be even greater.

The preponderance of the places where the wages are low and the working conditions poor, and health and environmental risks abound, can be found in semi-peripheral or semi-core countries. These "sweat shops" are able to thrive because of differences in the economy and the political system and ultimately the culture between nation-states. Several things are worth noting here. One is that the sweatshops typically are not in the poorest places. Those places, the true periphery, are too far out of the way of the world economy to even be players on the world stage. It is much more likely for exploitative factories to be placed in rapidly developing countries such as China, Mexico, India, and Brazil.

These countries have an abundance of people willing to work for low wages. In Marxist terms, they have a large combination of a proletariat or working class, spurred on, and kept from striking from perhaps an even larger lumpenproletariat, or reserve army of the unemployed. This potent combination, driven by the demography of high birth rates and population growth, with young people coming into working age with dizzying rapidity, yet without the prospect of a steady job, gives multinational corporations a tremendous upper hand in dictating wages and working conditions.

Because of this, workers are willing to work for very low wages and poor working conditions. On the more macro level, the developing countries, desperate to have something for these reserve armies of the unemployed to do, lest they turn their attention perhaps to other things such as revolution or violence (Homer-Dixon 1999; Marx 1867/1967), enable the process by having lax or no environmental or occupational safety and health laws, or if they do have laws on the books, tending not to enforce them.

As a result, some of the worst environmental catastrophes have taken place in developing countries. In Bhopal, India, for example, a Union Carbide factory that was engaged in manufacturing practices deemed too dangerous to do in a developed country, exploded, killing or injuring huge numbers of people—some half a million were affected. It was the worst industrial accident in history.

The Environment and Health in Developing Countries

Some of the most polluted places in the world are in developing countries. This has serious consequences that are likely to become worse before they get better. As we saw in the chapter on environment and health, India and China have some of the worst pollution problems in the world. Thus, it should come as no surprise that they also lead the world in deaths attributable to air pollution, with about 3 million per year between the two of them and rising.

More generally speaking, while risk is a general problem in modern society (Beck 1992), developing societies are at disproportionate risk, due to their relative position in the global hierarchy (Burns, Kentor, and Jorgenson 2003). Most of the factories and manufacturing plants for a wide array of products are found in developing societies. These are places where there is an abundant supply of cheap labor, combined with lax occupational safety and health oversight and negligible environmental regulation.

In addition to the vast array of products available to global markets, such as clothing and cosmetics, these places also manufacture dangerous chemicals, fertilizers, and pesticides that may be outlawed in developed countries such as the United States and Canada and Western Europe. For example, although DDT has been outlawed in the United States, largely as a result of the pioneering work of Rachel Carson and others, it nonetheless is manufactured and used just south of the border between the United Sates and Mexico in the *Maquiladora* region (Frey 2003). Here, some of the most toxic activity takes place on a regular basis and, thanks to the North American Free-Trade Agreement (NAFTA), the products are then exported back into the United States on just as regular a basis. More broadly, foreign investment tends to come into sectors of the economies of developing countries with little oversight or environmental controls. This, in turn, leads to situations that enable toxic and risky conditions (Dick and Jorgenson 2010).

The herbicide atrazine has a number of toxic effects, including being a hormone disrupter that causes dangerously high levels of estrogen, which in turn can lead to higher risk of certain kinds of cancers, birth defects, as well as liver and kidney disease (Steingraber 2010). Because of these significant risks, it has been banned in the countries of the European Union. However, due to the strong lobbying efforts of the chemical industry, and their ability to sway elections directly through campaign contributions, and indirectly through Super PACs and the control of information, the United States has failed to ban it. Atrazine continues to be used widely in the United States, entering waterways and contaminating everything downstream of it. Its toxic effects have redounded in increased rates of cancer and birth defects. In animal populations, the effects can be seen dramatically when, for example, there are cases of male frogs which, having been exposed to heavy doses of atrazine in river systems in agricultural areas where its use is rampant (e.g., the central valley of California), over time turning into fully functional females.

Yet, as problematic as atrazine has become in the United States, its use has become more widespread by orders of magnitude in some developing countries. India, for example, uses something like 30 times as much atrazine as the United States. It is no wonder then, that so many diseases and birth defects that had been rare have become more common in India.

These problems are even more overwhelming in and around the town of Jadugora in eastern India, where there was a functional uranium mine for 47 years. Although the mine is now shut, the people there—those who are still alive—feel the aftermath of radiation poisoning. Virtually everyone in the town was affected. Children born there regularly had serious birth defects, including swollen heads, blood disorders, and partial paralysis.

In most cases, the people responsible for causing exposure to toxins were not held accountable. They were able to profit, while the local people typically were powerless to fight back, and in any case were lacking in knowledge about the risks to which they were unwittingly being exposed until it was too late to do anything about it.

In a rapidly globalizing world, exposure can come in many ways, and under many guises (Austin and McKinney 2012). Moving forward into the third millennium, it will be important to remember these sorts of mistakes, so that we may avoid them in the future (Chew 2008). Yet, the pattern continues to repeat itself—the poor, the disenfranchised, those lacking knowledge, and those without political connections and clout, remain particularly vulnerable (McKinney 2014; Austin, McKinney, and Thompson 2012).

Figure 9.1 Industrial Accidents in Developing Countries

Abandoned Union Carbide (later purchased by Dow Chemical) plant in Bhopal, India. The 1984 leak of methyl isocyanate gas caused approximately 8,000 deaths in the first two weeks following the disaster.

For data collection purposes, the United Nations Environmental Programme (UNEP) defines major accidents as:

- 25 or more deaths; or
- 125 or more serious injuries; or
- 10,000 or more people evacuated; or
- 10,000 or more people deprived of water.

In reviewing all of the major industrial accidents over the course of the last century, a number of patterns emerge. More major accidents occurred in developed countries than in developing countries. However, the most serious of the accidents tended to occur in the developing countries. Researchers attribute these differences to better enforcement of safety regulations in developed countries.

By far, the worst industrial accident occurred in December of 1984 in Bhopal, India, when there was an explosion in a Union Carbide plant there. There was a highly toxic substance released into the air called methyl isocyanate. It caused about 8000 deaths in two weeks, and 1000 more from related causes over longer periods of time. And it should be noted, that those were excruciating deaths. The methyl isocyanate poisoning caused coughing to the point of choking and respiratory failure for some people, and eye irritation to the point of blindness for others. In the longer term, it caused stillbirths and neonatal mortality, respiratory problems, pulmonary fibrosis, and other brain and neuro-muscular difficulties. Second only to the Bhopal incident, in terms of loss of life, was a gasoline explosion in Jesse, Nigeria in October of 1998.

Another horrific industrial accident occurred in April, 1986 in Chernobyl, Ukraine, when it was part of the former Soviet Union. During the accident itself, 31 people died. High levels of radiation were expelled into the atmosphere and were detected as far away as Warsaw, Poland and Helsinki, Finland. To this day, people living in the wake of the Chernobyl accident are at higher risk for cancer and other diseases.

Bhopal, Jesse, and Chernobyl are high profile instances of disasters in developing countries—in two of the three cases, in the BRIC countries. As Ulrich Beck (1992) points out in *Risk Society: Towards a New Modernity*, increasing risk of accidents is ubiquitous throughout the globe. Yet, people in developing societies are particularly at risk. In the cases of India, Nigeria, and Ukraine, there was a lack of oversight and a lack of regulation. Those catastrophes could have been avoided, and faulty equipment found with more rigorous inspection and replaced in a timelier manner.

The British Petroleum (BP) oil spill off the coast of Louisiana in the Gulf of Mexico had its primary effects on a developed country—the United States. As horrific as it was, and environmentally catastrophic, it did not have the loss of human life as did the other instances. However, something it did have in common with the tragedies in India, Nigeria, and Ukraine, was that during that time leading to the accident, there was slipshod maintenance and poor inspection, bordering on negligence. The cleanup that was so costly in so many ways could have been avoided, had there been greater attentiveness to keeping the equipment up to date and in working order.

More broadly however, these accidents beg a number of ethical questions. What was Union Carbide doing with such toxic chemicals in the first place? This American company would not have been allowed to have used these chemicals in the United States. In fact, the CEO of

Union Carbide was indicted by Indian courts on multiple charges of manslaughter. He never was extradited by the United States, and never did stand trial.

Should BP have been making incursions in the Gulf of Mexico at all? If so, to what extent? Did the Soviet Union really need a nuclear reactor? If so, why in Chernobyl? Was placing a gasoline refinery at that location in Nigeria a good idea in the first place? If so, for whom?

The abandoned city of Pripyat, Ukraine, inside the exclusion zone or "alienation zone"–an area of approximately 30 kilometers in all directions surronding the Chernobyl nuclear reactor. Chernobyl can be seen in the background. It has been estimated that the area will not be safe for human habitation for 20,000 years.

The point is not to answer those questions here, or even to imply that there is one right answer. Yet, by ignoring those questions, we allow others to ask them by default. Should Union Carbide be the sole arbiter of where it places its plants, and what chemicals or other substances it has in them when it does? If the answer to that is yes, then by default, we place untold numbers of people at substantial risk.

One of the take-away lessons from these catastrophes may be to take the precautionary principle seriously, and to practice it as an integral part of public policy. Rather than assuming that people in power have everyone's best interest at heart, and will proceed with all caution and due diligence, it may make more sense in the long run, even while hoping for the best, to take precautions that the worst case scenario does not occur. This would necessarily include building in some redundancies into the system, so that if a safety mechanism is down, there is a backup. Also, people with some level of expertise, as well as good will, need to inspect the equipment regularly and diligently, and to replace faulty parts of the system immediately, before they are allowed to spin out of control.

Ultimately though, it is important to move beyond mere technocratic solutions, and to grapple with the deeper issues about which of these enterprises even make sense doing from an environmental and culturally conscious standpoint. This works best to the extent that the environment is the central organizing principle in the culture. It brings us back to the ethical questions raised by John Cobb (1991, 2007)—will the culture revolve around trying to keep a perpetually growing economy, and in so doing, continue to degrade the planet—or will the culture revolve around making the planet a more livable place? These are questions that are valid and timely throughout the world, cross culturally, in developed and developing societies. They invite us to take a step back and re-examine where we are in this culture of late modernity. These are important questions for all of us.

Sources: Mihailidou et al. (2012); Kletz (2009); Fortun (2001); Medvedev (1992); Lustgarten (2012); United Nations Environmental Programme (UNEP 2016).

Chapter 9 Summary

- While environmental problems present themselves in countless ways around the world, they manifest differently in different regions and different levels of development.

- Emerging economies often have access to the technology to make incursions into the environment, but tend not to have the level of environmental protections found in more developed societies. As a result, some of the worst environmental degradation is found in rapidly developing societies, including but not limited to BRIC countries of Brazil, Russia, India and China.

- One of the artifacts of globalizing society, is the advent of "commodity chains," where a complex product such as an automobile or a computer might have components that, in fact, have been manufactured in over a dozen countries on a multitude of continents. This has profound environmental consequences.

- The law of comparative advantage has become a central idea in the capitalism of late modernity. This manifests in how these commodity chains come together, where the cheapest resources or component parts will be found around the globe, regardless of the environmental externalities, and the cheapest labor will be used, regardless of the human costs. The product is manufactured efficiently, thus making a profit for investors, most or virtually all of whom are removed from the production process itself. The results are often daunting to everyone else, in terms of the burden on the environment and human well-being.

- Some of the most polluted places on the planet are in the developing societies—neither in the richest nor in the poorest countries, but in the middle. To be even more precise, countries toward the higher end of the middle—the BRICs in particular—are experiencing some of the worst degradation.

- According to recent statistics from the World Health Organization, slightly over half of the deaths attributable to air pollution occurred in just two (albeit the two most populous) countries—India and China.

- Other countries, such as those in sub-Saharan Africa and in the poorest parts of Asia and Latin America are "catching up" rapidly, in terms of environmental degradation. Consumption patterns are rising rapidly around the globe, including even in the least developed countries, and this puts a strain on the natural environment and its resources.

- While the core, semi-periphery, and periphery of the world-system were originally conceptualized on the nation-state level, these hierarchies actually occur at a number of levels of analysis, from the global, to the national, to the more local. Within a nation-state there are regions that are more core and those that are more peripheral, with a semi-peripheral buffer in between. Put another way, the core-periphery hierarchy can be seen as a recursive structure.

- In the United States, for example, researchers have shown how tribal reservations have been, in many cases, relegated to peripheral status, as has much of the Appalachian region of the eastern United States (Dunaway 1996). They are used to extract resources and to bear the brunt of the externalities of the extractive process by being exposed to disproportionate shares of toxins and other risks.

- The environmental Kuznets curve highlights the curvilinear relationship between the level of economic development of the country and its level of environmental degradation, with the highest levels of pollution in developing societies and lower levels in the least and most developed societies. In world-system terms, this would predict the lowest levels of pollution to be found in the periphery and in the core, with the higher levels to be found in the semi-periphery and the semi-core. The empirical support for this, however, is mixed at best.

- It is important to consider the concept of the *ecological footprint*, which goes beyond how much pollution there is in one's own locale or country, and asks a deeper question: how much of the pollution and environmental degradation were *caused* by the consumption patterns in that country? The ecological footprint is a measure of consumption of an array of goods, including energy sources such as fossil fuels, food, and manufactured goods.

- Empirical work has shown a roughly linear relationship between the level of development and the ecological footprint, with the footprint being highest in the most developed countries.

- Countries with the highest per capita footprints at the beginning of the last decade of the twentieth century, also tended to be those with the greatest growth in footprint size over that decade.

- In a rapidly globalizing world, exposure can come in many ways, and under many guises. The poor, the disenfranchised, those lacking knowledge, and those without political connections and clout, remain particularly vulnerable.

Chapter Ten - Catalysts for Change and Growing Consciousness

In his book, *Earth in the Balance,* Al Gore calls for a "Global Marshall Plan," analogous to the rebuilding of Europe from the ruins of World War II, to address environmental problems. While there is a compelling warrant for such dramatic action, if it were to occur, it would need to be approached with great measures of care and humility, lest we create other problems in attempting to solve the ones we do have. In the absence of a concerted global effort, what can be done? Many of the issues we discuss have a fractal quality, which is to say that they manifest on multiple levels of analysis. As such, they need to be addressed in integrated ways. At the same time, however, it is crucial to keep in mind that meaningful change can occur in many ways, and can originate in what may at first blush seem unlikely places. A central theme of this chapter is that of the catalyst–a small addition to a mix that helps to bring about a large change. We look to incremental, achievable changes people and communities can make that could help to make huge differences. One example we discuss is the rise of a culture in which people are more likely to use low-impact transportation such as bicycles or go by foot. These changes on the individual level would best be facilitated on the community and perhaps even on the national level with a system of low-impact transportation. Ideally, a synergy emerges between individual interests and public projects so that there is a win-win for both, with environmentally friendly outcomes a major by-product.

Introduction

Previously, we reviewed five institutions that are often considered to be part of the solution to our contemporary environmental problems: governance, economics, education, science and technology, and social movements. We reviewed the ways in which socio-cultural studies have examined these institutions; we highlighted ways these institutions might be changed to minimize their negative environmental impacts; and we made recommendations for how to strengthen these institutions in proenvironmental ways. In this section, we review a variety of approaches set forth by experts for comprehensive changes to our society that can transform our personal behaviors, as well as our institutions, in ways that reorient our behaviors to be more in line with nature and environmental limits.

Specifically, we review three approaches that emphasize structural institutional changes and two approaches that focus on cultural and personal changes. Former Vice President of the United States Al Gore's framework for change emphasizes the need to expand governance, policies, education, and science.

Economist, author, and *New York Times* columnist Thomas Friedman emphasizes a complete reconstruction of our energy system, along with improved economics and educational systems. John Bellamy Foster suggests that the entire capitalist economic system is responsible for the over-consumption and accumulating inequality in our present system. On the cultural side, we look at the work of William James Gibson and Dan Wildcat, who argue that we need to reconnect to nature and build our lifestyles in ways that deeply integrate respect and reverence of our non-human plant and animal relatives.

We conclude with an analysis of the structural and cultural dimensions of these perspectives and the ways social scientists understand the roles of structure and personal change. Traditionally, there has been a strong divide between those who advocate for structural changes, such as legal changes, and those who emphasize the need to transform individual behaviors through education and lifestyle modifications. However, our approach recognizes the need to work for change on both of these levels.

Global Marshall Plan for the Environment

Former U.S. Vice President Al Gore laid out five central steps toward catalyzing environmental change in his book *Earth in the Balance* (1992). He equated these steps to a Global Marshall Plan, necessary to reorient the actions and relationships of European nations after WWII, just as now we so desperately need to reorient our actions and relationships with our planetary home.

The five steps Gore describes include:

1. Stabilizing world population
2. Rapid development of advanced environmentally sustainable technologies
3. True cost accounting of environmental degradation into global economic practices
4. Far-reaching education programs to increase awareness and understanding of the current environmental crisis among all global citizens
5. Establishment of the social and political conditions conducive to the emergence of sustainable societies

Gore argued that world population growth restructures our relationship fundamentally with natural resources by increasing stresses on the ability to provide for so many new arrivals. He was also concerned about the fact that, at the time, 94 percent of population growth was projected to take place in the developing world, rather than inside of industrialized nations. He recommended increased availability of birth control devices, targeted literacy programs, and decreased infant mortality as specific routes to reduce the stress of population

Al Gore accepting the 2007 Nobel Peace Prize, won jointly with the Intergovernmental Panel on Climate Change.

growth on environmental degradation.

In spite of the challenges often caused by new technologies, Gore took an ecological modernization approach toward the transition to a more sustainable society. Recall that ecological modernization theorists argue that superior technological advancement will increase the sustainability of economic growth via advanced materials and increased energy efficiency. Gore was an advocate for this approach. However, he also believed that the advanced technologies developed in the industrialized nations had to be shared/transferred to the developing nations to help them to leapfrog dirtier development strategies. Such technology transfer helps everyone, because it encourages an economy where no one is left behind. This builds trust across nations and increases the likelihood that the world will rally together to address environmental problems, rather than be mired in capitalist forms of competition that categorizes environmental damages as "externalities."

Technology transfer is just one piece of an overarching "New Global Eco-Nomics" called for by Gore. He notes that contemporary calculations in the economy excludes natural resources and their depletion, along with excessive industrial pollution. In other words, current economics considers natural resources to be "limitless and free." In fact, Gore points out that many times environmental degradation is actually subsidized by our governments around the world. For example, Gore describes programs in the United States, Australia, and Canada that encourage regular plowing of marginalized lands, which leads to increased soil erosion and decreased long-term productivity. Such programs are obviously irrational, according to Gore, and need to be discontinued. Similar subsidy programs reinforce the use of fossil fuels well past their peak energy potential. Thus, a complete reconsideration of current subsidy frameworks is in order, and changes must be made that incentivize more sustainable economic pathways over our current unsustainable practices. Gore also advocates for "green label" schemes that give consumers the knowledge to make sustainable product choices. Such programs encourage sustainable pollution prevention strategies within industry, because consumers generally prefer to purchase products they feel good about. Lifestyle branding in the industrialized world can serve as a strong catalyst to improve the sustainable practices and products of companies worldwide. As further assurance that increasingly sustainable practices are implemented by industry subsidiaries around the world, Gore recommends transparency and the integration of environmental oversight into free-trade agreements. Otherwise, he fears that industries will simply move their production plants to countries with less sustainable legal structures and "green wash" their products in their advertising. Finally, Gore recommends the establishment of cap and trade programs for CO2 that provide credits to the developing world for keeping large carbon "sinks," such as forests and peat bogs, which provide carbon sequestration services in exchange for financial incentives. This is another example of the full-participation economy that Gore envisions–one that brings everyone into exchange with one another in mutually beneficial ways.

Gore believes the foundation upon which these other changes can be made requires the creation of a series of internationally binding consensus agreements regarding sustainable environmental practices based on the model of the Montreal Protocol, which focused on eliminating the substances responsible for the ozone hole above the Arctic. The Montreal Protocol is considered the most successful international environmental treaty in history, in part because of the assessment committee structure used to create the terms of the treaty and to evaluate its implementation (Canan and Reichmann 2002). The three panels brought together members of industry, scientists, economists, and governments to evaluate the steps required to eliminate ozone-depleting substances. The critical difference between this approach and most other international treaties is that industry and economists were actively engaged in the discussion from the very beginning so that the recommendations of the panels were (1) reasonable in light of existing technological capabilities and (2) supported by those who would be required to change their practices if the treaty was ratified. We discussed this approach to governance in the earlier chapter on Governance and Policies, which is called hybrid governance; and, according to Gore, the world will require a base in international law that is built on a hybrid governance model that includes all governments and the stakeholders required to uphold international law.

Gore believed all of the above steps would be easier to implement if the final step–the creation of a new way of thinking about the natural world–was accomplished. Central to this goal, according to Gore, is to convince everyone that the global environment can be found outside their own back doors. A broad educational effort would be needed, and it would be BIG–NASA-scale big. A global effort to collect data that describes our atmosphere, oceans, terrestrial systems, plate tectonics, and provide insights for everyone on Earth to see just how fragile and under threat our planet truly is. These data can then be used to create books, documentaries, educational curriculum, and other scientific documentation to advance our understanding of Earth's global systems and to locate leverage points for combatting "self-interested cynics … seeking to cloud the underlying issue of the environment with disinformation" (Gore 1992:360).

Today's Date: 1 E.C.E

Al Gore isn't the only person arguing that we need an entirely new social structure that is designed around solving our environmental problems. Thomas Friedman, famous author of *The World Is Flat*, published *Hot, Flat, and Crowded: Why We Need a Green Revolution–and How It Can Renew America* in 2008 and offers a detailed analysis of why an entirely new social order is required as a result of the current environmental crisis. Friedman calls this new order the Green New Deal, because of the large number of economic changes that need to take place to make America more sustainable and more competitive in the new energy-climate era.

Friedman's concerns about our environmental problems stem from three related factors that converge to make the fate of our future look very bleak. The combination of climate change, rising education and standards of living around the world, and rising population, according to Friedman, require us to rework our relationship to the planet, energy, and consumption. In the past, only a few nations had high standards of living, and those countries also had low populations. Today, however, as globalization ushers higher standards of living to highly populated places like India and China, the stressors placed on natural resources, biodiversity, and the provision of energy are exponentially increasing and will continue increasing until population growth stabilizes around mid-century. Imagine billions of people desiring American-sized homes, multiple cars, and walk-in closets filled with clothes and shoes.

The Green New Deal consists of too many steps to detail here, but the primary areas where Friedman recommends we make significant changes include: energy production/consumption; conservation of biodiversity and forests; and the transformation of our economic system to reflect the full costs of environmental degradation. Friedman argues, in keeping with the best scientists around the world, that our energy system is the key step required to combat the threats of climate change. Citing Pacala and Socolow (2004), Friedman describes the need for us to stabilize greenhouse gas emissions through off-setting coal-burning power plants with cleaner energy sources. Particularly, he highlights solar, wind, and nuclear energy as hopeful alternatives that can curtail the global warming impacts of climate change. This strategy not only accomplishes the goal of reducing greenhouse gas emissions, but it also removes America from the petropolitics of acquiring oil and gas from foreign countries and increases America's energy independence.

Changing our energy supply isn't enough to solve all of our environmental problems, however. Friedman argues that we need to change the way we think about the natural world. We need to increase conservation of biodiversity and forests, because they make up the base of the life-support system of our planet. A denuded planet will fail to provide essential ecosystem services, including clean water supplies, medicinal discoveries, flood mitigation, protection from soil erosion, and provision of carbon storage for future generations. Because the average person doesn't really know or care about how forests and critters are affected by the production of the things we buy, Friedman argues that we have to create economic incentives to bring about the proper conservation efforts whether people realize it is necessary or not. Tax structures need to reflect the natural resource costs of production processes, including the water, plants, and minerals used in their making as well as the pollution produced along the way. Allan Schnaiberg called these costs *additions* and *subtractions* in his book *The Environment: From Surplus to Scarcity* (1980). Similar to Al Gore's Global Marshall Plan, Friedman emphasizes the need for changes to provide rising tides for all nations, but for this to happen the developing world has to be full partners in their own economic and environmental transitions. As Friedman puts it, we need a million Noahs and a million arks.

The key to implementing changes on this scale is to engage all levels of society in the challenge. Friedman highlights the need for policy changes–both globally and locally; economic incentives that discourage individuals from over-consumption, economic structures that encourage conservation on the part of industry, and tax structures that encourage full-cost accounting of the cost of further greenhouse gas emissions. In addition, nations will require private sector investors and local experts to bring conservation goals together with economic development opportunities. Each country will have to find its own path, but find a path that works they must. Finally, Friedman emphasizes the need for global and local educational initiatives that increase broad understanding of the fragility of our natural environment and the urgency to transition into the energy-climate era.

Ecological Revolution

John Bellamy Foster, a sociologist at the University of Oregon, has provided a framework for saving the planet that focuses critically on the expansion of capitalism as the primary driver of environmental degradation. His analysis is based on what he calls the *ecological rift*, which is the mismatch between the rate of resource consumption and the sustainability of that consumption rate. According to Foster, the "treadmill of production and consumption" that is at the center of the capitalist economic system drives humanity into a relationship of alienation from nature. The requirement that individual items taken from nature need to be measured, divided, commoditized and sold as a part completely separated from their ecological form and function fosters a relationship between people and the items they buy that perpetuates separation from the natural value of the product. We don't generally ask questions about how mercury is extracted from the earth or what dangers exist due to exposure to mercury, even though mercury is an important component in cell phones and accumulates in the fatty tissues of farmed fish. Mercury is also a toxic

Figure 10.1 Action Items from the Earth Charter Secretariat (web page)

The Action Guidelines

- Start with the Earth Charter. Let the Earth Charter be your basic guide when you are planning and undertaking activities to make the Earth Charter vision a reality.

- Be a Living Example. Strive to be a living example of the spirit of the Earth Charter in your day-to-day life — at home, in the work place, and in your community.

- Empower Yourself. Act boldly, and trust that you can make a difference as an individual and that your activities will catalyze the efforts of many others.

- Cooperate, Cooperate. Create the power to affect change by building partnerships and collaborating with others, and seek win/win solutions.

- Empower Others. Share power by being inclusive and providing others with opportunities to strengthen their capacities for problem-solving, decision-making, and leadership, unleashing human creativity.

- Promote Respect and Understanding. Endeavor to build relationships of mutual respect and trust among individuals and groups from diverse cultures and communities, and resolve differences through dialogue in a way that produces learning and growth.

- Facilitate Self-Organization. Facilitate the spread of initiatives inspired by the Earth Charter without trying to control them, counting on the capacity of human groups with a clear ethical purpose to self-organize and achieve positive outcomes.

- Focus on Root Causes. Focus thought and action on the root causes of the major problems and challenges facing humanity, and do not let the pressures of existing unsustainable systems and practices deter you from action.

- Be Committed Yet Flexible. Be unwavering in your commitment to fundamental principles and ensure that the means adopted to achieve your goals are consistent with Earth Charter values, but always be flexible and innovative in selecting means and methods as circumstances change.

- Be Resourceful. Do not let your thinking and acting be restricted by dependence on money; use your imagination and be resourceful in making things happen.

- Use Technology Wisely. Be mindful that large numbers of people do not have access to advanced technology, and when constructing technological solutions to problems, ensure that they are appropriate.

- Protect the Integrity of the Charter. When presenting, quoting from, or translating the Earth Charter, be faithful to the words and spirit of the original text, and link the Charter only with organizations, products and events that are consistent with its values and vision.

Sources: http://earthcharter.org/act/action-guidelines/.

substance that causes cancer in humans; however, our consciousness of the presence of mercury–or any range of ecologically derived substances–in the products we use every day is quite limited. This, according to Foster, is an example of the ways that capitalism alienates us from nature, because the natural dimensions of commodities are eclipsed by the human-created commodities themselves. We are in love with our new cell phones without being conscious of the many ecologically derived elements that make up those phones; our love of our phone–as a whole product–leads us to overlook what it is made of and the potential costs to the planet that were perpetrated during its production. This mental process of substituting the human-produced technology as the real item, while ignoring completely the myriad of items from the natural world that were either used to produce the technology or damaged in the process, is a form of alienation that has serious consequences for the planet.

Unfortunately, Foster points out that a lot of our over-exploitation of the planet's resources is not simply due to alienation. Rather, alienation is in some ways manufactured by those at the top of the capitalist system, purposely to distract us from the consequences of the products we buy and to perpetuate the economic advantages that accrue to the owners of the means of production. Not that the biggest fear of capitalist barons is that the masses will rise up to protect nature, but the whole image of capitalism as being fun, profitable, and the source of satisfaction of every human desire needs to be propagated without distraction in order to keep folks from questioning whether another economic system might bring more happiness to a wider population of people around the world. This apparatus of successful capitalists is called "ideology," and it is perpetuated by advertising, through all of our primary institutions–including education and religion, and we even see it in the contemporary environmental movement. According to Foster:

> Mainstream environmentalists seek to solve ecological problems almost exclusively through three mechanical strategies: (1) technological bullets; (2) extending the market to all aspects of nature; and (3) creating what are intended as mere islands of preservation in a world of almost universal exploitation and destruction of natural habitats" (as quoted in Caniglia et al. 2015:196).

Given the central challenges that capitalism presents to sustainability, Foster advocates a transition of our global economic system away from capitalism toward socialism. While he stops short of providing a specific definition of socialism, he states the following:

> Socialism has always been understood as a society aimed at reversing the relations of exploitation of capitalism and removing the manifold social evils to which these relations have given rise.

> This requires the abolition of private property in the means of production, a high degree of equality in all things, replacement of the blind forces of the market by planning by the associated producers in accordance with the genuine social needs, and the elimination to whatever extent possible of invidious distinctions associated with the division of town and country, mental and manual labor, racial divisions, and gender divisions (as quoted in Caniglia et al. 2015:196).

There is a two-fold message in this argument for how socialism improves our relations with nature. First, "collective planning by the associated producers in accordance with the genuine social needs," according to Foster and other socialist-leaning environmentalists, will encourage the development of much more balanced trade associations that will consider the long-term ecological costs of their production processes in comparison to the public goods that result. Sustainable approaches require that human use of natural resources be harmonized with ecological and cultural benefits. But, in addition to this more measured approach to production processes, socialism–in Foster's examination–encourages a reconnection to nature that overcomes our alienation from nature to the extent that: "Nothing of this earth is alien to me." In other words, a true transformation to socialism requires a reincorporation of ecosystems and their non-human occupants into a holistic interpretation of society. The reorganization of our economic system is only a start; to complete the transformation to a sustainable society, we must also transform how we see, comprehend, value, and relate to our planetary home.

Indigenous Realism

Another insightful argument is that we need to incorporate indigenous knowledge into our approaches to the planet. Dr. Daniel Wildcat, in his book *Red Alert!*, lays out several ways that indigenous perspectives can help the world revise the disastrous path we are on. Specifically, he describes climate change as a wake-up call that highlights how out of balance our lifeways have become. The ways we live are out of touch with the natural world, he argues. We approach the world as dominators and climate changers, without acknowledgement of the landscapes, seascapes, and non-human relatives who surround us. Wildcat points out that the ways we engage with the world allow actions that are not grounded in knowledge. In other words, we consume excessively without knowledge of how our consumption impacts the world around us; we engage with technologies without knowing the consequences of how our energy is produced; we drink water and eat food without knowing how it was produced or where it comes from. This disconnect between human activities and human knowledge are central to the environmental crises we now face, according to Wildcat. Furthermore, we spend so much time inside of our human dwellings that we have lost touch with the places where we live–the places right outside of our doors.

Wildcat invites us to consider indigenous approaches to the world as antidotes to our contemporary, technology-laden lifestyles and lifeboats for creating lifeways that are sustainable. For example, Wildcat (2009: 74) argues that indigenous knowledges "are grounded in the human realization that the life that surrounds us can teach us valuable life lessons, if we pay attention to our relationships and interactions with the land, air, water, and other-than-human living beings." Indigenous peoples have never approached the world with the "delusion" that they should control the natural world; rather, their knowledges–or native science "is a metaphor for a wide range of tribal processes of perceiving, thinking, acting, and "coming to know" that have evolved through human experience of the natural world" (Cajete 2000:2). In fact, it has been described that indigenous knowledges are "ecological in character"–being formed from and dependent upon their landscapes and the living inhabitants (plants, animals, the skies, seas, and peoples) who interact interdependently within them. Wildcat argues that: "The incredibly high cost of this climate change to our Mother Earth must be understood as related to humankind's development of societies and cultures disconnected in fundamental ways from the landscapes and seascapes, the places where they are situated" (2009:61). Reconnecting to our immediate places, including and especially the wildlife and ecosystems, is an essential step to saving the planet. And the reconnection needs to be deeper than merely romantic symbolism. We need to observe with "respectful attentiveness" and accept that we are "one small but powerful part of nature," relatives to the trees, plants, and animals surrounding us. Our "ecological amnesia"–our loss of connection and understanding of and respect for the ecological contexts in which we live–is a primary cause of a range of contemporary environmental problems.

To address this disconnect, Wildcat proposes we attend carefully to the culture-nature nexus. This nexus is the place where ecosystems and cultures connect, the place where our behaviors are directly influenced by the natural world we live in every day. Most people in industrialized nations, like the United States, Canada, Australia, Europe, and Japan, have deep divides between their cultures and nature. Our cultures are generalized, while our spaces are specific. Wildcat points out that indigenous communities tend to have a very tightly coupled culture-nature nexus; their practices, technologies, beliefs, and foods, for example, are directly connected to their homelands. The world around them is integral to their identities–not because they lack technologies to alter their environment, but because their orientation to the world is one of relationship with their places and the animals and plants that share those places. Wildcat highlights that, in fact, we all live in specific places–contexts that are rich with non-human relatives, plants and animals, and we are all responsible for the collective health and prosperity of those places. Our ignorance about the plants and animals that live in our places is an example of our contemporary lifeways, which act without knowledge. We emphasize our right to exploit our environments, yet we ignore our inalienable responsibilities to nurture and protect those same places. Wildcat argues that we must reconnect our culture-nature nexus through respectful attentiveness, and we must accept our responsibilities to the ecosystems and animals that sustain us. Tirso Gonzales, a Peruvian scholar focused on indigenous development, has offered the concept of re-nativization as a framework for native and non-native peoples alike to reconnect to nature at the culture-nature nexus. He writes (2008: 302): "Re-nativization [for Indian people] means to regain the strength of who you are and how you want to be connected to this world and to your specific community. Re-nativization may mean for non-Indian people who I have met in the North, a beginning to reconnect themselves to Mother Earth and revisiting the past, their histories, their family stories, and they want to procure balance and harmony among all living beings in the world."

Another insight Wildcat conveys is the indigenous obligation that requires all people to foster "seven generations thinking." This insight has been integrated into sustainability thinking around the world, but putting this thought into action is required to save the planet. This is translated by Wildcat into two important teachings. First, seven generations thinking engenders a responsibility to protect and steward resources for seven generations in the future. This type of respectful attentiveness requires that we connect knowledge of ecosystems, plants, and wildlife–their life-cycles and the extent that they can be harvested sustainably–to our harvesting, production and consumption, and conservation practices. Secondly, Wildcat passes along the teaching of his colleague and mentor Vine Deloria Jr. (2009:91): "Each of us is the seventh generation–at the center of life, preceded by three generations and followed by three generations. Our decisions," Deloria related, "should take into account the knowledge of our ancestors–an intellectual and spiritual inheritance–and the responsibilities we have for our children and future generations–a sort of intellectual and spiritual trusteeship." This is a cosmological relationship–an orientation toward our place in the world that acknowledges the insights and practices that have formed the foundation of our contemporary society, yet also recognizes our current power and responsibility to create or destroy the foundation of future generations. Such an orientation is not limited to a seven generations orientation toward human beings. For example, Wildcat shares the forest stewardship approach of the Nuxalk Nation in British Columbia, Canada. In a court case defending their responsibility to the forest, Chief Edward Moody stated (Wildcat 2009: 91): "We must protect the forests for our children, grandchildren and children yet to be born. We must protect the forests for those who can't speak for themselves such as the birds, animals, fish, and trees."

Wildcat's book provides us with an indigenous framework for reorienting our current practices in ways that incorporate lessons from indigenous lifeways. At the core of his appeal, is that we model our future behavior in ways that mirror indigenous wisdom, which is a "cooperative construction built on generations of attentive interaction between humans and the diversity of life found in the unique ecosystems and environments that we call home" (2009:139). Fostering our responsibility to understand the environmental consequences of our everyday actions is also a central component. By reorienting our lifeways–our eating, our entertainment, our everyday decisions–around the culture-nature nexus, Wildcat argues that we can reconnect to the animals, plants, and ecosystems where we live in ways that reform our behavior in sustainable ways.

Reenchanting Nature

William James Gibson offers a very similar set of recommendations to those given by Wildcat. For decades, most sociologists avoided recognizing the ties between religion, modernity, and environmental behavior. However, Gibson addresses these connections directly in his book, *A Reenchanted World: The Quest for a New Kinship with Nature* (2010). Gibson focuses especially on the concept of enchantment–a concept he believes differentiates the way modern societies relate to nature from the ways people related to nature before advanced modernity. When Gibson describes what it means for nature to be *enchanted*, he refers to the feelings of wonder, mystery, magic, and reverence that have characterized human descriptions of nature at various times and places around the world. Similar to Wildcat, Gibson doesn't see nature's enchantment as an outdated form of mysticism or naiveté. Instead, Gibson documents a resurgence of actions in very modern places that indicate strong beliefs about nature's innate beauty and special powers.

Enchantment of nature can be seen, according to Gibson, in the many environmental groups that have fought to protect endangered species and the places they call home. At the base of their commitment to this cause is a deep compassion for animals, a desire to end their suffering, and a belief that their right to a full life is as important as our own. Extensive documentation is now available to prove that animals and plants, indeed, have a level of consciousness, intelligence, and that their emotional capacity is in some cases as complex as the emotions found in human beings (Masson and McCarthy 1995; Bekoff 2003; Turner and D'Silva 2006). Gibson points out that Christianity and modern science have both long denied the intelligence and emotional capacity of animals, because each was driven to prove that human beings should be valued above all other living creatures–one for religious reasons; one for rational pursuits. In spite of this, increasing numbers of groups and individuals have felt compelled by science and intuition to protect the rights of animals, plants, and trees.

The fundamental changes that Gibson highlights in his book pertain to both personal transformation of the way we perceive nature and infrastructural changes that provide more opportunities for humans to interact with nature in beneficial ways. These two changes are mutually reinforcing. For example, community gardens bring greenery back into urban communities; they provide fresh food at a much lower cost than high-end grocery stores; they lower crime rates by eliminating empty lots and by increasing community presence in previously abandoned places. But they also introduce people to the magic of the soil–the smell of the earth, the sticky feeling of tomato vines when you pinch off the suckers, the cycles of the opening and closing of squash blossoms; the tyranny of the squash beetle and the wonder of the praying mantis; the abundance when the tomatoes come in and the ability to share with others. Community forestry is a similar catalyst that brings personal growth and community benefits. The trees mitigate flooding; careful management provides income through strategic culling of trees; and time in nature, amidst the cover of the trees and the squirrels, birds, and deer provides respite in times of struggle and a feeling of deeper purpose because of the many connections we share with the forest. Bike paths, urban green spaces, outdoor classrooms, and local stargazing clubs both represent the reenchantment that Gibson refers to, as well as bring opportunities for reenchantment among those who have been out of touch with nature.

Structure vs. Agency or Infrastructure vs. Personal Change

The authors' perspectives reviewed in this chapter emphasize two forms of proenvironmental catalysts. On the one hand, Gore, Friedman, and Foster highlight the need for large-scale changes on a structural level. These types of changes include the creation of new policies and laws, new school curricula, renewable technologies, bike routes, and mandatory recycling programs. On the other hand, Gibson and Wildcat suggest we also need to change our values and the ways we see the world, because our assumptions about what our ideal world should look like, in terms of environmental prosperity and social justice, shapes our everyday decisions in ways that add up to make a significant difference in environmental outcomes. Unless we hand over all of our liberties to those in charge of the social structural elements, we have to cultivate awareness and a sense of personal responsibility to keep our personal actions in balance with the needs of the planet.

To understand the role each of these approaches plays to bring about social change, let's review what social scientists have to say. Those who study social change focus on the ways attitudes, social institutions, social structures, behaviors, and culture evolve over time. Structural functionalists, like Talcott Parsons, emphasize relatively slow changes, where existing social institutions

Individual attitudes about such things as the environment, consumption and behavior are examples of *agency*, while solar farms, wind farms and mandatory recycling programs are examples of *structure*. Changes in both areas are necessary to effect social change.

are relatively stable and only change in response to technological changes or the emergence of new knowledge. In this perspective, slower change is best, because societies tend to function best when they achieve relative equilibrium (1977). In this framework, too, there is an assumption that existing social institutions have evolved to meet the functional needs of society; therefore, any large-scale changes are discouraged for fear of upsetting the current system. In other words, structural-functionalists assume that the current system is the ideal system. In contrast, conflict theorists, such as Karl Marx, encourage a much faster rate of change. Their assumption is that current social institutions have evolved primarily to serve the elite, capitalist class (often at the expense of the poor, women, and people of color); therefore, the faster society can rectify their social institutions, people's knowledge, and behaviors, the better off everyone will be.

Social scientists tend to consider catalysts for change at three levels of analysis. At the micro-level, we are concerned with the impacts of personal attitudes, values, knowledge, and behaviors. The sociology and psychology studies of these factors show that those who claim to make personal decisions based on environmental concern tend to be more educated (Kollmuss and Agyeman 2002). Another recent study found that people's conceptions of biodiversity are directly correlated with their opinions of how to address environmental problems (Fischer and Young 2007). Studies also show that those who spend time in nature regularly tend to place a higher value on conservation, because they observe directly the impact of their behavior on their surrounding environment (Ehrlich 2002).

The meso- and macro-level approaches emphasize larger-scale changes, such as the creation of social movement organizations or changes in education or policy institutions. The literature suggests that the rise of environmental movements, for example, is associated with broader acceptance of environmental views. Environmental groups provide education for the public through television commercials, bulletin boards, and door-to-door campaigns that actually change the hearts and minds of the general population (Tarrow 1998). Changes that make industry more sustainable are also important examples of meso-level changes that make a big difference. Environmental management guidelines and certification systems, such as the ISO 14001 industry certification system, have transformed the ways that industry relates to the environment and the surrounding community, placing a high premium on valuing cultural and environmental diversity in addition to profits (Mol 2003; Ciccantell et al. 2005). Bike paths, local trains, and buses are infrastructural changes that bridge the meso- and macro-levels, while large-scale, macro-level changes refer to the types of changes that impact an entire region, industry, nation, or body of water, for example.

Findings regarding the effectiveness of these types of changes is mixed and suggest that an integrated approach that addresses all of these levels is the best way to go. While very clear and consistent relationships are found between increased education and proenvironmental behavior, a large portion of the variance in proenvironmental behavior comes from factors outside of education (Klineberg et al. 1998; Jones et al. 1992). Deeper forms of personal commitment and awareness make a difference (Kollmuss and Agyeman 2002; Schor and White 2010; Heberlein and Warriner 1983). Meso-level programs, such as mandatory curbside recycling, tend to increase participation in recycling programs much more effectively than education alone (Derksen and Gartrell 1993). And we know from extensive research that who we elect as president of the United States, for example, definitely has an impact (Dunlap 1995). Policy changes, across the board, appear to make a big difference in behavior–both by limiting bad behavior and encouraging choices that are good for the environment (Hironaka 2014).

Conclusions: Take-Away Lessons about Catalysts for Change and Growing Consciousness

So, what does our examination of change catalysts suggest as the best way forward? We certainly see that there are many intervention points where changes can be made. There is social science evidence in support of changes at multiple levels; and changes at one level are often mutually supported by changes at another level. When we build social movements or develop community gardens, we increase our knowledge of the environments where we live and develop deeper appreciation for the nutrition and health benefits that environment can provide. Spending time in nature, wakes us up to the complexity of the web of life and can open our hearts to the intelligence and emotional capacity of all living things. And when we develop reverence and compassion for animals, plants and trees, we often realize the importance of passing laws that will protect ecosystems and wildlife for now and future generations. Sometimes, it may seem overwhelming when we try to figure out how to save the environment, so to speak. We hope this chapter has shown you that a series of approaches, both big and small, can be undertaken to make a big difference. All we have to do is start somewhere!

Chapter 10 Summary

- Traditionally, there has been a strong divide between those who advocate for structural changes, such as legal changes, and those who emphasize the need to transform individual behaviors through education and lifestyle modifications. There is a need to work toward change on both of these levels in order to reach sustainability for the planet.

- Former Vice President Al Gore points out how contemporary calculations in the economy exclude natural resources and their depletions. Because of this lack of consideration of these resources, pollution and degradation of the environment has increased considerably. Accordingly, a complete reconsideration of current subsidy frameworks is in order, and changes must be made that provide more sustainable economic pathways that will replace current practices.

- The model for the Montreal Protocol was successful as an environmental treaty because it was a global perspective that used a unique assessment committee containing members of industry, scientists, economists, and governments working together to evaluate the steps required to eliminate ozone-depleting substances. This panel actively engaged those manufacturing the products, as well as those assessing their effects on the environment. In so doing, all sides could be seen and appropriate measures taken to create a more sustainable way of operating.

- Thomas Friedman believes his Green New Deal can combat environmental problems stemming from climate change. By raising education and standards of living around the world, his hope would be to reestablish our relationship with the planet. Conserving resources and energy, reworking how we produce things, and transforming our economic system to include environmental degradation costs, would go a long way in saving our planet and providing us a way to reconnect to it.

- John Bellamy Foster uses ecological rift analysis as a framework to conceptualize saving the planet. It highlights the expansion of capitalism as the primary driver of environmental degradation by forcing humanity into a relationship of alienation from nature. This alienation then causes us to be distracted from the consequences of the products we buy and perpetuates the economic advantages that accrue to the owners of the means of production. Only by unwinding these processes and reconnecting with nature, will these ecological rifts come to be healed.

- Climate change, according to Dr. Daniel Wildcat, is a wake-up call that highlights how out of balance our lifeways have become. He posits that the ways we engage with the world are not grounded in knowledge, and we consume excessively because of this lack of knowledge. This consumption impacts the world around us, but we are blinded from seeing it due to being disconnected to nature and the planet.

- Indigenous communities have a different way of looking at our relationship with the world. Instead of seeing it as an unlimited resource that is open to all to consume without limits, they model their practices, technologies, beliefs, and foods with the thought in mind that they are connected to their homelands. A number of native communities hold that what they do today will affect not only themselves, but seven generations into the future from themselves as well.

- When we reconnect to the planet by doing things like community gardens, volunteer cleanup of parks, or develop social movements, we develop a more meaningful relationship with nature and the planet. When we find meaning in it, then there is hope that we will work harder to preserve it not only for ourselves, but for those who will inherit it from us in the future.

Chapter Eleven - Bringing It Together and Moving Ahead

In this final chapter, we address big-picture issues and consider possibilities for deeper cultural transformations as we look ahead. We then conclude with a model that helps tie together some of the major themes in environmental sociology and human ecology.

The Transformations of Modernity

As we saw throughout the book, humankind has always relied on the natural environment to make its living—to provide it with sustenance and meaning. Its relationship to the natural environment has changed radically over time. The first dramatic sea change was in the move from hunting and gathering to farming that began about 12,000 years ago. A second radical shift came with industrialization. Commencing a mere two-and-a-half centuries ago, the Industrial Revolution and its aftermath profoundly changed the relationship of humankind with the natural environment—so much so that we now may refer to it as being the Anthropocene Age—in which humankind has not only been affected by, but has profoundly *transformed*, the planet on which we live.

With modernity came profoundly new ways of relating to the planet. On the eve of the Industrial Revolution, even in the most "advanced" societies such as England, over 95 percent of the people in the society, directly or indirectly, were involved with farming. Now, in late industrialism, in advanced industrial societies like the United States and England, well over 95 percent (actually it is over 97 percent to be more accurate) of people work outside of farming.

On the eve of the Industrial Revolution there were fewer than 1 billion people in the world. Now there are over 7 billion and counting. The first city with 1 million people was London, several decades into the Industrial Revolution. Now there are many cities with over 10 million, some closer to 20 million, all over the world. Almost all of the largest cities are now in developing societies. Also, for the first time in history, in the lifetimes of those of us who are now alive, the world passed the point of having more people living in cities than outside of them.

World Population Milestones in Billions (United States Census Bureau estimates)									
Population	1	2	3	4	5	6	7	8	9
Year	1804	1927	1959	1974	1987	1999	2012	2025	2042
Years Elapsed	–	123	32	15	13	12	13	14	16

All of these factors have environmental consequences. With concentrations of people, there come concentrations of wealth and poverty, concentrations of production and waste, which in turn overwhelm the earth's capacity to recycle them. As societies came into industrialization, they developed a new set of institutions including economics and sociology. Those disciplines, while perhaps adequate to the task of concerns encountered in the nineteenth century, have proven inadequate in many ways when trying to understand complications of the environment wrought by the late twentieth and early twenty-first centuries. As we saw in the very beginning of the book, sociology as a discipline came about largely in response to issues of modernity. It did quite well at understanding problems such as stratification or social equality, and problems of alienation, egoism, anomie, and rationality. However, it was less adequate to the task of understanding the human environmental interface. The disciplines of environmental sociology and human ecology came about largely as correctives. They continue to develop, as we struggle to catch up to understand and deal with some of the wicked problems society must contend with here in the twenty-first century relative to humankind's relationship to the natural environment.

Much of the task moving forward will be to unwind problems created over the centuries, particularly with industrial technology. Technology can create problems it cannot solve. It is important as we move into the third millennium, to be aware of the limitations of technology, to have a humility about it, and to develop technologies that dovetail with the natural environment rather than trying to control it.

As we saw, many of the problems associated with modernity can be attributed to institutions that were developed early in the modernity process that did not keep apace with ways in which humankind interfaces with the natural environment. We saw, for example, some of the problems caused by the overweening use of technology, and also by mismatches between ways in which ecological cycles operate in nature, and the human creation of the world economy. We will go through and summarize some of the major findings that were presented earlier in the book here momentarily. But before we do, it is important to note a couple of things. One is that virtually nothing works in a vacuum in real ecological systems. What we discuss here are principles, but in practice, it is important to weigh actual factors as they come, realizing that everything is embedded in complex social and ecological systems.

Things only work perfectly in textbooks. In real life, ecological systems are messy and complex. A second crucial point is that the ecological problems we face took a long time to develop and no doubt will take a long time to unwind—and unwinding is probably a good metaphor for how we might address them. We will have to deal with them incrementally over time. We will not dispatch them with a magic bullet. There is no going back to a prior state.

Many of the material conditions of the world have changed significantly as have people's expectations and consumption patterns. That said, it is vitally important now, as ever, to make the environment a central organizing principle of our thinking and our living. We continue to pretend the environment is something we can control only at our own peril.

Thinking about Institutions

The Italian philosopher Antonio Gramsci observed that for a revolution to be complete, it must first take a "long slow march through the institutions." Let us now take a somewhat cursory march through the institutions and note some of the mismatches between how those institutions tend to operate and how the natural ecology of the earth actually works. As society moves into the twenty-first century, among the most urgent matters at hand will be to address those mismatches. It is not as though the mismatches we point out throughout the book are so much matters of opinion as they are matters of how nature actually works. By way of analogy, we might like the law of gravity or we might hate the law of gravity. But in walking over a cliff, our personal opinion about the law of gravity really doesn't matter—we are subject to the law of gravity, and we will fall accordingly. We might approach with a parachute, or we might figure out a more gradual way down, or we might keep from going over the cliff by wise action, but we never really defeat the law of gravity. At the very best, we figure out ways to live with it.

And so it is with the institutions such as the economy and the political system. We may wax rhapsodic about the laws of economics or how well or poorly the political system works, but if those institutions do not conform on some level to how *nature* actually works, then the earth, including the society and the people in it, will suffer for it. Using some of the stratagems of technology and affluence, we may put off some of the consequences temporarily, but, in putting them off, the consequences do not go away and in some cases become more severe by our not dealing with them as they arise.

The Industrial Revolution, as we have noted, marked a major turning point in the history of humankind. More so than in any time in history, we have been able to extract resources and use them at astonishing rates. Societies have become bigger, more complex, and are abler to use resources in novel ways.

The downsides of this are experienced at home and abroad. Domestically, there have been costs that are borne by everyone, but particularly those who are most vulnerable, including those who are in poor communities, such as urban minorities, those living in rural farming, mining, and less developed areas.

Internationally, the picture is challenging as well. With globalization, a possibility of taking resources from other places and peoples in the world has gone up tremendously, as has the ability to offload the costs of production, and to dump the refuse of affluence in other places, not just locally, but around the globe, including in the oceans.

According to a recent study, air pollution is the fourth leading cause of death in the world, accounting for 5.5 to 7 million deaths internationally. Of those, just over half, or about 3 million, are attributable to two countries: China (with 1.6 million deaths), and India (with 1.4 million deaths). These rapidly developing societies have, in their race for economic growth, taken what they have foolishly thought to be an expedient by cutting a number of corners with lax air pollution standards. We see this pattern in other developing countries. Even as research has shown that the cost of cleaner air need not come at the expense of well-being, some countries still go headlong into this abyss.

There are some hopeful signs. In the very recent Paris climate accord, which was signed onto by a number of countries including India and China as well as the United States, goals for more reasonable standards (from the standpoint of health and well-being of the planet and of human beings) were brought to the table. While it remains to be seen whether or not the citizens of the world will pull together to live up to the promise of these accords, they do offer a glimmer of hope.

In order to meet these goals, it is important that they are able to be implemented at a number of levels, including globally, nationally, and locally. The institutions such as the economy and the political system operate at each of these levels. It will be important for them to work together in ways that will be beneficial to the environment and health and well-being. Holding ecological principles as central will be vital to help organize thinking and fruitful action.

In so doing, it will be important to face some of the problems that these institutions have gotten caught up with over the course of the last two-and-a-half centuries since the Industrial Revolution, and begin to unwind from the tangled web we have woven. As the chapter on economics noted, there are some fundamental mismatches between the way the economy works on a number of different levels, but globally in particular, and the natural ecology. We revisit some of those ideas here, not to wallow in the problems, but in the spirit of addressing them as society moves into the future.

We look back, that we might look forward. If there is one text that stands as the canon of global capitalism, it would no doubt be Adam Smith's, *The Wealth of Nations*. First appearing on the eve of the Industrial Revolution in 1776, Smith, who had actually written his earlier work about moral philosophy, ventured into what became, over time (as it was modified and refined by others from David Ricardo to Paul Samuelson), something amounting to a series of rarely questioned truths, learned in business schools, nearly by rote, and constituting the vision for what businesses should achieve, and an almost default for the ideal society. Even the august Nobel Prize committee became so taken with what economics had become by the late twentieth century that it began to give a prize in economics.

The legacy of Adam Smith, bolstered over the years by adherents and true believers, is an assumption that there can be unending economic growth. As we move into the future, it will be crucial to come to grips with the limits of growth. One of the tenets of economics going back to Adam Smith is the idea of economies of scale. However, in ecological systems, as we saw, smaller-scale systems usually work better.

In economic systems, it is typically the case that environmental costs are "externalized," or offlaid to the natural environment and/or to people living downstream of the economic enterprise such as the factory. Moving into the future, it will be important to simply be honest. What are the externalities of production? In fairness to people living downstream and in consideration of the natural environment, externalizing costs will and should, in the future, become increasingly problematic.

Societies, and people of goodwill within them, have the moral obligation to keep this free riding to a minimum. Just as in a prior age, as we recognized bank robbing as a moral and legal problem, and the bank robber as selfish and criminal, it will be important for society to develop norms, and laws stemming from those norms, that make it clear that polluting, or taking disproportionate amounts of resources, is no more moral, and probably less so, than is robbing a bank. It is worth considering that the fact that we do not have just such a system of norms in place already, is more a function of cultural lag and a holdover from a prior time when resources were more abundant, than it is a reflection of current conditions.

Thinking about Time

The question becomes: What is sustainable over time? Time becomes a *crucial* variable here. On one hand, the world is running short on time. The longer we wait, the more severe problems become. Had we acted, for example, to develop our solar technology in a major way in the 1970s and wind energy in the 1980s when the opportunities presented themselves, some of the choices that now seem so pressing might seem less so. And yet here we are.

It is at once tempting to look back in hindsight at mistakes and assign blame, but that is of no use. However, what is of tremendous use now, today, is to take a hard look at the past, including the recent past, and see what lessons mistakes of the past offer.

Even as we run short on time, there is a cautionary note. An important social variable is the trajectory of change itself. Put another way, when social change takes place, *the rate of change affects how that change unfolds*. Something happening rapidly typically has very different social and environmental effects than when it develops more gradually over time. As Joseph Stiglitz (2002) points out in his book *Globalization and its Discontents*, the shock treatment model of change in the former Soviet Union did not work well in bringing about smooth social transition. Rather, it caused many social problems including dramatic rises in crime, social dislocation, and environmental degradation. Stiglitz makes a

Time is not on our side. The longer we take to replace fossil fuels with clean energy solutions, like this wind farm in Kansas, the more likely it becomes that the eventual transition will be disruptive to society.

compelling case that had the former Soviet Union made the transition more gradually, it would have achieved its goals without many of the latent dysfunctions that did occur because of making such dramatic social changes virtually overnight.

There is a lesson here for changes—even positive changes—in environmental policy. It sometimes takes other parts of the system, such as the economy, the polity, the culture, and the educational system, to adapt. In the meantime, as we discussed in the chapter on culture, there are the significant forces of cultural lag and cultural inertia to take into account.

By way of analogy, consider that when you are going the wrong way in your car at 80 miles an hour, there are various ways to stop. You can gradually apply the brakes and turn around. Of course, the quickest way to stop is probably to just simply crash into a wall—but that has the other problems that crashing brings, such as serious injury and sometimes death, that we, as sane people, typically try to avoid. Likewise, in changing social policy, even when the policy being changed is clearly dysfunctional, it may still make some sense to transition out of it gradually.

We know, for example, that fossil fuels pollute the environment and over time accumulate in the atmosphere causing greenhouse gas effects in the environment. As fossil fuels are by definition the product of fossils such as dinosaurs, the world is not making any more fossil fuels, we are running short on oil and coal and natural gas. As we run short on these, we also encounter the "low hanging fruit phenomenon" in which the extraction in early years, is done more efficiently, and is less costly, than later extractions. At some point we begin the "burning the rocks phenomenon" in which the last few drops are gotten, but at a very high cost and with low efficiency. In the meantime, it behooves us to develop alternative fuel sources. The earlier we start, the longer the grace period. The converse is also true. The longer we wait, the less graceful the transition.

The problem is exacerbated by entrenched interests. In our society, there is an asymmetry between the money and power in the oil industry, which is older and has been accumulating wealth for over a century, and the relatively newer startups in solar and wind and other alternative energies. Those entrenched energy companies have powerful lobbying groups and can fund political action committees and "Super PACs" to support political candidates that keep the entrenched businesses going at the expense of the newer and more environmentally friendly businesses. This sort of entropy of political will can be overcome, but it takes a rising tide of environmental consciousness in the culture.

Transforming the Tragedy of the Commons into the Drama of the Commons

As we saw earlier, in a culture where selfishness is a major problem, so also is the tragedy of the commons. But this does not happen in a vacuum. Other demographic, social, structural, institutional, and, ultimately, cultural factors either enable the tragedy of the commons or make it less likely. In this section, we take a closer look at how societies might best transform themselves so that environmental awareness and stewardship become central organizing principles on which those societies can build sustainable futures for themselves, their progeny, and for the planet in the coming decades.

Building on what we have done throughout the book, let us now look more closely at the root causes of the tragedy of the commons, and then turn attention to what combination of things may be done on the individual and collective levels to keep that from happening. As society moves ahead, it will be increasingly important to embrace, rather, a "*drama of the commons.*"

Looking at the factors that drive the environmental change in the Anthropocene Age, we see the increase in demand for natural resources stemming from a culture of modernity, in which there is a rising tide of population and affluence, and a treadmill of production and consumption fueled by increasing technological sophistication.

This is facilitated by the rise of institutional arrangements that keep this apparatus going at a fever pitch. An economy based on many or most of the pernicious postulates that we examined earlier, in combination with a political system open to patronage and corruption, often enables the tragedy of the commons.

But the demographic and institutional arrangements are only parts (albeit important ones) of the overall picture. Each of these institutions is embedded within a larger culture, and individuals make choices that are constrained or facilitated, not only by the institutions, but by the norms, values, and beliefs held dearest by that culture. So, for a drama of the commons to emerge, it must do so in the context of individuals making choices, constrained by institutions that are embedded in a larger culture.

There is a growing body of research showing that the drama of the commons is most likely to emerge when all of these factors are in place, and are working well with each other. Dietz, Ostrom, and Stern (2003) review and synthesize a

Figure 11.1 The United Nations Climate Change Conference in Paris: COP 21

The Hall of Negotiations–COP21, Paris, France.

Over the course of the late twentieth and early twenty-first centuries, political leaders from around the world have been coming together somewhat regularly to discuss problems around global climate change, and sometimes to sign treaties to help ameliorate problems. Earlier treaties fell short for a number of reasons. The Kyoto Protocol (1992), for example, failed to be ratified by the two heaviest emitters of greenhouse gases—the United States and China.

Although it was eventually ratified by the requisite 55 countries (including some key players at the time, such as the Soviet Union), this crippling blow dealt by the largest emitters of greenhouse gas emissions caused some real damage at the time. It set the stage for a tragedy of the commons scenario, giving two of the major players a warrant to freeride the system, even as they were able to point at the "other" (with the United States pointing at China as a major offender, and China pointing at the United States). This had a cascading effect, with virtually all of the other countries in the world then able to point at both the United States and China as being worse offenders than themselves. Countries such as India, during the time between the Kyoto Protocol and now, have seen something akin to exponential growth in air pollution and, as a result, problems in morbidity and mortality.

This set up a classic lose-lose tragedy of the commons scenario. As we saw in the chapter on health and illness, one of the tragic legacies is that now air pollution is the fourth leading cause of death in the world (World Health Organization 2016). With China leading the way and India trailing closely behind, these two countries account for slightly over half of the total deaths worldwide.

Coming together in Paris in December 2015, parties to the UN framework convention on climate change (UN FCCC) were seeing some of these problems coming to roost, particularly in developing countries, and began to approach a consensus that earlier agreements had not gone far enough to deal with climate change. In that meeting (which was the 21st meeting of what has come to be known as the "conference of parties"—dubbed COP 21 for short), participants were determined to reach an accord that would go farther than any of the previous 20 meetings had toward establishing an international cooperative effort for environmental stewardship.

Acknowledging the seriousness of the problem, leaders from around the world were listening to people in their countries and abroad, and beginning to tune in to some of the real suffering environmental degradation was causing. Particularly in developing countries, acknowledging the enormity of the crisis, they were able to focus people's attention and will sufficiently to optimize the chances of their coming together to solve a common problem so large, they could not solve it by themselves. This set the stage for the emergence of the drama of the commons, in which people were willing to set aside their selfish short-term interests for the longer-term collective interests of humankind and for the planet more generally.

This, then, was the backdrop against which COP 21 took place. Unlike earlier conferences, where free riding was rampant, COP 21 appeared to make some major inroads into addressing the wicked environmental problems we all face. The denial that had been a long-term stratagem of the selfish and free riders, was remarkably and refreshingly in short supply at COP 21.

Some of the major outcomes of the UN climate change conference in Paris, known as COP 21, were to:

- Reaffirm the goal of limiting global temperature increases to 1.5-2 degrees Celsius;
- Establish binding commitments for nations to make "nationally determined contributions" (NDCs), and to coordinate with countries to ensure they would pursue domestic measures aimed at meeting those commitments;
- Commit all countries to report regularly on their greenhouse gas and other toxic emissions, and to undergo international review;
- Commit all countries to submit new NDCs every five years, with the expectation that there will be a progression toward lower emissions over time;
- Reaffirm the binding obligations of developed countries under the UNFCCC to support the efforts of developing countries while for the first time encouraging voluntary contributions by developing countries as well;
- Extend the current goal of mobilizing $100 billion per year in support of pollution abatement by 2020 through 2025, with even higher goals in the future;
- Call for a new mechanism, similar to the Clean Development Mechanism under the Kyoto Protocol, enabling emission reductions in one country to be counted toward another country's NDC.

While it remains to be seen how this will all come out, the preliminary indications are positive. Leaders from developed nations such as the United States and thos of Europe, developing nations such as China and India, and less-developed nations, such as those from sub-Saharan Africa and the poorest parts of Asia and Latin America were all involved.

There is real hope for a drama of the commons scenario, in which people from around the world realize it is in all of our interests to pull together to combat serious climate degradation and to steward the planet wisely toward a reconnection between humankind and the natural environment. It will not take place on its own. Regardless of the system, or the wording of the treaties that may be signed, they still require people of good will working with the health of the planet and its inhabitants at heart. COP21 is a hopeful step in that direction.

Sources: Center for Climate and Energy Solutions (2016); United Nations Framework Convention on Climate Change (2016).

The heads of national delegations–COP21, Paris, France.

large body of work, and then they distill some of the key factors. For a Drama of the Commons to emerge, it is crucial that institutions have rules to reflect actual ecological conditions, to devise clear boundaries for who may use resources, to provide graduated sanctions for those who go over the boundaries, and to establish low-cost ways of resolving conflict when it does occur. This is predicated on there being a relatively free-flow of information about resources, as well as about how to comply with rules and deal with conflict.

This works best when the people involved draw from a common normative system. In fact, the above model works best when there is a feeling of ownership, not necessarily in the private property sense, but rather in the sense of feeling a part of the larger collective holding the common and its good as something sacred and dear among stakeholders in the system. When that is the case, they internalize a common system of norms and values that help keep them connected to the larger collective, and they are able to envision a future involving themselves and those coming after them in connection with the common ecological resource.

The converse is also true, and several things can cause this. There can simply be a breakdown in norms in the society in general—giving rise to what Émile Durkheim characterized over a century ago as *anomie*. When there is such a general breakdown, Durkheim pointed out, there is a host of other serious social problems, such as rises in crime, suicide, and delinquency. This is the stuff of post-modern apocalyptic fiction and drama, such as *The Hunger Games*. In fact, the recent popularity of this genre, is perhaps indicative of how close society has come to a general state of anomie.

Short of anomie, however, several scenarios still bear considering. Most notably, when there are competing normative systems that are fundamentally different, it is difficult, if not close to impossible, to keep a commons from being degraded. Put another way, when more than one social group is drawing on a resource, it is not uncommon for them to construct their norms in such a way that gives the benefit of the doubt to themselves at the expense of their neighbors. The Buddha famously noted this propensity over two millennia ago. More recently, this has come to be known by social psychologists as the *fundamental attribution bias*. When it comes to the degradation of a common area or resource, the juxtaposition of different normative systems, almost invariably backed up by different legal and political systems, can lead to serious problems.

We saw, for example, the celebrated case pointed out by Al Gore in his book *Earth in the Balance*, of the Aral Sea being desertified, largely as a result of different normative expectations of peoples in different nations—in this case, in Azerbaijan and Kazakhstan. Each saw the other drawing down on the water resources in such a way that they felt their own normative systems were being disregarded (And as Durkheim pointed out, normative battles often harden into legal or physical ones.). This gave each additional incentive to draw down even more in what became a race to take what was left of a diminishing pool of resources. The tragic result was that it was now no longer able to sustain even a small fraction of what it had been able to do just a few decades earlier. With the hydrological cycle now permanently altered by this unfortunate situation, what was once the fourth largest landlocked body of water in the world is now a mere vestige of what it once was.

What would have been an alternative? If, before this lose-lose situation of resource drawdown became the socio-cultural reality, it would have been good for people of good faith on all sides to have negotiated a more universal normative system that was able to sustain the livelihoods of those dependent upon it. If they were able to do that in such a way that a critical mass of people felt a sense of belonging and ownership in the ecosystem, and had a vision for how they could play a part in sustaining ecosystems into the future, even as they were able to make a living, there may have been a good chance of a different result. Moving into the future, it will be crucial to learn from these mistakes, not wallowing in them, but building on them to make a good-faith effort to find ways to move toward sustainability.

A number of theorists (e.g., Coleman 1986) have pointed out, there is an asymmetry between the tragedy of the commons and the drama of the commons. It takes more people following a system of generally accepted social norms to keep the system going, than it does to break the system down. Consider the example of a group house near your local college campus. Suppose everyone is doing his or her chores and the house is running smoothly. Along come the first set of exams, and people start to put off chores. The dishes don't get done, and perhaps as a result, others who see the dishes not getting done stop doing their chores. In very little time, the otherwise smoothly running group house has degenerated into a crash pad.

To give another brief example from criminology, there is the celebrated "broken windows hypothesis." It could be that there is little crime in a neighborhood. However, a random act of vandalism, in which a house has its windows broken, has the unfortunate effect of attracting more crime in the neighborhood. There is a lesson for the environment here. Environmental degradation, even if it is inadvertent at first, has a way of attracting more degradation to it. This is perhaps because there is an unintended message that the norms keeping a place free from harm and clean are not as stringent there as in other places.

Once a place begins to develop a reputation as a dumping site, it is as if the social norms are now working against it instead of for it. This can, of course, be overcome when there is a strong normative system of environmental stewardship that pervades the society in general, and informs the activity of the individuals in it.

Members of a given community can be seen as a group of people *networked* together, or connected by normative, social, political, and cultural bonds. These bonds are what help make people accountable to one another, and keep people from free riding on the system (Coleman 1986). It is important to note how open or closed the feedback loop is in these networks. If someone who does free ride feels they can "get away" with it (which in network terms, means not being held accountable by someone in their own network), then there is the danger of a system breakdown, and the danger of the tragedy of the commons.

Again, the solution here is to work to achieve a social and cultural situation in which people feel like they belong to a larger collective, where using a common resource, whether it be the ocean, underground oil or coal, or the air we breathe, is something that we all have a right to and we all have a responsibility to steward. This is facilitated by well-done research that is clearly communicated, well structured dialogue (Rosa et al. 2003), in institutional arrangements that are complex and crosscutting (Burns and Clark 2009), and nested within a system of ecologically connected values (Dietz et al. 2003; Burns 2013, 2014). The net effect is that people feel involved, rather than excluded and managed. This then facilitates a culture in which the drama of the commons can most likely flourish.

No amount of economic or political sanctions or infrastructure in itself will solve the problem, however. Yet, with an emergent value system in which the environment is a central organizing principle and stewardship is a value held dear to all, the governance mechanisms we have been discussing will help to facilitate it, at least *optimizing the chances* of its running smoothly on the human institutional level.

A recent example of a drama of the commons can be witnessed in the recent United Nations climate change conference in Paris, known in short as COP 21. It was a conference in which political leaders from nearly every country in the world came together to confront the serious problems of climate change. Like any conference, it had pluses and minuses, yet it did have many of the characteristics we would hope to see looking ahead. Leaders, many of whom had theretofore been in denial, came together. We examine this more closely in the accompanying box.

Rebuilding Connection With the Natural Environment

We began the book with the observation that, over time, humankind's relationship with the natural environment has changed dramatically. The two most significant changes in human history in this regard, were the Neolithic Revolution beginning about 12,000 years ago, and the Industrial Revolution, beginning about 250 years ago. In the first, humankind gradually went from being hunters and gatherers to farmers, and in so doing, became sedentary town dwellers, invented writing, developed stratification systems, and many other social institutions that have been with us through the millennia.

Even more significant, in terms of humankind's relationship with the natural environment, was the Industrial Revolution. It was during this time, that we first developed the technology to use inanimate energy for things such as automobiles and electricity, and then progressively made deeper incursions into the natural environment. It was during and subsequent to this time, that humankind so profoundly changed its relationship with the natural environment, that it came to be known as the Anthropocene Age.

While there were some wonderful things that came about as a result of industrialization, it is our contention, that humankind gradually lost much of its connectedness with the natural environment during this time. The institutions it developed, including economics and sociology, largely wrote the environment out their equations, taking its abundance for granted, but never fully appreciating the complexities of the human-environmental interface.

Ultimately, people need to feel connected to the natural environment. In a culture characterized by "nature deficit disorder" (Louv 2008, 2012) in which people are alienated from nature, and more likely to reach for a noisy video game than go for a walk in the woods, more likely to take the car to the mall to buy something, the demand for which has been artificially created through the hype of advertising than to create something themselves, more likely to drive through a fast food joint than to raise their own backyard garden, we recognize the need for reconnection.

As we saw in the last chapter, a number of things, singly or in combination, can help to catalyze this reconnection. There are several common themes. By definition, when we do reconnect with nature, it is local. When we walk in the woods, it is immediate. As wonderful as the national parks are—and they are—there is a desperate need for places where people can reconnect with nature, close to where they live and work.

Within the lifetimes of most people reading this book, the majority of the people worldwide became urban dwellers. The trend that started with the Industrial Revolution eventually led to more people now living in cities than outside of them (with 2008 being the approximate tipping point). What are we to make of this? Even as fewer than 5 percent of the people in industrial societies are directly involved in farming, and agribusiness claims ever wider swathes of land in rural areas, there is room for growth in things like urban gardening and other local ways of reconnecting with the environment.

There is no substitute for green space. Communities can and should respect that, and keep that sacrosanct. If people have a way to walk or bicycle to work and to the market rather than relying on cars and freeways, it could transform the society. Examples of this sort of forward looking vision can be seen in the design of New York City's Central Park, the Back Bay Fens and Arnold Arboretum in Boston, or Golden Gate Park in San Francisco, where people have a chance to reconnect in the midst of a vast metropolis. The designers of these, Frederick Law Olmsted (1822-1903) and William Hammond Hall (1846-1934), respectively, had a forward looking vision about how green space could be conserved and incorporated into growing and thriving cities. Far from detract-

Landscape architect, Frederick Law Olmsted, designed many famous urban parks, such as Central Park in New York City.

ing from those cities, the green spaces became a central part of their identity, where residents could go to reconnect with the natural world and revitalize themselves. Nature needs to be treasured and stewarded on all levels--including the local communities where people live and actually spend most of their time--as well as nationally and worldwide. As our culture of late modernity moves into the next millennium, it will be vital for a new generation of forward looking people to build on the ecological genius of visionaries like Olmsted and Hall, to help society find its best uses of green spaces (Rybczynski 1999).

It is vital that environmental sociology and human ecology recover the lost connection for the social sciences. More broadly, it is the task of humankind, in the third millennium, to recover this lost connection. Even as we live within the institutional culture of late modernity, we seek to recover the humanity that has been gradually degraded.

Ultimately, we need to connect with the natural environment, even now in the age of late modernity. The institutions and culture with which we are most familiar give us mixed signals, and yet there is hope and longing for rebirth. This is what is at stake for us now (Borden 2014).

Toward a Comprehensive Model of Humankind's Interaction with the Natural Environment

One of the defining characteristics of the culture of late modernity is humanity's insatiable propensity to exploit the environment. The POET and IPAT ecological models have proven useful in explaining and understanding humankind's relationship with the natural world. However, these models are not entirely adequate, nor are they the best tools available, for the exploration of humankind's relationship with the earth—and the formulation of much needed solutions to the existential environmental dilemma that we find ourselves in today (Borden 2014).

Sociologists are no less adept than other academics at finding and pointing out problems. At this point in time, the problems are well known—even if some choose to ignore or deny them. What is most desperately needed now, are workable alternatives to business as usual. Ideally, these alternatives will guide nations and individuals toward long-term and sustainable balance and harmony between people and the earth (Mumford 1981).

To realize this goal, we believe that the previous models developed by early human ecologists need to be updated in order to better understand and solve human-environmental problems (Burns 2012; Canan 2004).

To this end, we present the POETICAA model:

- **(P)opulation**

  Total population is a vital factor, yet it is not the only important variable when it comes to predicting types of environmental degradation. Other elements of population include urban/rural, age, and gender distributions.

- **(O)rganization**

  The societal institutions that humans use to act have a profound effect on how we impact the environment. Such institutions include, for example, the economy, the political and education systems, and religion.

- **(E)nvironment**

  This refers to all components of the environment—plants and forests, soil, water sources, and air. It also refers to the degradation of those systems. Different factors, impact the environment in different ways. For instance, rural population growth is associated with deforestation, while urban population growth is a strong predictor of greenhouse gas emissions.

  While the preponderance of research in environmental sociology does model the impact of social variables (such as population, affluence, and technology, in the case of the I=PAT model), on some aspect of the natural environment (e.g., deforestation, air pollution), there is a small but growing body of work that looks at social outcomes such as violence, illness, and economic decline that *result from* environmental deterioration. It is vital, as we study the connectedness between humans and the environment, also to consider models that move beyond isolating the environment in one part of the equation (viz., as the left side of the I=PAT equation, and consider more broadly how it interacts with humankind).

- **(T)echnology**

  Technology's relationship with the natural world has proven to be a two-edged sword. On one hand, the scale and scope of environmental damage and exploitation would not be possible without modern technology. Yet, on the other hand, clean technology has the potential to help the environment. Comprehending the complexities of the interplay of technology and other variables, particularly population, affluence, and culture, are keys to gaining insight into the interface between humankind and the natural environment.

- **(I)llness and Health**

  Today, there is a growing acceptance of the interconnectedness of human health (both individually and communally) and the health of the natural environment. Beginning with the pioneering work of Rachel Carson, much study has been devoted to examining the relationship between ecological imbalances and serious health issues such as the rise in cancers, birth defects, breathing diseases like asthma and emphysema, allergies, and decreased fertility. Darwinian medicine explores the mismatches between evolution—both human and other species—and the shock and challenges to our immune and adaptive systems caused by environmental pollution and a world out of balance.

- **(C)ulture**

  In many ways the culture of modernity is the story of humanity's alienation and detachment from the natural world. Late modernity, hyper-industrialization, and the increasing power of technology have increasingly exacerbated this process to the point where separateness from nature is a basic component of culture itself. Moving into the future, it will be important to consider aspects of culture that are sustainable into the current and future millennia.

- **(A)ffluence**

  The rich are able to consume more of everything (especially energy), and thus, have a disproportionate impact on the natural environment. Affluent societies, like the United States and Europe, have taken for granted things like automobiles, air conditioning, computers and televisions, a growing consumption of meat, and diverse and varied foods transported from distant sources. Unequal distribution of natural resources, both at the micro and macro levels, have detrimental effects on the environment. Furthermore, affluent capitalistic economies are based on the dilemma presented by "the treadmill of production." Economies grow by manufacturing more and encouraging greater consumption. As populous societies, like China and India, become more affluent, their consumption patterns will inevitably increase, and, will in turn, make matters more critical.

- **(A)ddressing Problems**

  No longer is it enough for sociology to simply find problems. In many cases, we know only too well the problems we face. And while it is still a primary duty to educate and publicize those very real dangers, environmental sociology must research and put forward practical solutions to the problem at hand. The sociological imagination can be harnessed to bring forth creative and workable solutions to the immense environmental troubles that we all face.

Classical sociologists shed a great deal of light on many of the problems of modernity (such as alienation, anomie and egoism, and the iron cage of rationality). However, until recent times, the human social causes of environmental degradation were not fully appreciated. This was, in part, due to the fact that the full extent of the ill effects of industrialization had not fully manifested themselves until more recently. At this stage of Late Modernity, we no longer have that excuse.

As society moves into the third millennium, it is crucial to address this lack of connectedness with nature. It is the task of environmental sociologists and human ecologists to engage these crucial questions head on, and to lead the way with engaged teaching and research. For humankind to survive and thrive from this point forward, it is incumbent upon all of us to address this crucial set of social problems that ultimately lead back to humankind's relationship with the natural environment.

Chapter 11 Summary

- Our relationship with the planet and nature has radically changed, especially over the last two-and-a-half centuries since the Industrial Revolution. This evolving relationship, sometimes referred to as modernity or the Anthropocene Age, has impacted the earth and transformed it greatly.

- Environmental sociology and human ecology were formed, at least partially, in response to a combination of increasing problems with pollution and overuse of resources, and the failure of sociology, up until that time, to address those problems. A profound need was created by the degradation of our planet, for disciplines examining how we live and coexist, and perhaps even thrive, within nature.

- There has been a great cost borne from how we consume and exist since the Industrial Revolution. This has primarily been felt by those most vulnerable including the poor, minorities, rural farming communities, and other less developed areas. The benefits often are consumed by the affluent without conscious thought of this cost and strain on those more vulnerable parties, or on the fact that the earth is not a limitless supplier of resources.

- There is a real need for people of good faith to work together to find a common solution to the issues. Governments, including local, national, and global bodies as well as everyday citizens cannot work in a vacuum. The culture itself must nurture a more universal normative system that will sustain the environment. It will be crucial to learn from our mistakes and build from them in coming to a more sustainable way of living.

- No amount of economic or political sanctions or infrastructure in themselves will solve the daunting environmental problems faced by humankind. Only when a critical mass of people of goodwill come to see the natural environment as a central part of how we live and exist by being better stewards of the planet, can we see a change for the good really impact the imbalances that have been created in the past.

- As society moves into the third millennium, it is crucial to address the lack of connectedness with nature. It is the task of environmental sociologists and human ecologists to engage these crucial questions head on, and to lead the way with engaged teaching and research.

- For humankind to survive and thrive from this point forward, it is incumbent upon all of us to address this crucial set of social problems that ultimately lead back to humankind's relationship with the natural environment.

References and Suggested Readings

Adams, William M., Dan Brockington, Jane Dyson, and Bhaskar Vira. 2003. "Managing Tragedies: Understanding Conflict over Common Pool Resources." *Science* 302(5652):1915.

Agyeman, Julian. 2005. *Sustainable Communities and the Challenge of Environmental Justice.* New York City: NYU Press.

Alcott, Blake. 2005. " Jevons' Paradox. " *Ecological Economics* 54(1):9–21.

Alexander, Jeffrey C. 2003. *The Meaning of Social Life: A Cultural Sociology*. New York: Oxford University Press.

Antonio, Robert J. 2009. "Climate Change, the Resource Crunch, and the Global Growth Imperative." Pp. 3-73 in *Current Perspectives in Social Theory*, edited by Harry F. Dahms. Bingley, UK: Emerald.

Antonio, Robert J., and Robert J. Brulle. 2011. "The Unbearable Lightness of Politics: Climate Change Denial and Political Polarization." *Sociological Inquiry* 52:195-202.

Archer, Margaret S. 1988. *Culture and Agency: The Place of Culture in Social Theory.* New York: Cambridge University Press.

Austin, Kelly. 2012. "Coffee Exports as Ecological, Social and Physical Unequal Exchange: A Cross-National Investigation of the Java Trade." *International Journal of Comparative Sociology* 53(3):155-180.

Austin, Kelly F., and Laura A. McKinney. 2012. "Disease, War, Hunger, and Deprivation: A Cross-National Investigation of the Determinants of Life Expectancy in Less-Developed and Sub-Saharan African Nations." *Sociological Perspectives* 55(3):421-47.

Austin, Kelly F., Laura A. McKinney, and Gretchen Thompson. 2012. "Agricultural Trade Dependency and the Threat of Starvation: A Cross-National Analysis of Hunger as Unequal Exchange." *International Journal of Sociology* 42(2):68-69.

Baker, Carolyn, and John Michael Greer. 2013. *Collapsing Consciously: Transformative Truths for Turbulent Times.* Berkeley, CA: North Atlantic Books.

Bakker, Karen, and Christina Cook. 2011. "Water Governance in Canada:

Innovation and Fragmentation." *Water Resources Development* 27(2):275-289.

Barrett, Deirdre. 2010. *Supernormal Stimuli: How Primal Urges Overran Their Evolutionary Purpose.* New York: W.W. Norton.

Bartlett, Frederick C. 1932. *Remembering.* Cambridge, UK: Cambridge University Press.

Beck, Tony, and Cathy Nesmith. 2001. "Building on Poor People's Capacities: The Case of Common Property Resources in India and West Africa." *World Development* 29(1):119-133.

Beck, Ulrich. 1992. *Risk Society: Towards a New Modernity.* London: Sage.

Beck, Ulrich. 1995. *Ecological Politics in an Age of Risk.* New York: Polity.

Becker, Gary, Michael Grossman, and Kevin Murphy. 1984. "An Empirical Analysis of Cigarette Addiction." *American Economic Review* 84:396-418.

Bekoff, Marc. 2003. *Minding Animals: Awareness, Emotions, and Heart.* New York: Oxford University Press.

Bell, Daniel. 1973. *The Coming of Post-Industrial Society.* New York: Basic Books.

Bell, Daniel. 1976. *The Cultural Contradictions of Capitalism.* New York: Basic Books.

Bell, Michael. 2004. *Farming for Us All: Practical Agriculture and the Cultivation of Sustainability (Rural Studies).* University Park: Penn State University Press.

Bell, Shannon Elizabeth, and Richard York. 2010. "Community Economic Identity: The Coal Industry and Ideology Construction in West Virginia." *Rural Sociology* 75(1):111-143.

Benford, Robert D., and David A. Snow. 2000. "Framing Processes and Social Movements: An Overview and Assessment." *Annual Review of Sociology* 26(1):611-639.

Berger, Peter, and Thomas Luckmann. 1967. *The Social Construction of Reality: A Treatise in the Sociology of Knowledge.* New York: Anchor.

Berman, Marshall. 1982. *All That Is Solid Melts into Air: The Experience of Modernity*. New York: Simon and Schuster.

Berry, Wendell. 2015. *The Unsettling of America: Culture & Agriculture.* Berkeley, CA: Counterpoint Press.

Bewes, Timothy. 2002. *Reification: Or the Anxiety of Late Capitalism.* London: Verso.

Bonanno, Alessandro, and Douglas Constance. 1996. *Caught in the Net: The Global Tuna Industry, Environmentalism, and the State.* Lawrence: The University Press of Kansas.

Borden, Richard. 2014. *Ecology and Experience: Reflections from a Human Ecological Perspective.* Berkeley, CA: North Atlantic Books.

Boudet, Hilary Schaffer, and Leonard Ortolano. 2010. "A Tale of Two Sitings: Contentious Politics in liquefied Natural Gas Facility Siting in California." *Journal of Planning Education and Research* 30(1):5-21.

Boudon, Raymond. 1982. *The Unintended Consequences of Social Action.* London: Macmillan.

Bourdieu, Pierre. 1977. *Outline of a Theory of Practice.* London: Cambridge University Press.

Bourdieu, Pierre. 1984. *Distinction: A Social Critique of the Judgement of Taste.* Translated by R. Nice. Cambridge, MA: Harvard University Press.

Bowler, Kate. 2013. *Blessed: A History of the American Prosperity Gospel.* New York: Oxford University Press.

Bowring, Finn. 2003. "Manufacturing Scarcity: Food Biotechnology and the Life Sciences Industry." *Capital & Class* 27(79):107–44.

Boyce, James K. 2013. *Economics, the Environment and Our Common Wealth.* Northampton, MA: Edward Elgar.

Braverman, Harry. [1974] 1998. *Labor and Monopoly Capital: The Degradation of Work in the Twentieth Century*, anv. ed. New York: Monthly Review Press.

Brechin, Steven R., Peter R. Wilshusen, Crystal L. Fortwangler, and Patrick C. West, eds. 2003. *Contested Nature: Promoting International Biodiversity with Social Justice in the Twenty-First Century.* Albany, NY: SUNY Press.

Broadbent, Jeffrey. 1989. "Strategies and Structural Contradictions: Growth Coalition Politics in Japan." *American Sociological Review* 54(5):707-743.

Brooks, Harvey. 1973. "Technology Assessment as a Process." *International Social Science Journal* 25(3):247.

Brown, Phil. 1997. *No Safe Place: Toxic Waste, Leukemia, and Community Action.* Berkeley, CA: University of California Press.

Brown, Phil. 2007. *Toxic Exposures: Contested Illnesses and the Environmental Health Movement*. New York: Columbia Univ. Press.

Brown, Richard Harvey. 1987. *Society as Text.* Chicago: University of Chicago Press.

Brulle, Robert. 2000. *Agency, Democracy and Nature: The U.S. Environmental Movement from a Critical Theory Perspective.* Cambridge, MA: MIT Press.

Brulle, Robert. Forthcoming. "Environmentalism in the United States." In *Global Perspectives on Environmentalism,* edited by Timothy Doyle and Sherilyn MacGregor. New York, NY: Praeger.

Buchanan, James, Gordon Tullock, and Robert Tollison. 1980. *Toward a Theory of Rent-Seeking Society.* College Station, TX: Texas A&M University Press.

Bullard, Robert D. 1994. *Dumping in Dixie: Race, Class and Environmental Quality*. Boulder, CO: Westview Press.

Bunker, Stephen G., and Paul S. Ciccantell. 2005. *Globalization and the Race for Resources.* Baltimore: Johns Hopkins University Press.

Burke, Kenneth. 1966. *Language as Symbolic Action: Essays of Life, Literature, and Method.* Berkeley: University of California Press.

Burke, Kenneth. 1969a. *A Grammar of Motives.* Berkeley: University of California Press.

Burke, Kenneth. 1969b. *A Rhetoric of Motives.* Berkeley: University of California Press.

Burns, Thomas J. 1992. "Class Dimensions, Individualism and Political Orientation." *Sociological Spectrum* 12(4):349-362.

Burns, Thomas J. 1993. "Crunch Times and Orphan Issues: The Quid Pro Quo of Collective Decisions." Paper presented at annual meeting of the American Sociological Association, Miami, Florida.

Burns, Thomas J. 1999. "Rhetoric as a Framework for Analyzing Cultural Constraint and Change." *Current Perspectives in Social Theory* 19:165-185.

Burns, Thomas J. 2009. "Culture and the Natural Environment." Pp. 56-72 in *Current Trends in Human Ecology*, edited by Priscila Lopes and Alpina Begossi. Newcastle upon Tyne, UK: Cambridge Scholars Press.

Burns, Thomas J. 2012. "Toward an Overarching Theory of Environmental Sociology." Paper presented at the annual conference of the American Sociological Association, Denver, Colorado.

Burns, Thomas J. 2013. "A Theory of Ecological Mismatch in a World-Systems Perspective." Paper presented at the joint conference of the Political Economy of the World-System Section of the American Sociological Association and the World Society Foundation, Riverside, California.

Burns, Thomas J. 2014. "Issues in Environmental Governance in the Context of Global Risk." Invited Lecture to the Global University Summit, Moscow, Russian Federation.

Burns, Thomas J. 2016. "Reconsidering Scripture in Late Industrial Society: Religious Traditions and the Natural Environment." Pp. 43-60 in *Rise of Environmental Consciousness: Voices in Pursuit of a Sustainable Planet,* edited by Beth Schaefer Caniglia, Thomas J. Burns, Rachel M. Gurney, and Erik L. Bond. San Diego: Cognella.

Burns, Thomas J., Tom W. Boyd, and Colleen M. Burns. 2014. "Engaging Complexity in Business and Technology: Rethinking Old Ideas Humanistically and Ecologically." *International Journal of Business, Humanities and Technology* 4(1):1-9.

Burns, Thomas J., and Robert V. Clark. 2009. "Global Integration and Environmental Treaty Ratifications." Paper presented at the annual conference of the American Sociological Association, San Francisco, California.

Burns, Thomas J., Byron L. Davis, and Edward L. Kick. 1997. "Position in the World-System and National Emissions of Greenhouse Gases." *Journal of World-Systems Research* 3(3):432-466.

Burns, Thomas J., and Andrew K. Jorgenson. 2007. "Technology and the Environment." Pp. 306-312 in *21st Century Sociology: A Reference Handbook*, edited by Clifton D. Bryant and Dennis L. Peck. Thousand Oaks, CA: Sage.

Burns, Thomas J., Jeffrey D. Kentor, and Andrew K. Jorgenson. 2003. "Trade Dependence, Pollution and Infant Mortality in Less Developed Countries." Pp. 14-28 in *Emerging Issues in the 21st Century World-System.* Vol. 3. Edited by Wilma A. Dunaway. Westport, CT and London: Praeger.

Burns, Thomas J., Edward L. Kick, David A. Murray, and Dixie A. Murray. 1994. "Demography, Development, and Deforestation in a World-System Perspective." *International Journal of Comparative Sociology* 32:221-239.

Burns, Thomas J., Edward L. Kick, and Byron Davis. 2003. "Theorizing and Rethinking Linkages between the Natural Environment and the Modern World System: Deforestation in the Late 20th Century." *Journal of World-Systems Research* 9(2):357-390.

Burns, Thomas J., Edward L. Kick, and Byron L. Davis. 2006. "A Quantitative, Cross-National Study of Deforestation in the Late 20th Century: A Case of Recursive Exploitation." Pp. 37-60 in *Globalization and the Environment*, edited by Andrew K. Jorgenson and Edward L. Kick. Leiden, the Netherlands: Brill.

Burns, Thomas J., Edward L. Kick, with Dallos Paz, 2015. *Foundations of Social Understanding: A Theory and Instructions Based Introduction to Sociology.* Norman, OK: Line-In Publishing

Burns, Thomas J., and Terri LeMoyne. 2001. "How Environmental Movements Can Be More Effective: Prioritizing Environmental Themes in Political Discourse." *Human Ecology Review* 8(1): 26-38.

Burns, Thomas J., and Terri LeMoyne. 2003. "Epistemology, Culture and Rhetoric: Some Social Implications of Human Cognition." *Current Perspectives in Social Theory* 22:71-97.

Burns, Thomas J., and Thomas K. Rudel. 2015. "Meta-Theorizing Structural Human Ecology at the Dawn of the Third Millennium." *Human Ecology Review* 22(1):13-33.

Burt, Ronald. 1982. *Toward a Structural Theory of Action: Network Models of Social Structure, Perception, and Action.* New York: Academic Press.

Buttel, Frederick H. 2000a. "World Society, the Nation-State, and Environmental Protection: Comment on Frank, Hironaka, and Schofer." *American Sociological Review* 65(1): 117-121.

Buttel, Frederick H. 2000b. "Ecological Modernization as Social Theory." *GeoForum* 31(1):57-65.

Buttel, Frederick. 2003. "Environmental Sociology and the Explanation of Environmental Reform." *Organization and Environment* 16(3): 356-400.

Butts, Rachel. 2009. "The Jevons Paradox and the Myth of Resource Efficiency Improvements." *Human Ecology Review* 16(2):224–25.

Buzbee, William W. 2003. "Recognizing the Regulatory Commons: A Theory of Regulatory Gaps." *Iowa Law Review.*

Buzbee, William W. 2005. "The Regulatory Fragmentation Continuum, Westway and the Challenges of Regional Growth." *Journal of Law & Politics* 21: 323.

Cajete, G. 2000. *Native Science: Natural Laws of Interdependence*. Santa Fe, NM: Clear Light Publishers.

Canan, Penelope. 2004. "Integrating the 'Human Dimensions' into Earth System Science: The Global Carbon Project." A lecture presented to the Science Council of Japan, Tokyo, July 3.

Canan, Penelope, and Nancy Reichman. 2002. *Ozone Networks: Expert Network in Global Environmental Governance.* South Yorkshire, UK: Greenleaf.

Caniglia, Beth Schaefer. 2011. "Global Environmental Governance and Pathways for the Achievement of Environmental Justice." In *Environmental Injustice Beyond Borders: Local Perspectives on Global Inequalities*, edited by Julian Agyeman and JoAnn Carmin. Cambridge, MA: MIT Press.

Caniglia, Beth S., Thomas J. Burns, Rachel M. Gurney, and Erik L. Bond. 2015. *The Rise of Environmental Consciousness: Voices in Pursuit of a Sustainable Planet.* San Diego: Cognella Academic Publishing.

Caniglia, Beth Schaefer, Beatrice Frank, Daisha Dalano, and Bridget Kerner. 2014. "Enhancing Environmental Justice Research and Praxis: The Inclusion of Human Security, Resilience and Vulnerabilities Literature." *International Journal of Innovation and Sustainable Development* 8(4): 409-426.

Čapek, Stella M. 1993. "The 'Environmental Justice' Frame: A Conceptual

Discussion and an Application." *Social Problems* 40(1):5-24.

Carolan, Michael. 2004. "Ecological Modernization and Consumption: A Reply to Mol and Spaargaren." *Society and Natural Resources* 17(3): 267-270.

Carson, Rachel. [1962] 2002. *Silent Spring*. Boston: Mariner Books, Houghton Mifflin Company.

Cash, David W., W. Neil Adger, Fikret Berkes, Po Garden, Louis Lebel, Per Olsson, Lowell Prichard, and Oran Young. 2006. "Scale and Cross-Scale Dynamics: Governance and Information in a Multilevel World." *Ecology and Society* 11(2): 8.

Catton, William R., Jr. 1994. "What Was Malthus Really Telling Us?" *Human Ecology Review* 1920:234-236.

Catton, William R., Jr., and Riley E. Dunlap. 1978. "Environmental Sociology: A New Paradigm?" *The American Sociologist* 13:41-49.

Catton, William R., Jr., and Riley E. Dunlap. 1980. "A New Ecological Paradigm for a Post-Exuberant Sociology." *American Behavioral Scientist* 24:15-47.

Chase-Dunn, Christopher, and Thomas D. Hall. 1994. "The Historical Evolution of World-Systems. " *Sociological Inquiry* 64:257-280.

Chase-Dunn, Christopher, and Thomas D. Hall. 1997. *Rise and Demise: Comparing World-Systems.* Boulder, CO: Westview.

Chase-Dunn, Christopher, Yukio Kawano, and Benjamin D. Brewer. 2000. "Trade Globalization Since 1795: Waves of Integration in the World-System." *American Sociological Review* 65:77-95.

Chew, Sing. 2001. *World Ecological Degradation: Accumulation, Urbanization, and Deforestation, 3000 B.C.-A.D. 2000.* Walnut Creek, CA: AltaMira.

Chew, Sing C. 2008. *Ecological Futures: What History Can Teach Us.* Lanham, MD: AltaMira.

Church, J. A., and N. J. White. 2006. "A 20th Century Acceleration in Global Sea Level Rise." *Geophysical Research Letters* 33, L01602.

Ciccantell, Paul, David A. Smith, and Gay Seidman. 2005. *Nature, Raw Materi-*

als, and Political Economy. Oxford, UK: JAI/Elsevier Press.

Citron, Rodger D. [2007] 2008. "Charles Reich's Journey From the Yale Law Journal to the New York Times Best-Seller List: The Personal History of The Greening of America." *New York Law School Law Review* 52: 387-416.

Clark, Brett, John B. Foster, and Richard York. 2007. "The Critique of Intelligent Design: Epicurus, Marx, Darwin, and Freud and the Materialist Defense of Science." *Theory and Society* 36:514-546.

Clarke, Lee. 1988. "Explaining Choices Among Technological Risks." *Social Problems* 35(1):22-35.

Clausen, Rebecca, and Brett Clark. 2005. "The Metabolic Rift and Marine Ecology: An Analysis of the Ocean Crisis Within Capitalist Production." *Organization & Environment* 18(4):422-444.

Clelland, Donald A. 2012. "Surplus Drain and Dark Value in the Modern World-System." Pp. 197-205 in *Routledge Handbook of World-Systems Analysis*. Edited by Salvatore J. Babones and Christopher Chase-Dunn. New York: Routledge.

Cobb, John B. Jr. 1991. "Economism or Planetism: The Coming Choice." *Earth Ethics* 3(1):1-3.

Cobb, John B. Jr. 2007. *Sustainability: Economics, Ecology, and Justice*. Eugene, OR: Wipf & Stock.

Cohen, Joel E. 1995. *How Many People Can the Earth Support?* New York: W.W. Norton.

Colborn, Theo, Dianne Dumanoski, and John Peterson Myers. 1997. *Our Stolen Future: Are We Threatening Our Fertility, Intelligence, and Survival? – A Scientific Detective Story*. New York: Plume/Penguin.

Coleman, James S. 1986. *Individual Interests and Collective Action*. Cambridge, UK: Cambridge University Press.

Commission for Racial Justice. 1987. *Toxic Wastes and Race in the United States*. New York: United Church of Christ.

Committee on the Human Dimensions of Global Change. 2002. *The Drama of the Commons*. Washington, DC: National Academies Press.

Commoner, Barry. 1971. *The Closing Circle*. New York: Knopf.

Commoner, Barry. 1992. *Making Peace with the Planet.* New York: The New Press.

Cook, Christina L. 2011. "Putting the Pieces Together: Tracing Jurisdictional Fragmentation in Ontario Water Governance." University of British Columbia Thesis for PhD.

Cooper, Joel. 2007. *Cognitive Dissonance: Fifty Years of a Classic Theory.* London: Sage.

Cordner, Alissa, Margaret Mulcahy, and Phil Brown. 2013. "Chemical Regulation on Fire: Rapid Policy Advances on Flame Retardants." *Environmental Science & Technology* 47(13):7067-7076.

Crane, Jeff. 2014. *The Environment in American History: The Nature and Formation of the United States.* New York: Routledge.

Crenshaw, Edward M., Matthew Christenson, and Doyle Ray Oakey. 2000. "Demographic Transition in Ecological Focus." *American Sociological Review* 65:371-391.

Crosby, Alfred W. 1986. *Ecological Imperialism: The Biological Expansion of Europe, 900-1900.* New York: Cambridge University Press.

Crowder, Kyle, and Liam Downey. 2010. "Interneighborhood Migration, Race, and Environmental Hazards: Modeling Microlevel Processes of Environmental Inequality." *American Journal of Sociology* 115.4: 1110–1149.

Crutzen, Paul J. 2002. "Geology of Mankind: The Anthropocene." *Nature* 415:23.

Daly, Herman E. 1996. *Beyond Growth: The Economics of Sustainable Development.* Boston: Beacon.

Daly, Herman E., and John B. Cobb, Jr. 1994. *For the Common Good: Redirecting the Economy toward Community, the Environment, and a Sustainable Future.* 2nd updated ed. Boston: Beacon.

Daly, Herman E., and Joshua Farley. 2011. *Ecological Economics: Principles and Applications.* 2nd ed. Washington, DC: Island.

Davis, Kingsley. 1945. "The World Demographic Transition." *Annals of the American Academy of Political and Social Science* 235:1-11.

Davis, Kingsley, and Mikhail S. Bernstam, eds. 1991. *Resources, Environment, and Population: Present Knowledge, Future Options.* New York: Population Council.

Denworth, Lydia. 2009. *Toxic Truth: A Scientist, A Doctor, and the Battle over Lead.* Boston: Beacon.

Derksen, Linda, and John Gartrell. 1993. "The Social Context of Recycling." *American Sociological Review* 58(3): 434-442.

Diamond, Jared. 1999. *Guns, Germs and Steel: The Fates of Human Societies.* New York: W.W. Norton and Co.

Diamond, Jared. 2005. *Collapse: How Societies Choose to Fail or Succeed.* New York: Viking.

Dick, Christopher, and Andrew K. Jorgenson. 2010. "Sectoral Foreign Investment and Nitrous Oxide Emissions." *Society and Natural Resources* 23:71-82.

Dickens, Peter. 2004. *Society and Nature: Changing our Environment, Changing Ourselves*. Cambridge: Polity Press.

Dietz, Thomas, Elinor Ostrom, and Paul C. Stern. 2003. "The Struggle to Govern the Commons." Science 302(12):1907-1912.

Dietz, Thomas, and Eugene A. Rosa. 1994. "Rethinking the Environmental Effects of Population, Affluence and Technology." *Human Ecology Review* 1(2):277-300.

Dilthey, Wilhelm. 1976. "The Construction of the Historical World in the Human Studies." Pp. 168-245 in *Wilhelm Dilthey: Selected Writings,* edited by H. P. Rickman. London: Cambridge University Press.

DiMaggio, Paul J. 1997. "Culture and Cognition." *Annual Review of Sociology* 23:263-287.

DiMaggio, Paul J., and Walter W. Powell. 1991. "The Iron Cage Revisited: Institutional Isomorphism and Collective Rationality in Organizational Fields." Pp. 63-82 in *The New Institutionalism in Organizational Analysis,* edited by Walter W. Powell and Paul J. DiMaggio. Chicago: The University of Chicago Press.

Douglas, Mary. 1970. *Natural Symbols.* London: Barrie and Rockliff.

Downey, Liam, and Susan Strife. 2010. "Inequality, Democracy, and the Environment." *Organization & Environment* 23(2):155-188.

Dryzek, John. 1997. *The Politics of the Earth: Environmental Discourses*. Oxford: Oxford University Press.

Dunaway, Wilma A. 1996. "The Incorporation of Mountain Ecosystems into the Capitalist World-System." *Review* 19:355-381.

Duncan, Otis D. 1964. "From Social System to Ecosystem." *Sociological Inquiry* 31:140-149.

Dunlap, Riley. 1995. "Public Opinion and Environmental Policy." Pp. 63-114 in *Environmental Politics and Policy*, edited by James P. Lester. Durham, NC: Duke University Press.

Dunlap, Riley E., and Robert J. Brulle, eds. 2015. *Climate Change and Society: Sociological Perspectives.* New York: Oxford University Press.

Dunlap, Riley, and William R. Catton, Jr. 1994. "Struggling with Human Exemptionalism: The Rise, Decline and Revitalization of Environmental Sociology." *American Sociologist* 25:5-30.

Dunlap, Riley, and William R. Catton, Jr. 2002. "Which Functions of the Environment Do We Study? A Comparison of Environmental and Natural Resource Sociology." *Society and Natural Resources* 14:239-249.

Dunlap, Riley E., and Aaron M. McCright. 2015. "Challenging Climate Change: The Denial Countermovement." Pp. 300-332 in *Climate Change and Society: Sociological Perspectives*, edited by Riley E. Dunlap and Robert J. Brulle. Oxford: Oxford University Press.

Durkheim, Émile. [1893] 1964. *The Division of Labor in Society*. New York: Free Press.

Durkheim, Émile. [1912] 1965. *The Elementary Forms of Religious Life*. New York: Free Press.

Durkheim, Émile, and Marcel Mauss. [1902] 1961. "Social Structure and the Structure of Thought." Pp. 1065-1068 in *Theories of Society: Foundations of Modern Sociological Theory*, edited by T. Parsons, E. Shils, K. D. Naegele, and J. R. Pitts. New York: Free Press.

Dwyer, John M. 1988. *The Body at War: The Miracle of the Immune System*. New

York: Mentor.

Edwards, Bob, and Anthony E. Ladd. 2000. "Environmental Justice, Swine Production and Farm Loss in North Carolina." *Sociological Spectrum* 20(3):263-290.

Egan, Timothy. 2005. *The Worst Hard Time: The Untold Story of Those Who Survived the Great American Dustbowl.* New York: Houghton Mifflin Harcourt.

Ehrhardt-Martinez, Karen. 1998. "Social Determinants of Deforestation in Developing Countries: A Cross-National Study." *Social Forces* 77:567-586.

Ehrlich, Paul R. 1968. *The Population Bomb.* New York: Ballantine.

Ehrlich, Paul. 2002. "Human Natures, Nature Conservation, and Environmental Ethics." *Bioscience* 52(1): 31-43.

Ehrlich, Paul R., and Anne H. Ehrlich. 1990. *The Population Explosion.* London: Hutchinson.

Eisenberg, Evan. 1998. *The Ecology of Eden: An Inquiry into the Dream of Paradise and a New Vision of Our Role in Nature.* New York: Vintage.

Eliade, Mircea. [1954] 1959. *Cosmos and History: The Myth of the Eternal Return.* New York: Harper and Row.

Eldredge, Niles. 2000. *The Triumph of Evolution and the Failure of Creationism.* New York: W.H. Freeman.

Elliott, James R., and Scott Frickel. 2013. "The Historical Nature of Cities: A Study of Accumulation and Hazardous Waste Accumulation." *American Sociological Review* 78:521–543.

Epstein, Steven. 2008. "Culture and Science/Technology: Rethinking Knowledge, Power, Materiality, and Nature." *The Annals of the American Academy of Political and Social Science* 619(1):165-182.

Fain, Heidi D., Thomas J. Burns, and Mindy Sartor. 1994. "Group and Individual Selection in the Human Social Environment: From Behavioral Ecology to Social Institutions." *Human Ecology Review* 1(2):335-350.

Festinger, Leon. [1957] 1962. *A Theory of Cognitive Dissonance.* Stanford, CA: Stanford University Press.

Fischer, Anke, and Juliette Young. 2007. "Understanding Mental Constructs of

Biodiversity: Implications for Biodiversity Management and Conservation." *Biological Conservation* 136(2): 271-282.

Fischer, Claude S. 1978. "Urban-to-Rural Diffusion of Opinions in Contemporary America." *American Journal of Sociology* 84(1):151-159.

Fisher, Dana R., and William R. Freudenburg. 2004. "Postindustrialization and Environmental Quality: An Empirical Analysis of the Environmental State." *Social Forces* 83(1):157-188.

Folke, Carl, Thomas Hahn, Per Olsson, and Jon Norgerg. 2005. "Adaptive Governance of Social-Ecological Systems." *Annual Review of Environmental Resources* 30:441-473.

Fortun, Kim. 2001. *Advocacy after Bhopal: Environmentalism, Disaster, and New Global Orders.* Chicago: University of Chicago Press.

Foster, John Bellamy. 1999. "Marx's Theory of Metabolic Rift: Classical Foundations for Environmental Sociology." *American Journal of Sociology* 105:366-402.

Foster, John Bellamy. 2005. "The Treadmill of Accumulation." *Organization & Environment* 18(1):7–18.

Foster, John Bellamy, Brett Clark, and Richard York. 2011. *The Ecological Rift: Capitalism's War on the Earth.* New York: Monthly Review Press.

Frank, Andre Gunder. 1978. *Dependent Accumulation and Underdevelopment.* New York: Monthly Review Press.

Frank, David John, Ann Hironaka, and Evan Schofer. 2000a. "Environmentalism as a Global Institution: Reply to Buttel." *American Sociological Review* 65:122-127.

Frank, David John, Ann Hironaka, and Evan Schofer. 2000b. "The Nation-State and the Natural Environment over the Twentieth Century." *American Sociological Review* 65:96-116.

Freud, Sigmund. [1923] 1990. *The Ego and the Id*. Stand. ed. New York: W.W. Norton.

Freud, Sigmund. [1930] 2010. *Civilization and Its Discontents*. New York: W.W. Norton.

Freudenburg, William R. 2005. "Privileged Access, Privileged Accounts: Toward a Socially Structured Theory of Resources and Discourses." *Social*

Forces 84.1: 89–114.

Freudenburg, William R., and Scott Frickel. 1995. "Beyond the Nature/Society Divide: Learning to Think about a Mountain." *Sociological Forum* 10:361-392.

Freudenburg, William R., Robert B. Gramling, Shirley Laska, and Kai Erickson. 2009. *Catastrophe in the Making: The Engineering of Katrina and the Disasters of Tomorrow.* Washington, DC: Island Press.

Frey, R. Scott. 2003. "The Transfer of Core-Based Hazardous Production Processes to the Export Processing Zones of the Periphery: The Maquiladora Centers of Northern Mexico." *Journal of World-Systems Research* 9:317-354.

Frey, R. Scott. 2006. "The International Traffic in Asbestos." *Nature, Society, and Thought* 19:173-180.

Freyfogle, Eric T. 2003. *The Land We Share: Private Property and the Common Good.* Washington, DC: Island Press.

Frickel, Scott. 2004. *Chemical Consequences: Environmental Mutagens, Scientist Activism, and the Rise of Genetic Toxicology.* New Brunswick, NJ: Rutgers University Press.

Friedman, Thomas L. 2008. *Hot, Flat, and Crowded: Why We Need a Green Revolution—and How It Can Renew America.* New York: Farrar, Straus and Giroux.

Fukuyama, Francis. 2013. "What is Governance?" *Working Paper 314.* Washington, DC: Center for Global Development. http://www.cgdev.org/content/publications/detail/1426906.

Gareau, Brian J., and E. Melanie DuPuis. 2009. "From Public to Private Global Environmental Governance: Lessons from the Montreal Protocol's Stalled Methyl Bromide Phase-Out." *Environment and Planning A* 41(10):2305-2323.

Garrett, Laurie. 1994. *The Coming Plague: Newly Emerging Diseases in a World Out of Balance.* New York: Penguin.

Gaskins, R.H. 1992. *Burdens of Proof in Modern Discourse.* New Haven, CT: Yale University Press.

Geertz, Clifford. 1973. *Interpretation of Cultures.* New York: Basic Books.

Geisler, Charles C. 2000. "Estates of Mind: Culture's Many Paths to Land." *Society & Natural Resources* 13: 51-60.

Gellert, Paul K., and Barbara D. Lynch. 2003. "Mega-Projects as Displacements." *International Social Science Journal* 55(175):15-25.

Gerstner, Wolf-Christian, Andreas König, Albrecht Enders, and Donald C. Hambrick. 2013. "CEO Narcissism, Audience Engagement, and Organizational Adoption of Technological Discontinuities." *Administrative Science Quarterly* 58(2):257–91.

Gibson, James William. 2010. *A Reenchanted World: The Quest for a New Kinship with Nature*. New York: Henry Holt and Company, LLC.

Giddens, Anthony. 1990. *The Consequences of Modernity*. Stanford, CA: Stanford University Press.

Giddens, Anthony. 1991. *Modernity and Self-Identity: Self and Society in the Late Modern Age*. Stanford, CA: Stanford University Press.

Gilbert, Dennis. 2002. *The American Class Structure in an Age of Growing Inequality.* 6th edition. Wadsworth Publishing.

Gill, Duane A., J. Steven Picou, and Liesel A. Ritchie. 2011. "The Exxon Valdez and BP Oil Spills: A Comparison of Initial Social and Psychological Impacts." *American Behavioral Scientist* 56(1):3-23.

Gille, Zsuzsa. 2010. "Actor Networks, Modes of Production, and Waste Regimes: Reassembling the Macro-Social." *Environment and Planning A* 42(5):1049-1064.

Givens, Jennifer, and Andrew Jorgenson. 2011. "The Effects of Affluence, Economic Development, and Environmental Degradation on Environmental Concern: A Multilevel Analysis." *Organization and Environment* 24(1):74-91.

Givens, Jennifer, and Andrew Jorgenson. 2012. "Individual Environmental Concern in the World Polity: A Multilevel Analysis." *Social Science Research* 42:418–431.

Goffman, Erving. 1974. *Frame Analysis: An Essay on the Organization of Experience.* New York: Harper.

Gold, Russell. 2014. *The Boom: How Fracking Ignited the American Energy Revolution and Changed the World.* New York: Simon and Schuster.

Gore, Al. 1993. *Earth in the Balance: Ecology and the Human Spirit.* New York: Plume/Penguin.

Gould, Kenneth. 2007. "The Ecological Costs of Militarization." *Peace Review* 19(3):331-334.

Gould, Kenneth A., David N. Pellow, and Allan Schnaiberg. 2008. *The Treadmill of Production: Injustice and Unsustainability in the Global Economy.* Boulder, CO: Paradigm.

Gould, Stephen J. 1992. *Ever Since Darwin.* New York: Norton.

Gould, Stephen J. 1999. *Rocks of Ages: Science and Religion in the Fullness of Life.* New York: Ballantine.

Granovetter, Mark. 1985. "Economic Action and Social Structure: The Problem of Embeddedness." *American Journal of Sociology* 91:481-510.

Grant, Don, Mary Nell Trautner, Liam Downey, and Lisa Thiebaud. 2010. "Bringing the Polluters Back In: Environmental Inequality and the Organization of Chemical Production." *American Sociological Review* 75.4: 479–504.

Green, Donald, and Jan Shapiro. 1994. *Pathologies of Rational Choice Theory: A Critique of Applications in Political Science.* New Haven, CT: Yale University Press.

Grubler, Arnulf. 1991. "Diffusion: Long-Term Patterns and Discontinuities." *Technological Forecasting and Social Change* 39:159-180.

Hacker, Jacob S. 2008. *The Great Risk Shift: The New Economic Insecurity and the Decline of the American Dream.* Revised and updated ed. New York: Oxford University Press.

Hage, Jerald, and Charles H. Powers. 1992. *Post-Industrial Lives: Roles and Relationships in the 21st Century.* Newbury Park, CA: Sage.

Handel, Warren. 1982. *Ethnomethodology: How People Make Sense.* Englewood Cliffs, NJ: Prentice Hall.

Hanneman, Robert, Jesse Fletcher, Christopher Chase-Dunn, Kirk Lawrence, Hiroko Inoue, Richard Niemeyer, and Jacob Apkarian. 2010. "The Dynamics of Synchronization in World Systems: A Formal Model." *Conference Papers at the American Sociological Association*, 1675.

Hard, Mikael, and Andrew Jamison. 2005. *Hubris and Hybrids: A Cultural History of Technology and Science*. New York: Taylor & Francis.

Hardin, Garrett. 1968. "The Tragedy of the Commons." *Science* 162(13 Dec.):1243-1248.

Hardin, Garrett, 1993. "Second Thoughts on the Tragedy of the Commons." In *Valuing the Earth: Economics, Ecology, and Ethics*, edited by Herman E. Daly and K. N. Townsend. Cambridge, MA: MIT Press.

Harlan, Sharon L., Anthony J. Brazel, G. Darrel Jenerette, Nancy S. Jones, Larissa Larsen, Lela Prashad, and William L. Stefanov. "In the Shade of Affluence: The Inequitable Distribution of the Urban Heat Island." *Research in Social Problems and Public Policy* 15:173-202.

Harvey, David. 1996. *Justice, Nature and the Geography of Difference.* Oxford, UK: Blackwell.

Haszeldine, R. Stuart. 2009. "Carbon Capture: How Green Can Black Be?" *Science* 325(5948):1647-1652.

Hauter, Wenonah. 2014. *Foodopoly: The Battle Over the Future of Food and Farming in America.* Reprint edition. New York: New Press.

Hawley, Amos. 1981. *Urban Society: An Ecological Approach.* New York: Wiley.

Hayes, Samuel P. 2000. *A History of Environmental Politics since 1945.* Pittsburgh: University of Pittsburgh Press.

Heal, Geoffrey M. 2000. *Nature and the Marketplace.* Washington, DC: Island Press.

Heberlein, Thomas A., and G. Keith Warriner. 1983. "The Influence of Price and Attitude on Shifting Residential Electricity Consumption from On- to Off-Peak Periods." *Journal of Economic Psychology* 4(1):107-130.

Heidegger, Martin. [1932] 1966. *Being and Time.* Albany, NY: SUNY Press.

Heidegger, Martin. 1999. *The Hermeneutics of Facticity*. Bloomington, IN: Indiana University Press.

Heidegger, Martin. 2006. *Mindfulness.* London: Continuum.

Heinberg, Richard. 2011. *The End of Growth: Adapting to Our New Economic Reality.* Gabriola, BC: New Society Publishers.

Henry, James P., and Patricia M. Stephens. 1977. *Stress, Health, and the Social Environment: A Sociobiologic Approach to Medicine.* New York: Springer-Verlag.

Hill, Carey, Kathryn Furlong, Karen Bakker, and Alice Cohen. 2008. "Harmonization Versus Subsidiarity in Water Governance: A Review of Water Governance and Legislation in the Canadian Provinces and Territories." *Canadian Water Resources Journal/Revue Canadienne des Ressources Hydriques* 33(4):315-332.

Hironaka, Ann. 2014. *Greening the Globe: World Society and Environmental Change.* New York: Cambridge University Press.

Homer-Dixon, Thomas. 1999. *Environment, Scarcity, and Violence.* Princeton, NJ: Princeton University Press.

Hooks, Gregory, and Chad Smith. 2004. "The Treadmill of Destruction: National Sacrifice Areas and Native American." *American Sociological Review* 69 (4 August): 558–575.

Horne, Alistair. 2015. *Hubris: The Tragedy of War in the Twentieth Century.* New York: Harper.

Hornborg, Alf. 1998a. "Ecosystems and World Systems: Accumulation as an Ecological Process." *Journal of World-Systems Research* 4(2):169-177.

Hornborg, Alf. 1998b. "Towards an Ecological Theory of Unequal Exchange: Articulating World Systems Theory and Ecological Economics." *Ecological Economics* 25:127-136.

Hornborg, Alf. 2001. *The Power of the Machine.* Walnut Creek, CA: AltaMira.

Hornborg, Alf, John Robert McNeill, and Juan Martinez Alier. 2007. *Rethinking Environmental History: World-System History and Global Environmental Change.* Lanham, MD: AltaMira.

Houghton, John. 1997. *Global Warming: The Completed Briefing.* 2nd ed. Cambridge, U.K.: Cambridge University Press.

Hughes, J. Donald. 2009. *An Environmental History of the World: Humankind's Changing Role in the Community of Life.* 2nd ed. New York: Routledge.

Hunter, Lori M. 2000. *The Environmental Implications of Population Dynamics.* Santa Monica, CA: Rand Corporation.

Husserl, Edmund. 1965. *Phenomenology and the Crisis of Philosophy.* New York: Harper and Row.

Ibarra, P. R., and J. I. Kitsuse. 1993. "Vernacular Constituents of Moral Discourse: An Interactionist Proposal for the Study of Social Problems." Pp. 25-58 in *Reconsidering Social Constructionism,* edited by J. A. Holstein and G. Miller. New York: Aldine deGruyter.

Imhoff, Daniel, ed. 2010. *CAFO: The Tragedy of Industrial Animal Factories.* San Rafael, CA: Earth Aware.

Inglehart, Ronald. 1990. *Culture Shift in Advanced Industrial Society.* Princeton, NJ: Princeton University Press.

Inglehart, Ronald. 1997. *Modernization and Postmodernization: Cultural, Economic, and Political Change in 43 Societies.* Princeton, NJ: Princeton University Press.

Inglehart, Ronald, and Wayne E. Baker. 2000. "Modernization, Cultural Change, and the Persistence of Traditional Values." *American Sociological Review* 65:19-51.

Ivanova, Maria, and Jennifer Roy. 2007. "The Architecture of Global Environmental Governance: Pros and Cons of Multiplicity." Pp. 48-66 in *Global Environmental Governance: Perspectives on the Current Debate,* edited by Lydia Swart and Estelle Perry. New York, NY: Center for UN Reform.

Jackson, Tim. 2011. *Prosperity without Growth: Economics for a Finite Planet.* London: Earthscan.

Jameson, Frederic. 1991. *Postmodernism, or, The Cultural Logic of Late Capitalism.* Durham, NC: Duke University Press.

Jasanoff, Sheila. 2004. *Earthly Politics: Local and Global in Environmental Governance.* Cambridge, MA: MIT Press.

Johnson, Erik W., Jon Agnone, and John D. McCarthy. 2010. "Movement Organizations, Synergistic Tactics and Environmental Public Policy." *Social Forces* 88(5):2267-2292.

Jones, Robert Emmet, and Riley E. Dunlap. 1992. "The Social Bases of Environmental Concern: Have They Changed over Time? *Rural Sociology* 57(1):28-47.

Jorgenson, Andrew K. 2003. "Consumption and Environmental Degradation: A Cross-National Analysis of the Ecological Footprint." *Social Problems* 50:374-394.

Jorgenson, Andrew K. 2004. "Uneven Processes and Environmental Degradation in the World Economy." *Human Ecology Review* 11:103-113.

Jorgenson, Andrew K. 2006. "Unequal Ecological Exchange and Environmental Degradation: A Theoretical Proposition and Cross-National Study of Deforestation, 1990-2000." *Rural Sociology* 71(4):685-712.

Jorgenson, Andrew K., and Thomas J. Burns. 2007. "The Political-Economic Causes of Change in the Ecological Footprints of Nations, 1991-2001: A Quantitative Investigation." *Social Science Research* 36:834-853.

Jorgenson, Andrew K., Brett Clark, and Jennifer E. Givens. 2012. "The Environmental Impacts of Militarization in Comparative Perspective: An Overlooked Relationship." *Nature & Culture* 7(3):314–37.

Jorgenson, Andrew K., James Rice, and Jessica Crowe. 2005. "Unpacking the Ecological Footprint of Nations." *International Journal of Comparative Sociology* 46:241-260.

Jung, Carl. 1959. *The Archetypes and the Collective Unconscious.* Collected works, Vol. 9. Princeton: Princeton University Press.

Jung, Carl. 1960. *The Structure and Dynamics of the Psyche.* Collected works, Vol. 8. Princeton: Princeton University Press.

Jung, Carl. 1970. *Civilization in Transition.* Collected works, Vol. 10. Princeton: Princeton University Press.

Kant, Immanuel. [1781] 1958. *Critique of Pure Reason.* Translated by N.K. Smith. New York: Random House.

Kant, Immanuel. [1783] 1950. *Prolegomena to Any Future Metaphysics,* edited by L.W. Beck. New York: Bobbs-Merrill.

Kareiva, Peter, Heather Tallis, and Taylor H. Ricketts. 2011. *Natural Capital: Theory and Practice of Mapping Ecosystem Services.* New York: Oxford University Press.

Kent, Jennifer, and Norman Myers. 2001. *Perverse Subsidies: How Tax Dollars Can Undercut the Environment and the Economy.* Washington, DC: Island Press.

Kerner, Bridget. 2015. "Socio-Ecological System (SES) Resilience and Water Governance in Oklahoma." Master's Thesis, Oklahoma State University. Advisor: Beth Schaefer Caniglia.

Kick, Edward L., Thomas J. Burns, Byron L. Davis, David A. Murray, and Dixie A. Murray. 1996. "Impacts of Domestic Population Dynamics and Foreign Wood Trade on Deforestation: A World-System Perspective. *Journal of Developing Societies* 12(1):68-87.

Kick, Edward L., and Laura A. McKinney. 2014. "Global Context, National Interdependencies, and the Ecological Footprint: A Structural Equation Analysis." *Sociological Perspectives* 57(2):256-279.

Kim, Eun-Sung. 2014. "Technocratic Precautionary Principle: Korean Risk Governance of Genetically Modified Organisms." *New Genetics & Society* 33(2):204–24.

Kirby, David. 2011. *Animal Factory: The Looming Threat of Industrial Pig, Dairy, and Poultry Farms to Humans and the Environment.* New York: St. Martin's Griffin.

Kitcher, Philip. 1983. *Abusing Science: The Case against Creationism.* Cambridge, MA: MIT Press.

Kitcher, Philip. 2007. *Living with Darwin: Evolution, Design, and the Future of Faith.* New York: Oxford University Press.

Klare, Michael T. 2002. *Resource Wars: The New Landscape of Global Conflict.* New York: Henry Holt.

Klein, Naomi. 2014. *This Changes Everything: Capitalism vs. The Climate.* New York: Simon & Schuster.

Kletz, Trevor. 2009. *What Went Wrong? Case Histories of Process Plant Disasters.* 5th ed. Burlington, MA: Elsevier.

Klineberg, Stephen L., Matthew McKeever, and Bert Rothenbach. 1998. "Demographic Predictors of Environmental Concern: It Does Make a Difference How It's Measured." *Social Science Quarterly* 79(4):734-753.

Kohn, Marek. 2004. *A Reason for Everything: Natural Selection and the English Imagination.* London: Faber and Faber.

Kollmuss, Anja, and Julian Agyeman. 2002. "Mind the Gap: Why Do People Act Environmentally and What Are the Barriers to Pro-Environmental Behavior?" *Environmental Education Research* 8(3): 239-260.

Krieg, Eric J. 1998. "The Two Faces of Toxic Waste: Trends in the Spread of Environmental Hazards." *Sociological Forum* 13(1) Kluwer Academic Publishers - Plenum Publishers.

Kumar, S. 2002. "Does 'Participation' in Common Pool Resource Management Help the Poor? A Social Cost–Benefit Analysis of Joint Forest Management in Jharkhand, India." *World Development* 30(5): 763-782.

Kuznets, Simon. 1955. "Economic Growth and Income Inequality." *American Economic Review* 45(1): 1–28.

Ladd, Anthony E., and Bob Edwards. 2002. "Corporate Swine and Capitalist Pigs: A Decade of Environmental Injustice and Protest in North Carolina." *Social Justice* 29(3):26-46.

Lakoff, George, and Mark Johnson. 2003. *Metaphors We Live By.* 2nd ed. Chicago: University of Chicago Press.

Lapegna, Pablo. 2014. "Global Ethnography and Genetically Modified Crops in Argentina: On Adoptions, Resistances, and Adaptations." *Journal of Contemporary Ethnography* 43(2):202–27.

Laska, Shirley, and Betty H. Morrow. 2006. "Social Vulnerabilities and Hurricane Katrina: An Unnatural Disaster in New Orleans." *Marine Technology Society Journal* 40(4):16-26.

Lemos, Maria Carmen, and Arun Agrawal. 2006. "Environmental Governance." *Annual Review of Environmental Resources* 31:297-325.

Lenski, Gerhard. [1966] 1984. *Power and Privilege: A Theory of Social Stratification.* Chapel Hill, NC: University of North Carolina Press.

Lenski, Gerhard. 2005. *Ecological-Evolutionary Theory: Principles and Applications.* Boulder, CO: Paradigm.

Lenski, Gerhard, and Patrick Nolan. 2008. *Human Societies.* 11th ed. Boulder, CO: Paradigm.

Leonard, H. Jeffrey. 2006. *Pollution and the Struggle for the World Product: Mul-*

tinational Corporations, Environment, and International Comparative Advantage. Cambridge: Cambridge University Press.

Leopold, Aldo. 1949. *A Sand County Almanac.* Oxford: Oxford University Press.

Lessig, Lawrence. 2011. *Republic Lost: How Money Corrupts Congress and a Plan to Stop It.* New York: Twelve/Hachette.

Lewis, Tammy. 2000. "Transitional Conservation Movement Organizations: Shaping the Protected Area Systems of Less Developed Countries." *Mobilization: An International Quarterly* 5(1):103-121.

Lieberman, Daniel. 2013. *The Story of the Human Body: Evolution, Health, and Disease.* New York: Pantheon Books.

Lieberman, Sarah, and Tim Gray. 2008. "GMOs and the Developing World: A Precautionary Interpretation of Biotechnology." *British Journal of Politics & International Relations* 10(3):395–411.

Lofdahl, Corey. 2002. *Environmental Impacts of Globalization and Trade.* Cambridge, MA: MIT Press.

Longo, Stefano B., Rebecca Clausen, and Brett Clark. 2015. *The Tragedy of the Commodity: Oceans, Fisheries, and Aquaculture.* New Brunswick, NJ: Rutgers University Press.

Louv, Richard. 2008. *Last Child in the Woods: Saving Our Children from Nature Deficit Disorder.* Chapel Hill, NC: Algonquin Books.

Louv, Richard. 2012. *The Nature Principle: Reconnecting with Life in a Virtual Age.* Chapel Hill, NC: Algonquin Books.

Lustgarten, Abrahm. 2012. *Run to Failure: BP and the Making of the Deepwater Horizon.* New York: W.W. Norton.

Lux, Kenneth. 1990. *Adam Smith's Mistake: How a Moral Philosopher Invented Economics and Ended Morality.* Boston: Shambhala.

Magdoff, Fred, and John Bellamy Foster. 2011. *What Every Environmentalist Needs to Know About Capitalism.* New York: Monthly Review Press.

Malin, Stephanie A., and Peggy Petrzelka. 2012. "Community Development Among Toxic Tailings: An Interactional Case Study of Extralocal Institutions and Environmental Health." *Community Development* 43(3):379-392.

Malthus, Thomas. [1798] 1993. *An Essay on the Principle of Population*. Oxford, UK: Oxford University Press.

Mandel, Ernest. 1998. *Late Capitalism*. 2nd ed. London: Verso.

Marcuse, Herbert. 1964. *One-Dimensional Man*. Boston: Beacon Press.

Markowitz, Gerald, and David Rosner. 2013. *Lead Wars: The Politics of Science and the Fate of America's Children*. Berkeley, CA: University of California Press.

Marshall, Brent K., and J. Steven Picou. 2008. "Postnormal Science, Precautionary Principle, and Worst Cases: The Challenge of Twenty-First Century Catastrophes." *Sociological Inquiry* 78(2):230-247.

Martenson, Chris. 2011. *The Crash Course: The Unsustainable Future of Our Economy, Energy, and Environment*. New York: Wiley.

Marquart-Pyatt, Sandra T. 2013. "The Implications of Structural Human Ecology for Environmental Concern's Global Reach." Pp. 159-186 in *Structural Human Ecology: New Essays in Risk, Energy, and Sustainability*, edited by T. Dietz and A. Jorgenson. Pullman, WA: Washington State University Press.

Marx, Karl. [1867] 1967. *Capital: A Critique of Political Economy*. Vol. 1. New York: International Publishers.

Marx, Karl, and Friedrich Engels. [1848] 1948. *Manifesto of the Communist Party*. New York: International Publishers.

Masson, Jeffrey Moussaieff, and Susan McCarthy. 1995. *When Elephants Weep: The Emotional Lives of Animals*. New York: Delacourte Press.

McAdam, Doug. 1996. "Conceptual Origins, Current Problems, Future Directions." Pp. 23-40 in *Comparative Perspectives on Social Movements: Political Opportunities, Mobilizing Structures, and Cultural Framings*, edited by D. McAdam, J. D. McCarthy, and M. N. Zald. Cambridge: Cambridge University Press.

McCloskey, D. N. 1985. *The Rhetoric of Economics*. Madison, WI: University of Wisconsin Press.

McCloskey, D. N. 1987. *The Rhetoric of the Human Sciences: Language and Argument in Scholarship and Public Affairs*. Madison, WI: University of Wisconsin Press.

McClure, John. 1991. *Explanations, Accounts, and Illusions: A Critical Analysis.* Cambridge, UK: Cambridge University Press.

McGee, Michael C. 1975. "In Search of 'the People': A Rhetorical Alternative." *Quarterly Journal of Speech* 61(3):235-249.

McGee, Michael C. 1980. "The 'Ideograph': A Link between Rhetoric and Ideology." *Quarterly Journal of Speech* 66(1):1-16.

McKinney, Laura A. 2014. "Foreign Direct Investment, Development, and Overshoot." *Social Science Research* 47:121-133.

McNeill, John Robert. 2000. *Something New under the Sun: An Environmental History of the Twentieth-Century World.* New York: W.W. Norton.

McNeill, William H. 1976. *Plagues and Peoples.* New York: Anchor/Doubleday.

Meadows, Donella H., Jorgen Randers, and Dennis L. Meadows. 2004. *Limits to Growth: The 30-Year Update.* White River Junction, VT: Chelsea Green.

Medvedev, Zhores. 1992. *The Legacy of Chernobyl.* New York: W.W. Norton.

Mehan, Hugh, and Houston Wood. 1975. *The Reality of Ethnomethodology.* New York: Wiley.

Mertig, Angela G., and Riley E. Dunlap. 2001. "Environmentalism, New Social Movements, and the New Class: A Cross-National Investigation." *Rural Sociology* 66(1):113-136.

Meyer, John. 1977. "The Effects of Education as an Institution." *American Journal of Sociology* 83:55-77.

Meyer, John. 1980. "The World Polity and the Authority of the Nation-State." Pp. 109-137 in *Studies of the Modern World-System,* edited by A. Bergesen. New York: Academic Press.

Meyer, John, David John Frank, Ann Hironaka, Evan Schofer, and Nancy Brandon Tuma. 1997. "The Structuring of the World Environmental Regime, 1870-1990." *International Organization* 51:623-651.

Mihailidou, Efthimia K., Konstantinos D. Antoniadis, and Marc J. Assael. 2012. "The 319 Major Industrial Accidents since 1917." *International Review of*

Chemical Engineering 4(6):529-540.

Mills, C. Wright. 1959. *The Sociological Imagination*. New York: Oxford University Press.

Mills, C. Wright. 2000. *The Power Elite*. New York: Oxford University Press.

Minter, Richard. 1994. "You Just Can't Take it Anymore." *Policy Review* 70:40-46.

Mix, Tamara L. 2009. "The Greening of White Separatism: Use of Environmental Themes to Elaborate and Legitimize Extremist Disclosure." *Nature and Culture* 4.2: 138–166.

Mohai, Paul, David Pellow, and J. Timmons Roberts. 2009. "Environmental Justice." *Annual Review of Environment and Resources* 34:405-430.

Mol, Arthur. 2003. *Globalization and Environmental Reform: The Ecological Modernization of the Global Economy.* Cambridge, MA: MIT Press.

Moore, Jason W. 2000. "Environmental Crisis and the Metabolic Rift in World-Historical Perspective." *Organization and Environment* 13:123-157.

Moore, Jason W. 2003. "The Modern World-System as Environmental History? Ecology and the Rise of Capitalism." *Theory and Society* 32:307-377.

Moore, Jason W. 2011a. "Ecology, Capital, and the Nature of Our Times: Accumulation and Crisis in the Capitalist World-Ecology." *Journal of World-Systems Research* 17(1):108-147.

Moore, Jason W. 2011b. "Transcending the Metabolic Rift: A Theory of Crises in the Capitalist World-Ecology." *Journal of Peasant Studies* 38(1):1-46.

Moore, Jason W. 2015. *Capitalism in the Web of Life: Ecology and the Accumulation of Capital.* London: Verso.

Moore, Kelly. 2009. *Disrupting Science: Social Movements, American Scientists, and the Politics of the Military, 1945-1975.* Princeton, NJ: Princeton University Press.

Morales, Lymari. 2010. "Green Behaviors Common in U.S., but Not Increasing." http://www.gallup.com/poll/127292/green-behaviors-common-not-increasing.aspx.

Mumford, Lewis. 1981. *The Culture of Cities.* Santa Barbara, CA: Praeger.

Myers, Norman, and Jennifer Kent. 2001. *Perverse Subsidies: How Tax Dollars Can Undercut the Environment and the Economy.* Washington, DC: Island.

Nash, Linda. 2007. *Inescapable Ecologies: A History of Environment, Disease, and Knowledge.* Berkeley, CA: University of California Press.

National Research Council. 1999. *Human Dimensions of Global Environmental Change: Research Pathways for the Next Decade.* Washington, DC: National Academy Press.

National Research Council (NRC), 2006. *Surface Temperature Reconstructions For the Last 2,000 Years.* National Academy Press, Washington, DC.

Neese, Randolph M., and George C. Williams. 1994. *Why We Get Sick.* New York: Vintage.

Norgaard, Kari Marie. 2006. " 'We Don't Really Want to Know': Environmental Justice and Socially Organized Denial of Global Warming in Norway." *Organization & Environment* 19(3):347-370.

O'Connor, James. 1994. "Is Sustainable Capitalism Possible?" Pp. 152-175 in *Political Economy and the Politics of Ecology*, edited by Martin O'Connor. New York: Guilford.

O'Connor, James. 1998. *Natural Causes: Essays in Ecological Marxism.* New York: Guilford.

Ogburn, William F. [1932] 1961. "The Hypothesis of Cultural Lag." In *Theories of Society: Foundations of Modern Sociological Theory*, edited by Talcott Parsons, Edward Shils, Kaspar D. Naegele, and Jesse R. Pitts. New York: Free Press.

Ogburn, William F. 1956. "Technology as Environment." *Sociology and Social Research* 41(1):3-9.

Olson, Mancur. 1965. *The Logic of Collective Action.* Cambridge, MA; Harvard University Press.

Olzak, Susan, and Sarah A. Soule. 2009. "Cross-Cutting Influences of Environmental Protest and Legislation." *Social Forces* 88(1):201-225.

O'Neill, Karen M. 2002. "Why the TVA Remains Unique: Interest Groups and the Defeat of New Deal River Planning." *Rural Sociology* 67(2):163-

182.

Ostrom, Elinor. 1990. *Governing the Commons: The Evolution of Collective Action.* Cambridge, UK: Cambridge University Press.

Ostrom, Elinor. 2009. "A General Framework for Analyzing Sustainability of Social-Ecological Systems." *Science* 325: 419-422.

Ostrom, Elinor. 2010. "Beyond Markets and States: Polycentric Governance of Complex Economic Systems." *American Economic Review* 100: 641-672.

Ostrom, Elinor, Joanna Burger, Christopher B. Field, Richard B. Norgaard, and David Policansky. 1999. "Revisiting the Global Commons: Local Lessons, Global Challenges." *Science* 284: 278-282.

Ostrom, Elinor, Christina Chang, Mark Pennington, and Vlad Tarko. 2012. *The Future of the Commons: Beyond Market Failure and Government Regulations.* London: Institute for Economic Affairs.

Ostrom, Elinor, Thomas Dietz, Nives Dolsak, Paul C. Stern, Susan Sonich, and Elke U. Weber, eds. 2002. *The Drama of the Commons*. Washington DC: National Academy Press.

Ostrom, Elinor, Marco A. Janssen, and John M. Anderies. 2007. "Going Beyond Panaceas." *PNAS* 104(39): 15176-15178.

Pacala and Socolow. 2004. "Stabilization Wedges: Solving the Climate Problem for the Next 50 Years with Current Technologies." *Science* 305:968-972.

Parsons, Talcott. 1951. *The Social System.* Glencoe, IL: Free Press.

Parsons, Talcott. 1966. *Societies: Evolutionary and Comparative Perspectives.* Englewood Cliffs, NJ: Prentice-Hall, Inc.

Parsons, Talcott. 1977. *The Evolution of Societies.* Lebanon, IN: Prentice-Hall.

Peek, Lori A., and Dennis S. Mileti. 2002. "The History and Future of Disaster Research." Pp. 511-524 in *Handbook of Environmental Psychology*, edited by Robert B. Bechtel and Arza Churchman. Hoboken, NJ: John Wiley & Sons, Inc.

Pellegrini, Giuseppe. 2009. "Biotechnologies and Communication: Participation for Democratic Processes." *Comparative Sociology* 8(4):517–40.

Pellow, David Naguib. 2007. *Resisting Global Toxics: Transnational Movements for Environmental Justice.* Cambridge, MA: MIT Press.

Pellow, David N., and Robert J. Brulle, eds. 2005. *Power, Justice, and the Environment: A Critical Appraisal of the Environmental Justice Movement.* Cambridge, MA: MIT Press.

Perrow, Charles, and Simone Pulver. 2015. "Organizations and Markets." Pp. 61-92 in *Climate Change and Society: Sociological Perspectives*, edited by Riley E. Dunlap and Robert J. Brulle. New York: Oxford University Press.

Petersen, Alan. 2005. "The Metaphors of Risk: Biotechnology in the News." *Health, Risk & Society* 7(3):203–8.

Piaget, Jean. 1951. *The Child's Conception of the World.* New York: Humanities Press.

Piaget, Jean. 1954. *The Construction of Reality in the Child.* New York: Basic Books.

Poggi, Gianfranco. 1993. *Money and the Modern Mind: Georg Simmel's Philosophy of Money.* Berkeley, CA: University of California Press.

Polimeni, John M., Kozo Mayumi, Mario Giampietro, and Blake Alcott. 2008. *The Jevons Paradox and the Myth of Resource Efficiency Improvements.* London: Routledge.

Pollot, Mark. 1993. *Grand Theft and Petit Larceny: Property Rights in America.* Pacific Research Institute.

Ponting, Clive. 1991. *A Green History of the World.* London: Sinclair Stevenson.

Ponting, Clive. 2008. *A New Green History of the World: The Environment and the Collapse of Great Civilizations*. 2nd ed. New York: Penguin.

Porter, Gareth and Janet Welsh Brown. 1991. *Global Environmental Politics.* Boulder: Westview Press.

Postel, Sandra. 2003. *Rivers for Life: Managing Water for People and Nature.* Washington, DC: Island Press.

Prechel, Harland. 1994. "Economic Crisis and the Centralization of Control over the Managerial Process: Corporate Restructuring and New-Fordist Decision-Making." *American Sociological Review* 59(5):723-745.

Pulver, Simone. 2007. "Making Sense of Corporate Environmentalism: An Environmental Contestation Approach to Analyzing the Causes and Consequences of the Climate Change Policy Split in the Oil Industry." *Organization & Environment* 20(1):44-83.

Purdy, Jedediah. 2015. *After Nature: Politics after the Anthropocene.* Cambridge, MA: Harvard University Press.

Reich, Charles A. 1970. *The Greening of America.* New York: Random House.

Revkin, Andrew C., Shan Carter, Jonathan Ellis, Farhana Hossain, and Alan McLean. 2008. "On the Issues: Climate." *New York Times*, http://elections.nytimes.com/2008/president/issues/climate.html.

Ricardo, David. [1817] 2006. *On the Principles of Political Economy and Taxation.* New York: Cosimo.

Rice, James. 2007. "Ecological Unequal Exchange: Consumption, Equity, and Unsustainable Structural Relationships within the Global Economy." *International Journal of Comparative Sociology* 48:43-72.

Ridley, Matt, and Bobbi Low. 1994. "Can Selfishness Save the Environment?" *Human Ecology Review* 1(1):1 ff.

Ritzer, George. 1993. *The McDonaldization of Society.* Thousand Oaks, CA: Pine Forge.

Ritzer, George. 2011. *Sociological Theory.* 8th ed. New York: McGraw-Hill.

Roberts, J. Timmons, and Bradley Parks. 2007a. *A Climate of Injustice.* Cambridge, MA: MIT Press.

Roberts, J. Timmons, and Bradley Parks. 2007b. "Fueling Injustice: Globalization, Ecologically Unequal Exchange and Climate Change." *Globalizations* 4: 193-210.

Roberts, Paul Craig. 2013. *The Failure of Laissez Faire Capitalism.* Atlanta, GA: Clarity Press.

Robinson, William I. 2004. *A Theory of Global Capitalism.* Baltimore: Johns Hopkins University Press.

Rosa, Eugene, Aaron M. McCright, and Ortwin Renn. 2003. *The Risk Society: Theoretical Frames and State Management Challenges.* Department of Sociology, Washington State University, Pullman, WA.

Rosa, Eugene A., Thomas K. Rudel, Richard York, Andrew K. Jorgenson, and Thomas Dietz. 2015. "The Human (Anthropogenic) Driving Forces of Global Climate Change." Pp. 32-60 in *Climate Change and Society: Sociological Perspectives,* edited by Riley E. Dunlap and Robert J. Brulle. Oxford, UK: Oxford University Press.

Ross, Sheila M., ed. 1994. *Toxic Metals in Soil-Plant Systems.* New York: Wiley-Blackwell.

Rubin, Edward S. 2008. "CO2 Capture and Transport." *Elements* 4(5):311-317.

Rudel, Thomas, and Jill Roper. 1997. "Paths to Rainforest Destruction." *World Development* 25:53-65.

Rybczynski, Witold. 1999. *A Clearing in the Distance: Frederick Law Olmsted and America in the Nineteenth Century.* New York: Simon and Schuster.

Sanchez, Mikel L. 2013. *Causes and Effects of Heavy Metal Pollution.* Hauppauge, NY: Nova Science.

Sanderson, Matthew R., and R. Scott Frey. 2014. "From Desert to Breadbasket…To Desert Again? A Metabolic Rift in the High Plains Aquifer." *Journal of Political Ecology* 21:516-532.

Sanderson, Stephen, and Arthur Alderson. 2004. *World Societies: The Evolution of Human Social Life.* Boston: Allyn and Bacon.

Sbicca, Joshua. 2012. "Growing Food Justice by Planting an Anti-Oppression Foundation: Opportunities and Obstacles for a Budding Social Movement." *Agriculture and Human Values* 29(4):455-466.

Scanlan, Stephen J. 2009. "New Direction and Discovery on the Hunger Front: Toward a Sociology of Food Security/Insecurity." *Humanity & Society* 33(4):292-316.

Schnaiberg, Allan. 1980. *The Environment: From Surplus to Scarcity.* New York: Oxford University Press.

Schnaiberg, Allan, and Kenneth A. Gould. 1994. *Environment and Society: The Enduring Conflict.* New York: St. Martin's Press.

Schnaiberg, Allan, David N. Pellow, and Adam Weinberg. 2002. "The Treadmill of Production and the Environmental State." *Research in Social Problems & Public Policy* 10:15–32.

Schofer, Evan, and Ann Hironaka. 2005. "The Effects of World Society on Environmental Outcomes." *Social Forces* 84:25-47.

Schor, Juliet, and Karen Elizabeth White. 2010. *Plenitude: The New Economics of True Wealth.* New York: Penguin Press.

Schumacher, E. F. [1973] 1999. *Small Is Beautiful: Economics as if People Mattered.* Point Roberts, WA: Hartley and Marks Publishers.

Schumacher, E. F. [1975] 2000. *Small Is Beautiful, 25th Anniversary Edition: Economics As If People Mattered: 25 Years Later . . . With Commentaries.* Point Roberts, WA: Hartley and Marks.

Schutz, Alfred. 1972. *The Phenomenology of the Social World.* London: Heinemann.

Science Daily. 2015. https://www.sciencedaily.com/releases/2016/02/160212140912.htm (accessed 2/12/16).

Scott, Dayna Nadine. 2005. "When Precaution Points Two Ways: Confronting 'West Nile Fever.'" *Canadian Journal of Law & Society/Revue Canadienne Droit et Societe* (University of Toronto Press) 20(2):27–65.

Scott, Rebecca R. 2010. *Removing Mountains: Extracting Nature and Identity in Appalachian Coalfields.* Minneapolis: University of Minnesota Press.

Seldon, Thomas M., and Daqing Song. 1994. "Environmental Quality and Development: Is There a Kuznets Curve for Air Pollution Emissions?" *Journal of Environmental Economics and Management* 27: 147–62.

Seligman, Martin E.P., and Steven F. Maier. 1967. "Failure to Escape Traumatic Shock." *Journal of Experimental Psychology* 74:1-9.

Shandra, John M. 2007. "International Non-Governmental Organizations and Deforestation: Good, Bad, or Irrelevant?" *Social Science Quarterly* 88:665-689.

Shiva, Vandana. 2000. *Stolen Harvest: The Hijacking of the Global Food Supply.* Kings Cross, London: Zed Books.

Shriver, Thomas E., and Gary R. Webb. 2009. "Rethinking the Scope of Environmental Injustice: Perceptions of Health Hazards in a Rural Native American Community Exposed to Carbon Black." *Rural Sociology* 74(2):270-292.

Sicotte, Diane, and Samantha Swanson. 2007. "Whose Risk in Philadelphia? Proximity to Unequally Hazardous Industrial Facilities." *Social Science Quarterly* 88(2):515-534.

Simmel, Georg. [1907] 1978. *The Philosophy of Money.* London: Routledge and Kegan Paul.

Simmel, Georg. [1908] 1955. *Conflict and the Web of Group Affiliations.* New York: Free Press.

Simon, Herbert A. 1990. "Invariants of Human Behavior." *Annual Review of Psychology* 41:1-19.

Simon, Julian L. 1983. *The Ultimate Resource.* Princeton, NJ: Princeton University Press.

Sklair, Leslie. 1999. *The Transnational Capitalist Class.* Oxford, UK: Blackwell.

Sklair, Leslie. 2002. *Globalization: Capitalism and Its Alternatives.* Oxford, UK: Oxford University Press.

Smith, Adam. [1759] 1956. *The Theory of Moral Sentiments.* Indianapolis, IN: Liberty Classics.

Smith, Adam. [1776] 1999. *An Inquiry into the Nature and Causes of the Wealth of Nations.* New York: Penguin.

Smith, Jackie, and Dawn Wiest. 2005. "The Uneven Geography of Global Civil Society: National and Global Influences on Transnational Association." *Social Forces* 84:632-652.

Smith, Yves. 2010. *ECONned: How Unenlightened Self Interest Undermined Democracy and Corrupted Capitalism.* New York: Palgrave Macmillan.

Snow, Charles Percy. 1998. *The Two Cultures.* Cambridge, UK: Cambridge University Press.

Sonnenfeld, David A. 2002. "Social Movements and Ecological Modernization: The Transformation of Pulp and Paper Manufacturing." *Development and Change* 33(1):1-27.

Spaargaren, Gert, Arther Mol, and Frederick H. Buttel (eds.). 2000. *Environ-*

mental and Global Modernity. Sage: London.

Spaargaren, Gert, Arther Mol, and Frederick H. Buttel (eds.). 2006. *Environmental Flows: Global Challenges to Social Theory.* Cambridge: The MIT Press.

Speth, James Gustave, and Peter Haas. 2006. *Global Environmental Governance.* Washington, DC: Island Press.

Steingraber, Sandra. 2010 [1977]. *Living Downstream: A Scientist's Personal Investigation of Cancer and the Environment.* 2nd ed. Philadelphia: DaCapo.

Stern, David I., and Michael S. Common. 2001. "Is There an Environmental Kuznets Curve for Sulfur?" *Journal of Environmental Economics and Management* 41: 162–78.

Stern, Nicholas. 2007. *The Economics of Climate Change: The Stern Review.* Cambridge, UK: Cambridge University Press.

Stiglitz, Joseph E. 2002. *Globalization and its Discontents.* New York: Norton.

Stoll, Steven. 2007. *U.S. Environmentalisms since 1945: A Brief History with Documents.* New York: Palgrave Macmillan.

Suri, Vivek, and Duane Chapman. 1998. "Economic Growth, Trade, and Energy: Implications for the Environmental Kuznets Curve." *Ecological Economics* 25: 195–208.

Swidler, Ann. 1986. "Culture in Action: Symbols and Strategies." *American Sociological Review* 51:273-286.

Swidler, Ann. 2001. "What Anchors Cultural Practices?" Pp. 74-92 in *The Practice Turn in Contemporary Theory,* edited by T.R. Schatzki, K.K. Cetina, and E. VonSavigny. New York: Routledge.

Szasz, Andrew. 2007. *Shopping Our Way to Safety: How We Changed from Protecting the Environment to Protecting Ourselves.* Minneapolis, MN: University of Minnesota Press.

Tarlov, A. R. 1996. "Social Determinants of Health: The Sociobiological Translation." *In Health and Social Organization,* edited by D. Blane, E. Brunner, and R. Wilkerson. London: Routledge.

Tarrow, Sidney. 1998. *Power in Movement: Social Movements and Contentious*

Politics. Cambridge: Cambridge University Press.

Taylor, Dorceta E. 2000. "The Rise of the Environmental Justice Paradigm: Injustice Framing and the Social Construction of Environmental Discourses." *American Behavioral Scientist* 43(4):508-580.

Taylor, Peter J. 1997. "How Do We Know We Have Global Environmental Problems? Undifferentiated Science-Politics and its Potential Reconstruction." Pp. 149-174 in *Changing Life*, edited by P. J. Taylor, S. E. Halfon, and P. N. Edwards. Minneapolis: University of Minnesota Press.

Thompson, William Irwin. 1971. *At the Edge of History.* New York: Harper and Row.

Thompson, William Irwin. 1981. *The Time Falling Bodies Take to Light: Mythology, Sexuality, and the Origins of Culture.* New York: St. Martin's.

Tierney, K. J. 2007. "From the Margins to the Mainstream? Disaster Research at the Crossroads." *Sociology* 33(1):503.

Tilly, Charles. 1992. *Coercion, Capital, and European States, A.D. 990-1990.* Oxford, UK: Blackwell.

Tindall, David B. 1995. "What is Environmental Sociology? An Inquiry into the Paradigmatic Status of Environmental Sociology." Pp. 35-59, in *Environmental Sociology: Theory and Practice*, edited by Michael D. Mehta and Eric Ouellet. North York, Ontario: Captus Press.

Tönnies, Ferdinand. [1887] 2001. *Community and Society.* Cambridge, UK: Cambridge University Press.

Topik, Steven, and Kenneth Pomeranz. 2012. *The World That Trade Created: Society, Culture and the World Economy, 1400 to the Present.* 3rd ed. Armonk, NY: Routledge.

Torras, Mariano, and James K. Boyce. 1998. "Income, Inequality, and Pollution: A Reassessment of the Environmental Kuznets Curve." *Ecological Economics* 25(2): 147–60.

Turner, Jacky, and Joyce D'Silva, eds. 2006. *Animals, Ethics, and Trade: The Challenge of Animal Sentience.* New York: Routledge.

Turner, Jonathan. 2002. *The Structure of Sociological Theory*. 7th ed. Belmont, CA: Wadsworth.

Uekoetter, Frank. 2010. *The Turning Points of Environmental History.* Pittsburgh,

PA: University of Pittsburgh Press.

United Nations. 1992. *Long-Range World Population Projections: Two Centuries of Population Growth, 1950-2150.* New York: United Nations.

United States Department of Agriculture Economic Research Service Report. 2013. *Rural Poverty & Well-Being* from U.S. Census Bureau 2013 Annual Social and Economic Supplements. Suitland, MD: U.S. Census Bureau.

Vallas, Steven Peter, and Daniel Lee Kleinman. 2008. "Contradiction, Convergence and the Knowledge Economy: The Confluence of Academic and Commercial Biotechnology." *Socio-Economic Review* 6(2):283–311.

Wackernagel, Mathis, Larry Onisto, and Patricia Bello. 1999. "National Natural Capital Accounting with the Ecological Footprint Concept." *Ecological Economics* 29:375-390.

Wackernagel, Mathis, and William Rees. 1996. *Our Ecological Footprint: Reducing Human Impact on the Environment.* Gabriola Island, BC, Canada: New Society Publishers.

Wackernagel, Mathis, and Judith Silverstein. 2000. "Big Things First: Focusing on the Scale Imperative with the Ecological Footprint." *Ecological Economics* 32:391-394.

Wagner, Peter. 2012. *Modernity: Understanding the Present.* Cambridge, UK: Polity.

Walker, Brian, David Salt, and Walter Reid. 2006. *Resilience Thinking: Sustaining Ecosystems and People in a Changing World.* Washington, DC: Island Press.

Wallerstein, Immanuel. 1974. *The Modern World System.* Vol. 1. New York: Academic Press.

Wallerstein, Immanuel. 1989. *The Modern World-System III: The Second Era of Great Expansion of the Capitalist World-Economy, 1730-1840.* New York: Academic Press.

Wallerstein, Immanuel. 1999. *The End of the World as We Know It: Social Science for the Twenty-first Century.* Minneapolis, MN: University of Minnesota Press.

Weber, Max. [1896] 1976. *The Agrarian Sociology of Ancient Civilizations.* London: New Left Books.

Weber, Max. [1904-05] 1985. *The Protestant Ethic and the Spirit of Capitalism.* London: Unwin.

Weber, Max. [1921] 1968. *Economy and Society.* 3 vols. Totowa, NJ: Bedminster.

Weber, Max. 1948. From *Max Weber: Essays in Sociology.* Translated, edited and with an introduction by H. H. Gerth and C. W. Mills. London: Routledge and Kegan Paul.

Weber, Max. [1921] 1978. *Economy and Society: An Outline of Interpretive Sociology.* 2 Volume Set. Guenther Roth and Claus Wittich, eds. Berkeley: University of California Press.

Weigert, Andrew J. 1997. *Self, Interaction, and The Natural Environment: Refocusing Our Eyesight.* Albany, NY: SUNY Press.

Weitz, Rose. 1996. *The Sociology of Health, Illness, and Health Care: A Critical Approach.* Belmont, CA: Wadsworth.

White, Hayden. 1973. *Metahistory: The Historical Imagination in Nineteenth-Century Europe.* Baltimore: Johns Hopkins University Press.

Wildcat, D. R. 2009. *Red Alert. Saving the Planet with Indigenous Knowledge.* Golden, CO: Fulcrum Publishing.

Wilkenson, R. G. 1996. *Unhealthy Societies: The Afflictions of Inequality.* London: Routledge.

Wootton, David. 2015. *The Invention of Science: A History of Scientific Revolutions.* New York: Harper.

Wuthnow, Robert. 1987. *Meaning and Moral Order: Explorations in Cultural Analysis.* Berkeley: University of California Press.

Yeager, Peter C. 1987. "Structural Bias in Regulatory Law Enforcement: The Case of the US Environmental Protection Agency." *Social Problems* 34(4):330-344.

York, Richard. 2006. "Ecological Paradoxes: William Stanley Jevons and the Paperless Office." *Human Ecology Review* 13(2):143–47.

York, Richard, Eugene A. Rosa, and Thomas Dietz. 2002. "STIRPAT, IPAT and

ImPACT: Analytic Tools for Unpacking the Driving Forces of Environmental Impacts." *Ecological Economics* 46(3):351.

York, Richard, Eugene A. Rosa, and Thomas Dietz. 2003a. "Footprints on the Earth: The Environmental Consequences of Modernity. *American Sociological Review* 68:279-300.

York, Richard, Eugene A. Rosa, and Thomas Dietz. 2003b. "A Rift in Modernity? Assessing the Anthropogenic Sources of Global Climate Change with the STIRPAT Model." *International Journal of Sociology and Social Policy* 23(10):31-51.

Yunus, Muhammad. 1999. *Banker to the Poor: Micro Lending and the Battle against World Poverty.* New York: Perseus/Public Affairs.

Yunus, Muhammad. 2007. *Creating a World without Poverty: Social Business and the Future of Capitalism.* New York: Perseus/Public Affairs.

Zavestoski, Stephen, Phil Brown, Sabrina McCormick, Brian Mayer, Jaime Lucove, and Maryhelen D'Ottavi. 2004. "Patient Activism and the Struggle for Diagnosis: Gulf War Illness and Other Medically Unexplained Physical Symptoms in the U.S." *Social Science & Medicine* 58:161-175.

Zehr, Stephen C. 2000. "Public Representations of Scientific Uncertainty About Global Climate Change." *Public Understanding of Science* 9(2):85-103.

Zuckerman, Gregory. 2013. *The Frackers: The Outrageous Inside Story of the New Billionaire Wildcatters.* New York: Portfolio.

Internet Sources:

Center for Climate and Energy Solutions. 2016. www.c2es.org. Accessed 2/22/16.

Centers for Disease Control. 2015. Retrieved September 30, 2015. "Second Hand (SHS) Smoke Facts." (http://www.cdc.gov/tobacco/data_statistics/fact_sheets/secondhand_smoke/general_facts/).

Climatic Research Unit, University of East Anglia. (http://www.cru.uea.ac.uk/cru/data/temperature).

Drexal University. (http://www.pages.drexel.edu/~brullerj/Twenty%20Lessons%20in%20Environmental%20Sociology-Brulle.pdf accessed June 8, 2015).

Environmental Protection Agency (EPA)
Website: www.epa.gov
Integrated Risk Information System: www.epa.gov/iris

"From Peril to Progress." January 26, 2009. Remarks by President Barack Obama on Jobs, Energy Independence, and Climate Change. East Room of the White House. http://www.whitehouse.gov/blog_post/From-periltoprogress/.

Food and Drug Administration (FDA)
Website: www.fda.gov

Independent, The. 2009. "Forty years since the first picture of earth from space." http://www.independent.co.uk/news/science/forty-years-since-the-first-picture-of-earth-from-space-1297569.html

Institute for Health Metrics and Evaluation (IHME). Global Burden of Air Pollution. Seattle, WA: IHME, University of Washington, 2016. Available from http://www.healthdata.org/news-release/poor-air-quality-kills-55-million-worldwide-annually. (Accessed February 19, 2016.)

International Agency for Research on Cancer (IARC).
Website: www.iarc.fr
Agents Classified by the IARC Monographs, Volumes 1 – 114. 2015. Accessed at http://monographs.iarc.fr/ENG/Classification/List_of_Classifications_Vol1-114.pdf

International Agency for Research on Cancer (IARC).
Website: www.iarc.fr
IARC Carcinogen Monographs: http://monographs.iarc.fr

Monterey Bay Aquarium. 2015. Seafood Watch: Fishing and Farming Methods. (www.seafoodwatch.org/ocean-issues/fishing-and-farming-methods - accessed 9/26/15).

National Aeronautics and Space Administration Goddard Institute for Space Studies (http://data.giss.nasa.gov/gistemp).

National Cancer Institute
Website: www.cancer.gov
Cancer Causes and Risk Factors: www.cancer.gov/cancertopics/causes

National Centers for Environmental Information. (https://www.ncdc.noaa.gov/indicators/).

National Institute for Occupational Safety and Health (NIOSH)
Website: www.cdc.gov/niosh
NIOSH Safety and Health Topic – Occupational Cancer: www.cdc.gov/niosh/topics/cancer

National Institute for Occupational Safety and Health (NIOSH)
Website: www.cdc.gov/niosh
NIOSH Carcinogen List: www.cdc.gov/niosh/topics/cancer/npotocca.html

National Toxicology Program (NTP)
Website: http://ntp.niehs.nih.gov
Report on Carcinogens: http://ntp.niehs.nih.gov/pubhealth/roc/roc13 index.html

United Nations Environmental Programme (UNEP). 2016. www.unep.org/disastersandconflicts/

United Nations Environmental Program. (http://www.unep.org/geo/GEO4/report/GEO-4_Report_Full_en.pdf).

United Nations Framework Convention on Climate Change. 2016. Unfcc.int. Accessed 2/23/16.

U.S. Census Bureau. 2016. "World Population: Total Midyear Population for the World: 1950 - 2050." http://www.census.gov/population/international/data/worldpop/table_population.php (accessed 3/2/16).

U.S. Department of Health and Human Services. "Public Health Service, National Toxicology Program. Report on Carcinogens, Thirteenth Edition." 2014. (Accessed at http://ntp.niehs.nih.gov/pubhealth/roc/roc13/index.html)

U.S. Geological Survey. 2005. "Estimated Use of Water in the United States County-Level Data for 2005." (http://water.usgs.gov/watuse/data/2005/index.html).

U.S. Geological Survey. 2011. "High Plains Aquifer Water-Level Monitoring Study: Area-Weighted Water-Level Change, Predevelopment to 1980, 2000 Through 2009." (http://ne.water.usgs.gov/ogw/hpwlms/tablewlpre.html).

World Health Organization. (www.who.int/globalchange/environment/en/).

World Health Organization. 2014. (http://www.who.int/mediacentre/news/releases/2014/air-pollution/en/ accessed 2/14/16).

World Resources Institute. (www.wri.org).

Worldwatch Institute. (www.worldwatch.org).

Illustration Credits

pg. 21 Credit: By Little Mountain 5 (Own work) [CC BY-SA 4.0 (http://creativecommons.org/licenses/by-sa/4.0)], via Wikimedia Commons.

pg. 24 By Haines Photo Co. (Conneaut, Ohio) [Public domain or Public domain], via Wikimedia Commons.

pg. 26 By thisisbossi from Washington, DC, USA (2008 07 16 - 6009 - College Park - I95-495) [CC BY-SA 2.0 (http://creativecommons.org/licenses/by-sa/2.0)], via Wikimedia Commons.

pg. 27 By etching created by Cadell and Davies (1811), John Horsburgh (1828) or R.C. Bell (1872). [Public domain], via Wikimedia Commons.

pg. 33 {{PD-1923}} John Jabez Edwin Mayall [Public domain], via Wikimedia Commons, {{PD-1923}} [Public domain], via Wikimedia Commons, {{PD-1923}} [Public domain], via Wikimedia Commons.

pg. 40 By The original uploader was Cornischong at Luxembourgish Wikipedia (Transferred from lb.wikipedia to Commons.) [Public domain], via Wikimedia Commons.

pg. 46 By Ed Yourdon from New York City, USA [CC BY-SA 2.0 (http://creativecom.

pg. 49 By Siyuwj (Own work) [CC BY-SA 3.0 (http://creativecommons.org/licenses/by-sa/3.0)], via Wikimedia Commons.

pg. 52 By unknown, upload by Adrian Michael (Ortsmuseum Zollikon) [Public domain], via Wikimedia Commons.

pg. 53 By Klem, [Public domain], via Wikimedia Commons, Mezzotint by J. Faber by Wellcome Trust, [CC BY 4.0 (http://creativecommons.org/licenses/by/4.0)], via Wikimedia Commons.

pg. 56 By ENERGY.GOV (HD.11B.155) [Public domain], via Wikimedia Commons.

pg. 68 Gyrostat (Wikimedia, CC-BY-SA 4.0) [CC BY-SA 4.0 (http://creativecommons.org/licenses/by-sa/4.0)], via Wikimedia Commons.

pg. 69 By Dave Hoisington/CIMMYT [CC BY 2.5 (http://creativecommons.

org/licenses/by/2.5)], via Wikimedia Commons.

pg. 74 [Public domain], via Wikimedia Commons.

pg. 78 © CEphoto, Uwe Aranas / , via Wikimedia Commons.

pg. 79 Martyn Gorman [CC BY-SA 2.0 (http://creativecommons.org/licenses/by-sa/2.0)], via Wikimedia Commons.

pg. 90 By USGS [Public domain], via Wikimedia Commons., By SlimVirgin at en.wikipedia [Public domain], from Wikimedia Commons.

pg. 91 By Kbh3rd (Own work) [CC BY-SA 3.0 (http://creativecommons.org/licenses/by-sa/3.0) or GFDL (http://www.gnu.org/copyleft/fdl.html)], via Wikimedia Commons.

pg. 94 By Alex Rio Brazil (Own work) [Public domain], via Wikimedia Commons.

pg. 96 By NOAA (http://marinedebris.noaa.gov/info/patch.html) [Public domain], via Wikimedia Commons.

pg. 108 By Danny Cornelissen (http://www.portpictures.nl) [Attribution], via Wikimedia Commons.

pg. 112 epSos.de [CC BY 2.0 (http://creativecommons.org/licenses/by/2.0)], via Wikimedia Commons.

pg. 113 By NASA. Collage by Producercunningham. [Public domain], via Wikimedia Commons.

pg. 115 By Danny Cornelissen (http://www.portpictures.nl) [Attribution], via By JimChampion (Own work) [CC BY-SA 3.0 (http://creativecommons.org/licenses/by-sa/3.0) or GFDL (http://www.gnu.org/copyleft/fdl.html)], via Wikimedia Commons.

pg. 128 By Christopher Hurdzan (www.flickr.com) [CC BY-SA 2.0 (http://creativecommons.org/licenses/by-sa/2.0)], via Wikimedia Commons.

pg. 129 iStock Photos.

pg. 137 2016. Available from http://www.healthdata.org/news-release/

poor-air-quality-kills-55-million-worldwide-annually. (Accessed February 19, 2016.)

pg. 138 By Alexandrowicz, John L., Photographer (NARA record: 8452213) (U.S. National Archives and Records Administration) [Public domain], via Wikimedia Commons.

pg. 139 By Alexandrowicz, John L., Photographer (NARA record: 8452213) (U.S. National Archives and Records Administration) [Public domain], via Wikimedia Commons.

pg. 146 Mercury Academic.

pg. 153 By Fredrick Onyango from Nairobi, Kenya [CC BY 2.0 (http://creativecommons.org/licenses/by/2.0)], via Wikimedia Commons.

pg. 166 By Julian Nitzsche(Own work (own photograph)) [CC BY-SA 3.0 (http://creativecommons.org/licenses/by-sa/3.0)], via Wikimedia Commons.

pg. 167 By Jason Minshull (This photo is the author's own work) [Public domain], via Wikimedia Commons.

pg. 172 By Kjetil Bjørnsrud (Own work) [GFDL (http://www.gnu.org/copyleft/fdl.html) or CC-BY-SA-3.0 (http://creativecommons.org/licenses/by-sa/3.0/)], via Wikimedia Commons.

pg. 176 By Original photo: VISIONS Service Adventures (Cropped from File:Group21-029 (5271821005).jpg.) [CC BY 2.0 (http://creativecommons.org/licenses/by/2.0)], via Wikimedia Commons, By U.S. Fish and Wildlife Service [Public domain], via Wikimedia Commons.

pg. 177 By Frontier (Own work) [CC BY-SA 3.0 (http://creativecommons.org/licenses/by-sa/3.0)], via Wikimedia Commons.

pg. 184 By Shray.sharma (Own work) [CC BY-SA 4.0 (http://creativecommons.org/licenses/by-sa/4.0)], via Wikimedia Commons, By Thomas R Machnitzki (thomasmachnitzki.com) (Own work) [GFDL (http://www.gnu.org/copyleft/fdl.html) or CC BY 3.0 (http://creativecommons.org/licenses/by/3.0)], via Wikimedia Commons.

pg. 189 Mercury Academic

pg. 194 By Drenaline (Own work) [CC BY-SA 3.0 (http://creativecommons.org/licenses/by-sa/3.0)], via Wikimedia Commons.

pg. 196 By Surfnico (Own work) [CC BY-SA 4.0 (http://creativecommons.org/licenses/by-sa/4.0)], via Wikimedia Commons.

pg. 197 By Presidencia de la República Mexicana [CC BY 2.0 (http://creativecommons.org/licenses/by/2.0)], via Wikimedia Commons.

pg. 202 John Singer Sargent [Public domain], via Wikimedia Commons.

Index

Adaptive Culture, 56
Agricultural Revolution, 48,63
Alienation, 14, 27, 31, 33, 34,36, 41, 43, 88, 89, 175, 178, 179, 187, 190, 204
Anthropocene Age, 14, 60, 62, 70, 85, 190, 196, 202
Aristotle, 52, 71
Atrazine, 138, 165
Bacon, Francis,71
Barrett, Deirdre, 128
Berger, Peter and Luckmann, Thomas
    The Social Construction of Reality: A Treatise in the Sociology of Knowledge, 35
Bioaccumulation, 83, 136, 141, 143
Biodiversity, 21, 22, 26, 34, 76, 82, 132, 141, 143, 175-176, 185
Biomagnification, 83
Bisphenol-A (BPA), 135, 142
BRICs, 70, 160-161, 166, 169
Broken Windows Hypothesis, 200
Bryant, Bunyan, 151, 152
Buchanan, James Jr., 113
Bullard, Robert, 133, 152
Burns, Thomas, 36
Cancer Alley, 20
Carson, Rachel, 39, 43, 61, 64, 131, 132, 150, 165, 204
    Silent Spring, 61, 39
Center for Health and Environmental Justice, 151, 153
Classical Sociology, 31-34
    Limits of, 34
    Key Ideas of, 31-34
    Major Influences, 31-34
Clean Air Act, 139, 147, 157
Cobb, John Jr., 89, 99, 101, 102, 125, 137, 167
Commission on Sustainable Development
    see United Nations Commission on Sustainable Development
Comparative Advantage, 92, 100, 124, 161, 169
Concentrated Agricultural Feeding Operations (CAFOs), 22, 90-91, 92, 94, 98, 124, 134, 135
Contemporary Theory and the Environment, 36-40
    Critical Tradition, 36-37
    Functional Tradition, 38
    Human Ecology, 39
    Thought, Discourse and the Natural World, 35-36
Crutzen, Paul, 65
Cultural Diffusion, 56-57
Cultural Lag, 56-57
Culture, 45-64
    centrality, 46
    frameworks, 45-47, 103, 106

mechanism of socialization, 46
networks of meaning, 45, 46, 63
trajectory of modernity, 23, 24, 29, 34, 36, 48-49
Darwinian Medicine, 126, 128, 140, 142, 203
Darwinian Theory, 126
Deforestation, 14, 19, 22, 26, 28, 34, 35, 39, 66, 148, 162, 203
Deloria, Vine Jr., 181
Desertification, 19, 35, 52, 90-91, 148
Drama of the Commons, 104, 113, 195-200
Durkheim, Émile, 31-36, 41, 43, 88, 103, 106, 107, 111, 198
anomie, 33, 88, 190, 198, 204
egoism, 33, 36, 41, 88, 190, 198, 204
Gemeinshaft, 103, 107
social facts, 32, 33, 43
The Division of Labor in Society, 33
Dustbowl, 66
Earth Charter Secretariat, 176-177
Earth Day, 147, 153
Ecological Footprint, 37, 39, 75, 134, 162, 169
Ecological Marginalization, 133
Ecological Modernization Theory, 38, 108-110
Economic Truism, 89, 92-93, 99, 124
Economics, 14, 25, 27, 28, 50, 88-104, 109, 124, 125, 170, 171, 172, 190, 191, 192, 193, 201
cap and trade, 25, 154, 173
Default Lens, 25, 28
large-scale production, 28, 31, 49, 50, 54-55, 68, 76, 86, 89, 124
Economism, 89, 99, 101, 125, 137
Ecosystems, 20, 21, 22, 26, 30, 33, 42, 53, 55, 76, 78-79, 84, 100, 101, 118, 124, 179, 180, 181, 182, 186, 199
and Human Society, 20-22
Ehrlich, Paul and Anne, 39
and Paul Malthusian approach, 39
Enantiodromia, 52-53
Endangered Species Act, 147, 153, 157, 159
Engels, Friedrich, 52, 53, 106
Enlightenment, 23, 24, 49, 50, 52, 71, 72
Environmental Degradation, 19, 21, 23, 33, 34, 37, 47,58,61,64, 74, 77, 105, 126, 132, 133, 134, 141, 142, 160, 162, 168, 169, 171, 172, 174, 175, 187, 193, 199, 196, 203, 204
Environmental Governance, 105-125, 147, 149, 155, 156
institutional mismatch, 118-123
Environmental Justice Initiative, 151, 152
Environmental Movement, 144-159, 170-187
challenges and limits of, 153-157
Environmental Movement Organizations (EMOs), 144-145, 159
Environmental Problems
lenses of culture, 47

macro-level, 40, 112, 120
not new, 19
particular to modernity and late-modernity, 25
Environmental Protection Agency, 61, 81, 90, 144, 147, 158
Environmental Sociology
as a tool for understanding environment problems, 20, 40-41
living and vibrant field, 40
unique perspective of, 28
Externality, 27, 92, 94, 137
Fluoride, 136
Foster, John Bellamy, 171, 175, 187
Fracking 53, 77, 83, 94, 95
Fragmentation, 118-119
Freud, Sigmund
narcissism, 41,88
Friedman, Thomas
Hot, Flat and Crowded, 40
The World is Flat, 174
Fundamental Attribution Bias, 56, 198
GDP (Gross Domestic Product), 80, 83, 98
Geisler, Charles
possessive individualism, 104, 115, 116
Genetically Modified Crops (GMOs), 68-69, 73, 135, 142
Gibbs, Lois, 151, 152
Gibson, James William
A Reenchanted World: the Quest for a New Kinship with Nature, 36, 171, 182
Global Economic Market System, 120
Globalization, 40, 56, 62, 68, 103, 104, 106, 108, 111, 125, 174, 191, 193
Gonzales, Tirso, 181
Gore, Al
cultural lag, 57
Earth in the Balance, 112, 170, 171, 198
Global Marshall Plan, 170, 171-174
green label, 172
Green New Deal, 174 187
New Global Eco-Nomics, 172
Governance
classical theories, 106-107
contemporary theories, 108
traditional models, 105-106
Governance Gap, 119
Gramsci, Antonio, 191
hegemony, 56
Hardin, Garrett
see The Tragedy of the Commons
utility maximizing behavior, 114, 124
Hayes, Denis, 147
Hegel, G.W.F., 52

Heidegger, Martin, 58, 66, 70
Heraclitus, 52, 53
Hill, Julia Butterfly, 151
Homer-Dixon, Thomas, 40, 132, 133, 140, 164
    Environment, Scarcity and Violence, 40
Human Exemptionalism Paradigm, 137
Hybrid Governance, 121-122, 123, 173
Hydraulic Fracturing, *see* Fracking
Hyper-individualism, 46,49, 50, 56, 60
Indigenous Realism, 179-182
Industrial Revolution, 22, 24, 25, 26, 34, 39, 48, 50, 54, 61, 63, 65, 71, 72, 76, 80, 84, 88, 106, 130, 189, 191, 192, 200, 201, 205
    smaller-scale operations, 25, 79
Inequality, 132-140
Intergovernmental Organizations (IGOs), 148
IPAT (Impact, Population, Affluence and Technology), 39, 43, 202
    STIRPAT model variation, 39
Irish Potato Famine, 19
Jevons Paradox, 58, 73
Jung, Carl, 52
Kuznets, Simon
    Kuznets Curve, 162, 169
Kyoto Protocol, 157, 159, 196, 197
Laissez-faire economics, 50, 61
Large-scale farming
    Herbicides, pesticides, chemical fertilizers, GMOs 24
    wave of the future, 28
Late Modernity
    capitalism, 27, 88-104
    environmental problems, 25
    Individual and Modern Society, 49-51
    Mismatches between culture and Substainability, 51-55
    Mismatches between Evolution and Technology, 51-54
    Mismatches between Large-Scale Economies and the Natural Ecology, 54-55
    several distinctive features, 24
    see treadmill of production
Lead Poisoning, 138, 139
Lenski, Gerhard, 67, 77
Leopold, Aldo
    A Sand County Almanac, 149
Love Canal, 151, 152
Maathai, Wangari, 151, 153, 156
Malthus, Thomas
    Four Horsemen, 39, 93
    over-population, 93
Marx, Karl
    see alienation
    commodity chains, 24, 31, 43, 161, 168

Critical Tradition, 36
historical materialism, 38
metabolic rift, 31, 33, 37, 43
reification, 35
Material Culture, 56
Mesopotamia,
Cradle of Civilization, 19, 26
Metabolic Rift, 31, 33, 37, 43, 49, 52, 75, 97, 113, 125
Mills, C. Wright, 28, 110
Modernity, 22-25
bigger is better principle, 22
Montreal Protocol, The, 173, 187
Moody, Chief Edward, 181
Multinational Corporations (MNCs), 161, 163
Neese, Randolph and Williams, George C.
Why We Get Sick: The New Scienc of Darwinian Medicine, 126
Neolithic Revolution, 48, 80, 200
Netherlands Fallacy, 162
New Ecological Measures (NEMs), 81,82,100
Newtonian Revolution, 82
NIMBY (Not in My Back Yard), 37, 95, 134
Nongovermental Organizations (NGOs), 74, 121, 123,148, 157, 158
North American Free-Trade Agreement (NAFTA), 164
O'Connor, James
second contradiction of capitalism, 52, 125
Ogallala Aquifer, 90, 91, 124
Ogburn, William
crossing traditional boundries, 38
cultural lag, 32, 38, 56, 120
Olmsted, Fredrick Law, 201, 202
Ostrom, Elinor, 96, 97, 113, 115, 117, 119, 195
Pacific Trash Vortex, 23, 96, 112
Parabens, 136
Parsons, Talcott, 104, 107, 184
synthesizing theory, 107
Pellow, David, 37, 76, 118, 133, 134, 152
Perflurorooctanoic acid (PFOA), 136
Periphery, 160, 161, 162, 163, 168, 169
Phenomenological theories, 38
Plan for the Book, 29
Planetism, 89, 101, 125, 137
POET model (Population, human Organization, the natural Environment, and Technology), 39, 43, 202
POETICCA model, 203-204
Political Opportunity Structure, 144, 153, 154, 155, 158
Polyvinyl Chloride (PVC), 135
Population, 14, 20, 22, 24, 25, 27, 28, 30, 33, 39, 40, 43, 57, 80, 84, 85, 87, 93, 114, 127, 132, 133, 137, 141, 143, 160, 163, 171, 172, 174, 189, 195, 203

Postel, Sandra
    Last Oasis: Facing Water Scarcity, 150
Recursive Exploitation, 37, 75
Recursive Structure, 161, 169
Reich, Charles A.
    The Greening of America, 149, 151
Reification, 35, 46
Re-nativization, 181
Re-poisoning Effect, 138
Resource Capture, 132, 133
Sagan, Carl, 150
Schnaiberg, Allan, 76, 98, 125, 134, 175
    The Environment: From Surplus to Scarcity, 175
Scientific Management Principle, 23
Semi-periphery, 110, 111, 160, 161, 162, 163, 168, 169
Simmel, Georg, 31, 32, 34, 35, 52, 88
    social action, 32
    social networks, 32
Simon, Julian, 93
Smith, Adam, 24, 25, 27, 50, 74, 88, 93, 96, 100, 101, 124, 192, 193
    The Wealth of Nations, 24, 27, 50, 88, 124, 192
Social Change and the Environment, 22-23, 24, 88, 183, 184, 193, 194
Social Darwinism, 50
Socialism, 178, 179
Sophocles
    Oedipus Rex, 71
Steingraber, Sandra, 39, 76, 95, 131, 132, 134, 165
Stockholm Conference on the Human Environment, 148, 149
Super PACs, 165, 195
Supernormal Stimulus, 128-129, 130
Taylor, Frederick Winslow, 23
    scientific management principle, 23
Technology
    human condition, 24, 65-87
    Macro-level Variable, 80
Tragedy of the Commodity, The, 78
Tragedy of the Commons, The, 20, 33, 41, 46, 51, 79, 90, 96, 104, 112-113, 114, 124, 195, 199, 200
    see also, Hardin, Garrett
Toxic Substances Control Act, 147
Treadmill of Production, 37, 41, 54, 63, 76, 98, 124, 125, 158, 175, 195, 204
Two-Party System, 154-155
Unequal Ecological Exchange, 25, 75, 120, 163
United Nations Climate Change Conference Paris (COP 21), 196-197, 200
United Nations Commission on Sustainable Development (UNCSD), 121, 123, 155-157, 159,
United Nations Environmental Programme (UNEP), 158, 166
United Nations Framework Convention on Climate Change (UNFCCC), 156, 157,

197
Volatile Organic Compounds (VOCs), 134, 138
Weber, Max, 31, 32, 33, 34, 35, 36, 42, 43,44, 45, 50, 88, 103, 106, 107
the Bourgeois Marx, 32
Economy and Society, 107
ideal types, 32, 43
Iron Cage of Rationality, 33, 88, 103, 204
organizing behavior around something, 32
The Protestant Ethic and the Spirit of Capitalism, 33, 50
Wildcat, Dr. Daniel, 171, 179, 180, 181, 182, 183, 188
Red Alert!, 179
World Economic Forum, 156
World Polity Theory, 38, 58, 111
World Social Forum (WSF), 156
World System and the Environment, 110-111, 120, 160-163, 168-169

Made in the USA
San Bernardino, CA
11 January 2017